Journeys Through Bookland

PROSPERO AND MIRANDA

The Tempest

Journeys Through Bookland

A NEW AND ORIGINAL
PLAN FOR READING APPLIED TO THE
WORLD'S BEST LITERATURE
FOR CHILDREN

BY

CHARLES H. SYLVESTER
Author of English and American Literature

VOLUME EIGHT
New Edition

Chicago
BELLOWS-REEVE COMPANY
PUBLISHERS

CONTENTS

For Classification of Selections, see General Index, at end of
Volume X

vii

ILLUSTRATIONS

RINGROSE AND HIS BUCCANEERS[1]

UST two days after we took possession of the town of Santa Maria, we departed thence on Saturday, April 17th, 1680. We all embarked in thirty-five canoes, which we had taken while lying at anchor at the front of the town. Thus we sailed, or rather rowed, down the river in quest of the South Sea upon which Panama is seated. Our prisoners, the Spaniards, begged very earnestly that they might be permitted to go with us and not be left to the mercy of the Indians, who would show them no favor and whose cruelty they so much feared, but we had such difficulty in finding boats for ourselves that we could assist them little. However, they found soon after either logs or old canoes, so that they were able to come along with us.

1. This selection is taken from *The Dangerous Voyage and Bold Attempts of Captain Bartholomew Sharp and Others*, written in 1685 by Basil Ringrose, one of the pirates who sailed with Captain Sharp.

The expedition was organized with a general design to pillage and plunder on the Isthmus of Darien and the continent of South America. At the original rendezvous there were seven ships containing four hundred and seventy-seven men under the command of experienced pirate captains. The natural leaders were Captains Coxon, Sawkins and Sharp. At first the expedition met with comparatively little opposition, and they captured the town of Santa Maria, but the plunder was so small here that they were dissatisfied with what they were doing and decided again to take and plunder Panama. It is at this point that we take up the narrative of Ringrose.

Where the account appears in the first person, it is practically as it came from the pen of Ringrose, though omissions have been made and occasionally the phraseology has been changed.

1

It was my misfortune to have a canoe which was very heavy and consequently sluggish. Because of this we were left behind the rest a little way, there being only four men beside myself in the boat. As the tide fell it left several shoals of sand naked, and hence we, not knowing the location of the channel amongst such a variety of streams, steered for over two miles into a shoal where we were forced to lie by until high water came. As soon as the tide began to turn, we rowed away, but in spite of all our endeavors, we could neither find nor overtake our companions. At ten o'clock, when the tide became low, we stuck an oar in the sands and by turns slept in our canoe, where we were pierced to the skin by the showers that fell in the night.

The next morning, as soon as the day had come, we rowed away down the river in pursuit of our people, and after going about two leagues we were so fortunate as to overtake them at an Indian landing place, where they had been taking in water. They told us that we would not find water again for six days, and that we must without fail fill our jars. Although we made what haste we could, by the time our jars were filled our friends had all departed and were already out of sight. Such is the nature of the pirates; they care not in the least whom they lose or leave behind.

We rowed after them as fast as we possibly could, but all in vain, for here in the mouth of the river the islands were so numerous that it was very easy for us to lose them a second time. After much trouble and toil we did at last find the mouth of the river, but here the tide was again coming in, so that though we were within a stone's throw from the mouth of the river, we could not go through it, but were forced to put ashore and wait for better water. Accordingly we hauled our canoe close by the bushes and fastened it to a tree which the tide had almost covered.

As soon as the tide began to turn, we rowed away again, crossing the Gulf of Miguel. Here

WE ROWED AWAY DOWN THE RIVER IN PURSUIT

we had a very hard time fighting the waves, which dashed against our canoe and might easily have filled and overwhelmed it, for the boat was nearly twenty feet long and not over one and a half broad where it was widest. At dark we landed on an island where we had the most sorrowful resting place I ever experienced in my whole life. It rained impetuously all night long, in so much that we were wet from head to foot and had not one dry thread

about us; and so violent was the rain that we could
not keep any fire going to warm or dry ourselves.
Not one minute's sleep did we get during the whole
night, and our plight was indeed an awful one, remote from our companions and wholly destitute
of all human comfort. As morning broke, our
plight was little relieved, for a vast sea surrounded
us on one side, and on the other we could see nothing but high mountains and rocks. Our boat was
but an eggshell, and we had few clothes to defend
us from the weather. In fact, not one of us at
that time had a shoe to his foot.

Wet and cold as we were, however, we put forth
to sea and rowed away, passing several islands. In
the open sea the smallness of our vessel put us again
in deadly peril, and it always required one man
and sometimes two to bail out the water that came
over the sides of the boat. When we had struggled
for some time with these difficulties, and when we
were near one of the smaller islands, a huge wave
overturned our boat and we were all forced to
swim for our lives, but did manage to get to shore,
where soon our canoe was thrown after us. All
our bread and fresh water were spoiled, but as our
guns were lashed to the boat and were kept in
waxed cases, we lost none of them. Our first business was to take them out and clean them.

Scarcely had this been done when we saw another
boat suffering from the same misfortune at a little
distance from us. The persons thus cast ashore
proved to be six Spaniards from the garrison at
Santa Maria who had followed us to escape the
Indians. Presently they joined us, and we built
a fire, broiled our meat on the coals, and all ate

amicably together. We were suffering terribly for
water, as we had none to drink and knew not where
to get any. Fortunately our canoe was thrown on
edge and very little injured, but the one on which
the Spaniards came split itself against the rocks,
being old and slender, and was broken into a hundred pieces.

My company was now much discouraged and
wished to return, but after much persuasion I induced them to go forward at least one day longer,
saying I would then be willing to do whatever they
saw fit. About the time they concluded to follow
me, our watchman espied an Indian, who as soon
as he knew he had been seen, ran hastily to the
woods. Immediately I sent two of my companions
after him. Finding he was one of our friendly Indians, they followed him along the shore to where
seven more of his companions with a great canoe
were resting on the seashore. By means of signs
I asked him what had become of my companions,
and the Indians assured us that if we would take
their boat instead of our own, we would overtake
our friends before morning.

We were rejoicing over this news when the Indians noticed that six of the men of our company
did not seem to be of the same language and kind
as ourselves. We told them they were *Wankers,*
which is the name the Indians commonly give to
the Spaniards. Their next question was, "May we
kill those Spaniards?" I answered them, "By no
means; I will not consent to have it done." To this
the Indians seemed to consent, but after a little
while, when my back was turned, some of my company, thinking to oblige the Indians, beckoned to

them to kill the Spaniards. Perceiving their dan‚ ger, the Spaniards made a great outcry, which I heard, and I turned around in time to save their lives. Although I was able to accomplish this, I could not prevent them, however, from taking one of the Spaniards as a slave. To the others, however, I gave the canoe in which I came and bade them to get away as speedily as possible in order to save their lives from the Indians.

Then joining company with the Indians we entered a very large canoe, which was able to carry at least twenty men more easily than our canoe could carry five. Moreover the Indians had also fitted a good sail to the canoe, so that, having a fresh breeze, we set sail and moved rapidly away, to the infinite joy and comfort of our hearts. In one place we ran into a heavy sea, which was caused by a strong current and the heavy winds, and many times our boat was filled with spray. Again at night it rained heavily for several hours and was very dark.

About nine o'clock we discovered two fires on the shore of the mainland. The Indians began to shout and to cry out joyously that these fires were made by their companions. Accordingly we made for the shore as fast as we could drive, but as soon as we had reached it about sixty Spaniards, armed with clubs and other arms, rushed out into the breakers, laid hold of our canoe on both sides and pulled it out of the water. Thus were we all taken and made prisoners. I laid hold of my gun, thinking to defend myself, but it was all in vain, for four or five of them stopped and overpowered me. The Indians leaped overboard and got away very nimbly into the woods, though my companions were too much amazed to make any attempt to escape.

Our captors could speak neither French nor English, but I was able to talk, in Latin, with one of them who seemed more intelligent than the rest, and from him I learned that these were Spaniards who had been put ashore by our other boats for fear that some of them might escape and warn Panama that we were on our way to capture it. For this reason the Spaniards were much rejoiced at taking us, and they designed to treat us very severely for plundering their town of Santa Maria.

But even while the Spaniard was talking to me, there came in a poor wretch that I had saved from the Indians. When he reported how kindly I had treated him and the rest of his companions, the captain rose from his seat and embraced me, saying, "You Englishmen are very friendly enemies and good people, but the Indians are rogues and a treacherous nation. Come and sit by me and eat of the victuals which your companions left us when they turned from shore." For the kindness I had shown their countrymen, the Spaniards agreed to give us our lives and liberty, but it was only after long persuasion that I could induce them to spare the lives of the Indians. However, I accomplished this and was bidden to take my canoe and go in God's name, with the wish that we might be as fortunate as we had been generous.

Having found the Indians, we took our departure soon after, although the Spaniards invited us to stay with them longer. All that night it rained very hard and we found no place where we could land. About ten o'clock the next morning, however, after a night of rowing and paddling, we espied a canoe coming toward us at great speed. The men in it proved to be of our old English company, who supposed us to be Spaniards and were coming to attack us. They had given me and my companions up for lost, but now we were all mutually rejoiced, and were soon reunited on the shore of a deep bay which lay concealed behind a point of rocks.

On the morning of the second day after, that is, on the twenty-third of April, the day sacred to Saint George, our patron of England, we came before sunrise within view of the city of Panama, which makes a pleasant show to vessels that are at sea. At that time there lay at anchor near the Island of Perico, which is distant about two leagues from Panama, five great ships and three smaller men-of-war called *The Little Fleet*. The latter, it appeared, had been suddenly manned with a design to fight us and prevent us from making any further attempts upon the city or seacoast.

Accordingly, as soon as they spied us, they instantly weighed anchor and came directly to meet us. Two of our boats were very heavy and could not row as fast as the canoes, and accordingly we were already far in advance. There were five canoes in this company, and among them only thirty-six men in a very unfit condition to fight, being tired and worn with so much rowing. The enemy sailed toward us directly before the wind, and we feared greatly lest they should run us down. So we rowed straight up into the "wind's eye," as the sailors say, and got close to windward of them. While we were doing this, other of our boats in

which were thirty-two more men overtook us, so that
altogether we were sixty-eight men engaged in the
fight that day.

In the three vessels of the Little Fleet that opposed us were altogether two hundred and seventy-
eight men, of whom more than two hundred were
native Spaniards, the rest being Indians or Mulat-
toes. The commanders of these ships had issued
orders that no quarter was to be given to any of
the buccaneers. But such bloody commands as
these seldom or never prosper.

The canoe of Captain Sawkins and that wherein
I was were much to the leeward of the rest. The
third of the Spanish ships came between us two and
fired on me to the windward and on Captain Sawkins to the leeward, wounding with these broadsides
four men in the Captain's canoe and one in mine.
Nevertheless, he paid so dear for his passage between us that he was not very quick in coming about
again and trying it a second time; for with our first
volley we killed several of his men upon the decks.
Thus we got to the windward of the enemy as our
other canoes had already done. At this moment the
Admiral of the Little Fleet came up with us suddenly, scarcely giving us time to charge, and thinking to pass by us with as little damage as the first
of his ships had received, or even less. But it fell
out much worse for him, for we were so fortunate
as to kill the man at the helm, so that his ship ran
into the wind and her sails lay "a-back" as the
mariners say. This gave us time to come up under
the stern of his vessel, and firing continually into
the vessel we killed as many as came to the helm,
and cut in two his mainsail and brace.

At this time the third Spanish vessel was seen coming up to the aid of the Admiral's ship. Captain Sawkins left the latter to our four canoes and rowed away to meet the oncoming Spaniards. The dispute or fight between them was very hot, as they lay close together, and fought from one side of the deck to the other, both giving and receiving death as fast as they could charge. Meanwhile the first ship tacked about and came up to relieve the Admiral. We determined to prevent this design, and two of our canoes, Captain Springer's and my own, stood out to meet the new arrival, who made direct upon the Admiral, who stood upon the quarter-deck waving at him with a handkerchief what to do. But we met him in the middle of his way, and came so close to him that if he had not turned his course, we should have been on board him. As it was, we killed so many of his crew that the vessel had scarcely men enough left alive and unwounded to carry her off. Fortunately for them, the wind sprang up fresh, and they were able to sail away and save their lives.

Having put to flight the vessel which was to relieve the Admiral, we turned about and with a loud halloo joined our friends in the other boat, and came so close under the stern of the Admiral's ship that we wedged up the rudder and at the same time killed both the Admiral and the chief pilot. Seeing how disabled their ship was, and disheartened by the slaughter, for at least two-thirds of their men had been killed and many others wounded, they cried for quarter, which had several times been offered them, but had been always stoutly denied. So we took possession of the Admiral's ship and put on board all our wounded men, including Captain Harris, who had been shot through both his legs. As soon as this was done, we instantly sent some of our ships to go and aid Captain Sawkins, who had been fighting against the second Spanish ship. Indeed, to give our enemies their due, no men in the world ever fought more bravely than these same Spaniards.

Coming up close under the Spaniard's side, we gave him a full volley of shot and expected to have a like return from him, but of a sudden we saw his men that were abaft the mast, blown up in the air, some of them falling into the deck and others into the sea. This disaster was no sooner seen by their valiant Captain than he leaped overboard, and in spite of all our shot succeeded in rescuing some of his men, although he was much burned in both his hands himself. But while he was rescuing these men to reinforce the ship and renew the fight, another jar of powder took fire and blew up several others upon the forecastle.

Under cover of the smoke from these explosions, Captain Sawkins led his men on board and took the ship. Soon after I went on board myself, and indeed, such a miserable sight I never saw in my life. For not one man was to be found but was either killed, desperately wounded or horribly burned with powder, in so much that their black skins were turned white in several places where the powder had torn it from their flesh and bones.

Having compassionated their misery, I afterwards went on board the Admiral's ship, and here what I saw did much astonish me, and would scarcely be believed by others than ourselves who

saw it. There were found on this ship only twenty-
five men alive, where before the fight there were
four-score and six. And out of these twenty-five
men, only eight were able to bear arms, all the rest
being desperately wounded, and by their wounds
totally unable to make any resistance. Their blood
ran down the decks in whole streams, and scarcely
one place in the ship was free from blood.

Having once possessed ourselves of two vessels
of the little fleet, Captain Sawkins asked the prisoners how many men there were on the largest ship
that we could see lying in the harbor of Perico, and
also how many were upon the smaller ships. Peralta, the heroic captain of the second vessel, tried
to dissuade Sawkins from attacking the Spanish
vessels at anchor, saying in the biggest one alone
there were three hundred and fifty men, and that
all the other vessels would be found too well provided for defense against the small number of the
buccaneers. One of the Spaniards, however, who
lay dying on the deck, told Captain Sawkins that
there was not a single man on board any one of
the great ships in the harbor, for they had all been
drawn away to fight on the ships of the Little Fleet.
Believing the dying man's story, we sailed into the
harbor and went on board the ships, finding, as we
had been told, not one person there. They had
set on fire the biggest ship and made a hole in her
hull, but we put out the flames and stopped the
leak. All our wounded were then placed on this
ship, which for a time became our hospital.

Having counted up our own loss and damages,
we found eighteen of our men killed and twenty-
two wounded.

The three captains against whom we fought were esteemed by the Spaniards as the bravest in the South Seas, nor was this reputation undeserved by them, as may easily be seen from the story of this bloody battle. We began the fight about a half hour after sunrise, and by noon had finished the battle. While Captain Peralta was our prisoner, he would often break out and say: "Surely you Englishmen are the valiantest in the whole world, and always design to fight in the open; while all other nations have invented all kinds of ways to barricade themselves and fight as close as possible"; and yet notwithstanding, we killed more of the enemy than they have of us.

The journal of Basil Ringrose is a very interesting document, and we should enjoy following it to the end if we had the space and if it were not for the fact that he devotes so much space to information that is valuable chiefly to a sailor. Accordingly it seems best to give a brief summary of his journal in our own words:

Captain Peter Harris, whom Ringrose calls "a brave and stout soldier and a valiant Englishman, born in the county of Kent," died of his wounds, and they buried him with the usual honors of war —a volley from all their guns.

The buccaneers captured the five ships that lay near the Island of Perico and divided the spoils among themselves. Within the next two or three days, however, dissensions arose among them, and Captain Coxon, taking with him a large number of men together with most of the Indian allies, deserted the expedition and returned. During this time Captain Sharp was absent, and after the de-

parture of Coxon, Captain Sawkins was chosen
to command. For some weeks the buccaneers remained in the Bay of Panama, capturing vessels
and ravaging the adjacent islands.

While they were at Taboga, the governor of
Panama sent a message to Captain Sawkins inquiring why he came to this locality. Captain Sawkins replied, "We came to assist the Indian King
of Darien, who is the true lord of Panama and all
the country round about. Since we came so far,
there seems to be no reason why we should not have
some satisfaction. Accordingly, if you will send
us five hundred pieces of eight for each man and a
thousand for each commander and will promise no
longer to annoy the Indians or deprive them of
their liberty, we will go away peaceably: otherwise,
we will stay here, get what we can and cause all
the damage possible to you."

In answer to this, the governor inquired by
messenger—"From whom do you have your commission and to whom shall I complain for the
damages which you have already done?"

The reply of Captain Sawkins to this message
was prompt and decisive, for he said, "All my company have not yet arrived, but as soon as they come,
we will visit you at Panama and bring our com-
missions on the muzzles of our guns, at which time
you may read them as plain as the flame of gunpowder can make them."

On the 22nd of May, Captains Sawkins and
Sharp took with them about sixty men and attacked
the town of Pueblo Nueva. The buccaneers found
that the inhabitants of this town were well prepared
for the defense. They had cut down great trees

and laid them across the narrow river which led to
their town in such a way as to prevent the ascent
of any boats.

Sawkins and his followers landed at the mouth
of the river and made their way by land until
they reached some heavy breastworks which had
been thrown up by the Spaniards. With undaunted courage, Sawkins stormed the defenses,
and was killed at the head of his men. His loss
was a sad one to the pirates, because they regarded
him as their most valiant leader, and because, next
to Captain Sharp, he was best beloved by them.
In fact, his loss meant the desertion of a number
more of the buccaneers, who left their companions
and returned over land, as Captain Coxon and his
officers had done.

Thus all the adventurers who wished to remain
in the South Seas and still further ravage the coast
of South America, elected Captain Sharp com-
mander-in-chief, and vowed themselves to be faithful to him in all things. A large number, however,
of the pirates deserted, preferring the dangers of
land travel in the rainy season to continued adventure in the South Seas.

Basil Ringrose was among those who were tired
of the expedition and wished to return home, but
he finally decided to remain with Captain Sharp
because of the great difficulties he foresaw in returning by the shorter way.

It was the last day of May when the mutineers
departed, and it was on the sixth of June, a dark
and rainy day, that they set sail on the long and
adventurous voyage. Almost from the start they
met with most vexatious delays which gave an op-

portunity for the Spanish on shore to send ahead
news of their coming. In consequence of this, they
were almost everywhere expected, and most of the
towns which were unable to defend themselves succeeded in concealing their wealth, provisions and
supplies so that the buccaneers were unable to seize
treasures of any great value. As a whole, the voyage was a disappointment, but from time to time
the adventurers succeeded in taking sufficient food
and occasionally gold and silver in such quantities
that the voyage was somewhat profitable to those
who survived.

The journal of Ringrose is full of interesting little details, which show how exciting the trip must
have been, and how great were the perils and privations of its followers.

In one place we find them anchored for four or
five days, trying to dry their sails so that they could
be able to take them down and repair the hull of
their ship, yet all the time the rain fell in such tor-
rents that they were unable to work. At another
place he tells of killing a snake which was fourteen
inches in circumference and eleven feet in length.
On this part of the coast they saw every day whales
and grampuses, which often came and dived
under the ship, and although the men fired at them
several times, the bullets rebounded from their
tough skins. At this place, too, the best food consisted of Indian conies, snakes, oysters, periwinkles,
a few small turtles and a variety of small fish.

Again, we find some of the most valuable of the
men dying from malignant fevers, and all suffering from want of provisions. For a long time they
had nothing but flour and water, and then again

they were able to revel in small particles of meat, with a good supply of sugar which they took from some of the mills along the coast. Now and then they seized a flock of goats, and then for days the feasting was continuous, while the surplus flesh was salted and stored away for future use.

On the 24th of August they discovered a vessel some distance from them, and because of the darkness, ran very close to it before they were discovered. When they were within hail, they called in Spanish to the ship and commanded it to lower its sails. "Not we," replied the Spaniards; "we will soon make you lower your own." The pirates immediately fired upon them, and they responded at a lively rate from their own guns. For half an hour or more the fight was very brisk, and undoubtedly would have lasted much longer had not the buccaneers been fortunate enough to kill the man at the helm, after which no one of the Spaniards dared to take his place, and the ship drifted aimlessly. About the same time another lucky shot tore off the mainsail, and seeing their helpless condition, the Spaniards begged for quarter and gave up their ship. Afterwards they declared that they fought the pirates only out of bravado, for they had agreed on a wager before they left shore to do so in case they met with Captain Sharp. Although the fight was short, the pirates themselves had suffered considerable damage to their ship, and several of their men were sadly wounded.

The captain of the captured vessel gave the buccaneers a great deal of information as to what had happened after they left Panama, and also as to the preparations which were being made to defend the towns against the adventurers, and to capture the vessel if possible whenever it appeared.

At Tumbes they heard that this was the first settlement made by the Spanish after Panama, and that at the time of the settlement a priest went ashore with a cross in his hand, while ten thousand Indians gathered on the hillsides and stood watching him. As he landed, two lions came out of the woods toward him, but when he laid the cross gently over their backs, they fell down and worshiped him; moreover, two tigers following did the same thing. The Indians seeing these wonderful things recognized the power of the Christian religion and at once embraced it.

By the end of October they were near the Fort of Hilo on the coast of Peru, far south of the equator. Here at night they anchored about two miles from the village, while they sent four canoes with fifty men in them to seize and plunder the town. In the morning they discovered by the flags which the men had put out, that the town was in the hands of the English. Accordingly, all the men that could be spared from the ship landed and learned that the enemy had been put to flight after a few volleys had been exchanged. In the town they secured great quantities of pitch and tar, besides oil, wine, flour and several other kinds of provisions. Most of the Spaniards had fled to the hills, and the pirates were afraid that at any moment they might be attacked. About sixty men were sent out to search the valley and the country round about the town. The whole region was found to be very pleasing, thickly set with groves of figs, olives, oranges, lemons and other

fruits. About four miles up the valley appeared a
great sugar factory, where sugar, oil and molasses
were found in abundance. The mill was deserted,
and the pirates were unable to capture any of the
inhabitants, though from time to time the Spaniards were seen marching along the hilltops whence
they tumbled down great stones and fired at random among the buccaneers.

At the sugar factory, under a flag of truce, the
Spaniards promised to deliver eighty beef cattle at
the port the next day by noon as a ransom for the
building. Captain Sharp accordingly sent word
that no violence was to be offered to those who
brought the beeves down to the ship.

The next morning, the Spaniards, bearing a flag
of truce, came to Captain Sharp and told him that
sixteen of the cattle were already at the port, and
the rest would be there the next morning. Accordingly, the raiders began their retreat to the sea,
expecting to re-embark on the ship. Ringrose
thought that at least twenty men should be left behind at the sugar house for a lookout to keep watch
of the Spaniards, but he was overruled on this and
all went on to the port, where, however, no cattle
were found, nor was there evidence that any effort
had been made to bring them. The next morning
Captain Sharp went again to the hills and met the
Spaniards, who promised that the cattle would certainly be there by night, and accordingly it was
decided to wait one day more. The next morning
the experience was repeated, but that day passed
without any of the beeves appearing, and on the
following morning the pirates marched to the village and burned not only the sugar mill but all of

the buildings round about, breaking the machinery
and destroying all of the oil and other provisions
which they could not carry away.

This done, they returned to the port by a new
route over the mountains, and in doing so escaped
an ambuscade which would inevitably have destroyed them all. As it was, they reached the shore
only to find more than three hundred cavalrymen
charging upon them from the north. As quickly
as possible the buccaneers threw themselves into a
posture of defense and charged to meet the advancing horsemen. The horsemen retreated as the
pirates advanced, with the intention of leading the
latter away from the village and the rocks near the
port. Detecting the stratagem, the pirates returned
to the port, and a battle at long range commenced,
which lasted the entire day. Meanwhile the Spaniards had been receiving continuous reinforcements,
and appeared in numbers on the hills on all sides, so
that the pirates, fearing they would be overpowered
by force of numbers, resolved that night to escape
and sail away from the coast which had brought
them so much trouble. Nevertheless, they had
gathered a great quantity of provisions, which were
very acceptable under the circumstances.

Early in December the buccaneers had another
series of exciting experiences at the town of La
Serena. Here a force was landed and sent toward
the city, but it quickly discovered that the inhabitants had been warned of the approach of the pirates
and were rallying to defend themselves, led by a
troop of a hundred Spanish horse. The advance
guard of the buccaneers, however, was able to rout
the Spaniards and drive them from the town. At

a short distance away, however, the cavalry rallied, and appeared ready to offer battle in a more favorable place, but the pirates brought up their rein-

A BATTLE AT LONG RANGE COMMENCED

forcements, and when they offered to attack the Spaniards, the latter fled again. A third time they formed and a third time retreated. This method of fighting they continued until the English were drawn far away from the town, which was evidently the plan of the Spaniards, although they lost three of their officers and several horses. The buccaneers, abandoning the chase, crossed the green fields and waded the irrigating streams which enclosed them, finding here and there a house, but all destitute of both inhabitants and provisions. The Spaniards had taken good care that little should be left for the pirates. Near the town they found fine fruit orchards and gardens, and regaled themselves with strawberries, which are described as being big as walnuts and very delicious to the taste. In fact, everything about the place pleased them, excepting the fact that most of the valuables had been transported and hidden. It appeared, too, that the Spaniards, fearing a revolt among their Chilian slaves, had killed nearly all of them. Nevertheless a few were found who served as guides and showed the pirates where much plate and many kinds of valuable goods had been stored away.

The buccaneers spent that night in the village, and the next morning the Spaniards came bearing a flag of truce and offered to treat with their conquerors. The buccaneers finally agreed to depart, providing a ransom of ninety-five thousand pieces of eight was paid. This was promised by the inhabitants, and it was agreed that it should be paid the next day.

That night an earthquake shook the surrounding country and badly frightened the pirates, who were sleeping in one of the largest churches. Moreover, during the night the Spaniards turned the mountain streams through the streets of the town, apparently hoping to drive out the buccaneers, or at least to prevent the burning of the town.

Until noon the next day the pirates waited for
the ransom, but when it did not appear they were
satisfied that the Spaniards had never intended to
pay it, and accordingly the buccaneers burned the
town and retreated to the coast. Here they found
that the Spaniards had tried to burn the ship by
rather an extraordinary stratagem. They took the
hide of a horse, blew it up till it floated like a great
bladder, and upon it put a man who paddled himself under the stern of the ship. Here he crammed
oakum, brimstone and other combustibles between
the rudder and the sternpost, and set the whole on
fire. In a few moments the vessel was covered
with smoke, and in the confusion the Spaniard
escaped. However, his plot was not successful, for
the pirates had the good fortune to discover the
cause of the fire and put it out before any serious
damage was done.

Three weeks later, the pirates visited the island
of Juan Fernandez, where they spent several days
and where they celebrated their Christmas holiday
by firing three volleys of shot. They found an
abundance of goats on the island and were able
to replenish their larder. The water supply was
excellent, but at one time when Ringrose with nine
of his companions in two canoes had landed to fill
their jars, a storm came up which prevented them
from returning to the ship. The wind grew so
violent that the ship itself was forced to sail out
into the open sea. About noon, Ringrose and his
companions tried to follow the ship, but were driven
back upon the shore by a raging sea. Early in the
evening they tried a second time, and got some
little distance from land, but the waves were so

violent that they were forced to throw overboard all their jars of water to lighten their boats. Even then they were unable to reach their ship, but went ashore in the darkness and hauled up their canoes. They were unable to rest where they landed because of the great numbers of noisy seals that troubled them exceedingly. Therefore they went higher up into the islands, kindled a fire and spent a wet, hungry and uncomfortable night. All about them were the nests and roosting places of a multitude of birds, one of which fell down into their fire and was killed. Early the next morning they put to sea again, and finally found their ship half a league from them at anchor in a bay which furnished them a better anchorage than any they had previously discovered. More days were spent in taking on water, chopping wood, catching fish and killing goats. Terrible storms struck them, and the death of one of their mates made the stay an unhappy one.

Here they were told the story of a man who was cast upon this island, the only one saved from a large ship, and who lived five years there before any one came to carry him off. This was probably Alexander Selkirk, from whose adventures on the island Defoe wrote his *Robinson Crusoe*. Ringrose tells us that he on a trip into the island one day found cut in the bark of a tree a cross with several letters beside it, and that on the same tree he cut his own name with a cross above it. On the twelfth of January, seeing three ships which appeared to be men-of-war sailing toward them, they hurriedly left the island, abandoning there one of their Indian allies because he could not be found in time. Thus a second Man Friday was deposited upon Robinson Crusoe's island.

While at the island, some of the buccaneers mutinied, deposed Captain Sharp, and chose Watling to be their commander. When they left the island they went directly to the coast and made a

A CROSS WITH SEVERAL LETTERS BESIDE IT

second attempt upon the town of Arica, but they were beaten off with a great loss of men, among the killed being Captain Watling. After their return to the ship, Sharp was again chosen captain, and remained as such until the end of the voyage.

It seems that about the first of February, Ringrose was taken sick, and that thereafter he was unable to keep a constant diary, so that our accounts of the remainder of the voyage are brief and broken.

In March, sick and discouraged by the misfortunes they had met, the buccaneers decided not to continue the voyage, but to land, abandon their ship and return home across the continent. For one reason and another, however, they delayed leaving the ship, and continued to work their way north until about the middle of April. Forty-seven of the men who had been discontented all along were then put ashore, while the rest of the party decided to remain loyal to Captain Sharp, and to go home around the southern part of the continent. Before the mutineers were put ashore, the ship had come north almost to the equator, so that the journey of the deserters was materially lessened. Two of the mutineers reached the Isthmus, crossed it and subsequently published some brief accounts of their experiences.

Sharp's vessel cruised about in the vicinity of the equator, raiding small towns and capturing Spanish vessels, and piling up a large amount of treasure, until the end of August, when the buccaneers turned south with a determination to make the voyage home as quickly as possible.

About the twentieth of September they passed the Tropic of Capricorn, and by the middle of October they were almost opposite the Straits of Magellan. On this voyage they had kept most of the time far away from the coast, and had landed only when necessary to re-stock their ship with water and provisions.

In the wildest kind of weather they searched the rocky coast, trying to find the opening into the Strait of Magellan, but were unable to do so. Provisions ran low, and many times they feared actual starvation little less than destruction by storms and hidden rocks. Most of them were sick, and all were discouraged. At last they abandoned the idea of going through the straits, and sailed south around Tierra del Fuego through rain and fogs and frost. About the middle of November they were able to turn their course to the north, and from that time we find them working steadily forward, till, on the twenty-eighth of January, they sighted the island of Barbados. Here they were told that peace was declared between Spain and England, but as they saw one of the British men-of-war lying at anchor, they did not dare to put into the harbor, fearing they would be seized as pirates, for throughout their whole expedition they had had no commission. Still they were overjoyed to see some of their country-men again and to talk with them, as they did with the mariners on some of the small vessels that were putting out from the island.

They set free at this place a negro who had served them as shoemaker, giving him his liberty because he had worked so faithfully. Besides this, they presented Captain Sharp with a mulatto body servant as a mark of the respect and admiration they had for his skill in conducting them through so many dangerous adventures. Then they divided the last of their prize money and started a fund for the celebration of their return. As a nucleus, there were a hundred pieces of eight, prize money which they could not divide satisfactorily. To this they added the price of a little Spanish dog which they had found on one of their prizes, and which they had fed and cared for to the present time. Captain Sharp bought the dog, paying forty pieces of eight for him, with the understanding that the money should go into the "jollification fund."

On the thirtieth of January they sighted the island of Antigua, and sent a canoe on shore to get tobacco and find out whether the governor would permit them to come into port. They found everybody excepting the governor willing and anxious to see them, but the latter flatly denied them entry. Accordingly, the ship was given to those of the pirates who had lost all their money at play, while the remainder separated themselves into two groups and took passage for England.

Ringrose and thirteen of his companions reached England on the twenty-sixth of March. There they were tried for piracy in the South Seas, at the instigation of the Spanish ambassador, but were not convicted. On the most serious charge they were released on the plea of self-defense, as it was claimed that the Spaniards had fired first upon them. Three of Sharp's crew were tried at Jamaica. One pleaded guilty and was hanged, but the other two fought their cases in court and were finally acquitted for lack of evidence.

DAVID CROCKETT

NIQUE among the characters in American history and one of the most interesting men of pioneer days was David Crockett, who was born on the 17th of August, 1786, in the backwoods district of what has since become the State of Tennessee. His father, who was of Irish parentage, during his youth lived with his parents in Pennsylvania, but afterwards moved to North Carolina and thence into the Tennessee country. David's grandparents were both murdered in their own house by the Creek Indians. At the same time, one uncle of David's was badly wounded, and a second, a younger one, who was deaf and dumb, was captured by the Creeks and kept in captivity for seventeen years, when he was met and recognized by an elder brother, who purchased him from the Indians that held him. Hearing of such atrocities must have affected the young David, and undoubtedly accounts for some of the fierce hatred which the backwoodsman felt for the Creeks, and the callous way in which he looked upon their sufferings when later he fought against them with the militia from his neighborhood.

David had five brothers and three sisters; his father was a poor man who tried farming and other pioneer occupations, who built a mill and lost it in a freshet just as it was completed, and who finally established a little roadhouse or tavern on one of the Tennessee trails. So poor were they that much schooling was impossible for the children, yet David was sent at the proper time, and applied himself diligently for a few days to his letters. However, he was so unfortunate as to quarrel with one of his older companions who little realized the savage nature of the newcomer. That night Davy lay in wait for the larger boy and set upon him so fiercely and beat him so unmercifully that he was soon ready to cry for quarter. On the way home Davy persuaded his brothers to say nothing about the fight, and the next morning instead of going to school, he ran off into the woods, where he stayed until the children returned at night. He kept this up for several days, fearing to return to school and take the whipping he knew he must get from his teacher. In the end his father heard that he was playing truant, and tried to force the boy back to school. Davy refused to go, and when his father tried to punish him, ran away from home and engaged himself to a drover. He was fifteen years old before he returned to his home, and then he had changed so much that his parents did not recognize him, and it was some time before one of his sisters discovered who he really was. They received him joyfully, and thereafter, until he reached his majority, he worked faithfully for his father, paying off the latter's indebtedness and assisting the family in every possible way.

His life during this time was that of a back-woods boy, working hard and finding his recreation in hunting, fishing and the sports of the border. It was during this time that he acquired the over-

powering taste for hunting in the woods, that lasted
all his life. During these years, too, he developed
that sturdy manhood which carried him through
many trying ordeals. Though he never had schooling, and his conversation and writings were lacking
in grammar, yet his speech was full of a sharp, rude
wit, and his ideas were characterized by shrewd
common sense.

Davy's motto, adopted early in life, was, "Be
sure you are right, then go ahead,"—words that
his own career made famous.

When the Creek War broke out, Crockett volunteered, and he served as soldier and spy till peace
was declared. His experiences there we will let
him tell himself, as he wrote them in his autobiography. (See page 37.)

After his return from the Creek War, he was
elected to Congress in 1826 and in 1828. He was
defeated in 1830 and re-elected in 1832. When he
was first elected he knew very little about the
government, and was totally ignorant of his duties
as a member of Congress, but here again his good
common sense and bright mind came to his aid; and
although he worked under great disadvantages, yet
he won respect and admiration from the other law-
makers. He was always a curious and noticeable
figure in Washington, both on account of his dress,
which was similar to that of his backwoods
companions, and because of his manner, which was
as strange as his clothes. Such a man could not
help being noticed, and on a trip which he made
to Philadelphia, New York and Boston, he was
received everywhere kindly and added not a little
to his fame.

He was defeated at the close of his third term in Congress, and being stirred by the exciting news that came from Texas, he left his home in Tennessee and went West to join those men who were fighting the Mexicans in an endeavor to make Texas really a free and independent state.

He kept a journal during this trip, and in it he describes very entertainingly his companions and their experiences. Among them were three curious characters: a bee hunter, who was well known through Texas and who left his wife Kate at Nacogdoches; a fierce old man, who had been a pirate and had abandoned the sea for more exciting events on shore; and a quaint gambler, whom Crockett picked up near the Mississippi and persuaded to abandon the petty shell game by which he was getting small sums from the people he met on the way. The real name of this man Crockett never told, but assigned to him the nickname "Thimblerig."

We shall tell of the fall of the Alamo in another place (page 141), but Crockett's connection with it is so intimate that we must borrow a little from his diary.

We find him writing at San Antonio on the nineteenth of February in high spirits, although he confesses to a shortage of provisions, but hopes to satisfy his appetite with fighting if in no other way. On the twenty-third the enemy came in sight, and the little garrison resolved to defend the Alamo to the last extremity. They made a large national flag of thirteen stripes, red and white alternately on a blue ground, with a large white star in the center, and between the points the word "Texas."

When the flag was raised, the bee hunter sang in
his wonderfully mellow voice the following patriotic
song, that roused the enthusiasm of his hearers to
the highest pitch:

> "Up with your banner, Freedom,
>   The champions cling to thee;
> They'll follow where'er you lead 'em,
>   To death, or victory;—
> Up with your banner, Freedom.
> Tyrants and slaves are rushing
>   To tread thee in the dust;
> Their blood will soon be gushing,
>   And stain our knives with rust;—
> But not thy banner, Freedom.
> While stars and stripes are flying,
>   Our blood we'll freely shed;
> No groan will 'scape the dying,
>   Seeing thee o'er his head;—
> Up with your banner, Freedom."

For the next nine days, Crockett gives an account of their privations and sufferings, their brave
and successful defense, and the marked execution
they were able to make among the Mexicans who
showed themselves within range. On the third of
March they had given up all hopes of receiving
assistance from without, and had promised to fight
to the last extremity, and in dying kill as many of
their foes as possible.

His entry for the fourth of March is substan-
tially as follows: "Shells have been falling into
the fort like hail during the day, but without effect.
About dusk this evening we saw a man running
toward the fort pursued by about a dozen Mexican
cavalry. The bee hunter immediately recognized
him as the old pirate who had gone to Goliad for

assistance, and calling to two others, the bee hunter sallied out of the fort to the relief of the old man, I following close after. Before we reached him the Mexicans were close upon his heels. He stopped suddenly, turned short upon his pursuers, discharged his rifle, and saw one of his enemies fall from his horse. After running a short distance again, the old pirate, finding that he would be taken and cut to pieces, turned fiercely, and to the amazement of the enemy clubbed his gun and dashed among them like a wounded tiger. By the time we reached him, his pursuers had fled like sparrows, and in the ardour of the moment we followed them some distance, not seeing that our retreat was cut off by another detachment of cavalry. Nothing was to be done but to fight our way through. We were all of the same mind. They were about twenty in number and stood their ground while we dashed among them, and for about five minutes a bloody conflict ensued. Then a detachment was seen coming from the fort to our relief, and the Mexicans scampered away, leaving eight of their men dead upon the field. We did not escape unscathed, for both the pirate and the bee hunter were mortally wounded, and I received a saber cut across the forehead.

"The old man died without speaking as soon as we entered the fort. We bore my young friend to his bed, dressed his wounds, and I watched beside him. He lay without complaint or manifesting pain, until about midnight, when he spoke. I asked him what he wanted. 'Nothing,' he replied with a sigh that seemed to rend his heart, and his eyes filled with tears as he continued his 'Poor Kate of

Nacogdoches; her words were prophetic, Colonel.'
Then he sang in a low voice,—

'But toom' cam' the saddle, all bluidy to see,
And hame cam' the steed, but hame never cam' he.'

"He spoke no more, and a few minutes afterward died. Poor Kate, who will tell this to thee?"
The last entry in Crockett's diary bears date
March fifth. It is as follows:
"Pop, pop, pop! Bom, bom, bom! throughout
the day.——No time for memorandums now.——
Go ahead!——Liberty and independence forever!"
Before daybreak the next morning, the final
assault was made on the Alamo, and when Santa
Ana entered in person, after the terrible butchery,
only six men, among whom was Colonel Crockett,
were found alive. The Colonel stood alone in an
angle of the fort, the barrel of his broken rifle in
his right hand, and in his left a huge Bowie knife
dripping blood. Across his forehead was a terrible
gash, while around him lay a barrier of dead Mexicans who had fallen at his hands. At his feet lay
the body of his friend Thimblerig with his knife
driven to the hilt in the throat of a Mexican, and
his left hand clenched in his hair.
"General Castrillon was brave and not cruel,
and disposed to save the prisoners. He marched
them up to that part of the fort where stood Santa
Ana and his murderous crew. The steady, fearless
step and undaunted tread of Colonel Crockett, on
this occasion, together with the bold demeanour of
the hardy veteran, had a powerful effect on all
present. Nothing daunted, he marched up boldly
in front of Santa Ana, and looked him sternly in

the face, while Castrillon addressed 'his Excellency,'—'Sir, here are six prisoners I have taken alive; how shall I dispose of them?' Santa Ana looked at Castrillon fiercely, flew into a violent rage, and replied, 'Have I not told you before how to dispose of them? Why do you bring them to me? At the same time his brave officers plunged their swords into the bosoms of their defenceless prisoners. Colonel Crockett, seeing the act of treachery, instantly sprung like a tiger at the ruffian chief, but before he could reach him a dozen swords were sheathed in his indomitable heart; and he fell, and died without a groan, a frown on his brow, and a smile of scorn and defiance on his lips. Castrillon rushed from the scene, apparently horrorstruck, sought his quarters, and did not leave them for several days, and hardly spoke to Santa Ana after."

It is only fair to say that the account which we have quoted above is denied by some authorities, who say that Crockett was killed before ever Santa Ana entered the Alamo.

DAVID CROCKETT IN THE CREEK WAR

ABRIDGED FROM HIS AUTOBIOGRAPHY

 WAS living ten miles below Winchester when the Creek warriors commenced their open hostilities by a most bloody butchery at Fort Mimms. There had been no war among us for so long that but few who were not too old to bear arms knew anything about the business. I for one had often thought about war and had often heard it described, and I did verily believe in my own mind that I couldn't fight at all; but my after-experience convinced me that this was all a notion, for when I heard of the mischief which was done at the fort, I instantly felt like going, and I had none of the dread of dying that I expected to feel.

In a few days a general meeting of the militia was called for the purpose of raising volunteers; and when the day arrived for that meeting, my wife, who had heard me say I meant to go to war, began to beg me not to turn out. It was mighty hard to go against her arguments, but my countrymen had been murdered, and I knew that the next thing would be that the Indians would be scalping the women and children all about there if we didn't put a stop to it. I reasoned the case with her as well as I could, and told her that if every man would wait till his wife got willing to let him go to war, there would be no fighting done until we would all be killed in our houses; that I was as able to go as any man in the world; and that I believed it was a duty I owed to my country. Whether she was satisfied with this reasoning or not, she didn't tell me; but seeing I was bent on it, all she did was to cry a little and to turn about to her work. The truth is my dander was up and nothing but war should bring it right again.

I went to Winchester where a muster was to be. When the men were paraded, a lawyer by the name of Jones addressed us; informing us he wished to raise a company, and that then the men should meet and elect their officers. I believe I was about the second or third man that stepped out; but on marching up and down the regiment a few times we found we had a large company.

We volunteered for sixty days, as it was supposed our services would not be longer needed. A day or two after this we met and elected Mr. Jones our Captain, and also elected our other officers. We then received orders to start on the next Monday week; the time arrived, I took a parting farewell of my wife and two little boys, mounted my horse and set sail to join my company. Expecting only to be gone a short time, I took no more clothing with me than I supposed would be necessary; so that if I got into an Indian battle, I might not be pestered with any unnecessary plunder to prevent my having a fair chance with them. We all met and went ahead till we passed Huntsville and camped at a large spring called Beaty's Spring. Here we stayed several days, in which time the troops began to collect from all

I SAID FAREWELL TO MY WIFE AND CHILDREN

quarters. At last we mustered about thirteen hundred strong; all mounted volunteers and all determined to fight, judging from myself, for I felt wolfish all over. I verily believe the whole army was of the real grit.

While we remained at the spring, a Major Gibson came and wanted some volunteers to go

with him across the Tennessee River and into the
Creek nation to find out the movements of the
Indians. He came to my Captain and asked for
two of his best woodsmen and such as were best
with the rifle. The Captain pointed me out to him,
and said he would be security that I would go as
far as the major would himself, or any other man.

I willingly engaged to go with him, and asked
him to let me choose my own mate to go with me,
which he said he would let me do. I chose a young
man by the name of George Russell, son of old
Major Russell of Tennessee. I called him out, but
Major Gibson said he thought he hadn't beard
enough to please him—he wanted men, not boys.
I must confess I was a little wrathy with this, for
I know'd George Russell and I know'd there was
no mistake in him and I didn't think that courage
ought to be measured by the beard; for here a goat
would have the preference over a man. I told the
major he was on the wrong scent; that Russell
could go as far as he could, and I must have him
along. He saw I was a little wrathy and said I
had the best chance of knowing, and agreed it
should be as I wanted it.

We took our camp equipage and mounted our
horses; and thirteen in number, including the
major, we cut out. We crossed the Tennessee
River and then traveled about seven miles further,
and took up camp for the night. The next morning, Major Gibson and myself concluded we should
separate and take different directions to see what
discoveries we could make; so he took six of the
men and I five. We were to meet that evening
where the roads came together, fifteen miles the

other side of the house of a Cherokee Indian named Dick Brown.

I and my men then started and went on to the place of meeting, but Major Gibson was not there. We waited till almost dark, but still he didn't come. We left the Indian trail a little distance and turning into the head of a hollow, we struck up camp. We stayed next morning till after breakfast; but in vain, for still the major didn't come. We started ahead and went about twenty miles to the house of a man by the name of Radcliff. He was a white man, but had married a Creek woman, and lived just in the edge of a Creek nation. He had two sons, large, likely fellows; and a great deal of potatoes and corn; so we fed our horses and got dinner with him. But he was bad scared all the time; he told us that there had been ten painted warriors at his house only an hour before, and if we were discovered there, they would kill us, and his family with us. I replied to him, that my business was to hunt for just such fellows as he had described, and I was determined not to go back until I had done it.

Our dinner being over we saddled up our horses and made ready to start; but some of my small company I found were disposed to return. I told them if we were to go back we should never hear the last of it; and I was determined to go ahead. I know'd some of them would go with me and the rest were afraid to go back by themselves; and so we pushed on to the camp of some friendly Creeks, which was distant about eight miles. The moon was about at the full, and the night was clear; we therefore had the benefit of her light from night to

morning, and I knew if we were placed in such
danger as to make retreat necessary, we could
travel by night as well as in the daytime. It was
after dark when we got to the camp, where we
found about forty men, women and children.

They had bows and arrows, and I turned to
shooting with their bows by the pine light. In this
way we amused ourselves very well for a while, but
at last a negro, who had been talking to the Indians,
came to me and told me they were very much
alarmed, for the *Red Sticks,* as they called the war
party of the Creeks, would come and find us there;
and if so, we should all be killed. I directed him
to tell them that I would watch, and if one would
come that night, I should carry the skin of his head
home to make me a moccasin. When he made this
communication, the Indians laughed aloud.

At about ten o'clock that night, we all concluded
to try to sleep a little, but that our horses might
be ready for use, we tied them up with their sad-
dles on them and put everything in readiness in
case in the night our quarters should get uncomfortable. We laid down with our guns in our arms,
and I had just gotten into a dozing sleep when I
heard the sharpest scream that ever escaped the
throat of a human creature. It was more like a
wrathy painter[1] than anything else. The negro
understood, and he sprang to me, for though I
heard the noise well enough, yet I wasn't wide
awake enough to get up; so the negro caught me
and said the Red Sticks was coming. I arose
quickly then and asked what was the matter. Our

i. The name *painter* is a corruption of *panther,* and is applied
in the United States to the cougar or American lion.

negro talked with the Indian, who had just fetched
the scream, and learned from him that he had come
into camp as a runner, and said that the war party
had been crossing the Coosa River all day at the
Ten Islands and was going then to meet Jackson.
This news very much alarmed the friendly Indians,
who were in the camp, and they were all off in ten
minutes.

I felt bound to make this intelligence known as
soon as possible to the army which we had left; and
so we all mounted our horses and put out in a long
lope to make our way back to that place. We were
about sixty-five miles off. We went on to the
Cherokee town we had visited on our way out, having called at Radcliff's, who was off with his family. At the town we found large fires burning, but
not a single Indian was to be seen. They were all
gone, and it appeared we must be in great danger.
We therefore stayed only a short time in the light
of the fires about the town, preferring the light of
the moon and the shade of the woods.

We pushed on till we got again to old Mr.
Brown's, which was still about thirty miles from
where we had left the main army. When we got
there, the chickens were just at the first crowing
for day. We fed our horses, got a morsel to eat
ourselves, and again cut out.

About ten o'clock in the morning we reached the
camp, and I reported to Colonel Coffee the news.
He didn't seem to mind my report a bit, and this
raised my dander higher than ever; but I know'd
I had to be on my best behavior, and so I kept it
all to myself; though I was so mad that I was burning inside like a tar-kiln, and I wonder that the

smoke hadn't been pouring out of me at all points. Major Gibson hadn't yet returned, and we all began to think he was killed.

The next day, though, the major got in, and brought a worse tale than I had, though he stated the same facts as far as I went. This seemed to put our colonel all into a fidget; and it convinced me clearly of one of the hateful ways of the world. When I made my report, it wasn't believed because I was no officer: I was no great man, but just a poor soldier; but when the same thing was reported by Major Gibson! why, then it was all as true as preaching, and the Colonel believed it, every word.

He therefore ordered breastworks to be thrown up nearly a quarter of a mile along; and sent an express to General Jackson, requesting him to push on like the very mischief, for fear we should all be cooked up to a cracklin before they could get there. "Old Hickory-face" made a forced march on getting the news, and on the next day he and his men got into camp with their feet all blistered from the effects of their swift journey. The volunteers therefore stood guard all together to let them rest.

About eight hundred of the volunteers, and of that number I was one, were sent on through Huntsville so as to get on the Indians in another direction. After we passed Huntsville, we struck the Tennessee River at Melton's Bluff. The river is here about two miles wide, and has so rough a bottom in many places as to be dangerous. At this place we left some of the horses with their feet held fast in the crevices of the rocks; their riders went on foot.

We pushed on till we got to what was called the

Black Warrior's town, which stood near the very spot where Tuscaloosa now stands. This Indian town was a large one, but when we arrived we

FOUND A DEER THAT HAD JUST BEEN KILLED

found the Indians had all left it, scared off no doubt by our arrival. There was a large field of corn standing out with a pretty good supply in some cribs. Without delay we secured the corn as well as a fine quantity of dried beans, which were very acceptable to us. Then we burned the town and left the place.

The next day we were entirely out of meat. I went to Colonel Coffee, who was then in command of us, and asked his leave to hunt when we marched. He gave me leave, but told me to take mighty good care of myself. I turned aside to hunt, and had not gone far when I found a deer that had just been killed, for his flesh was still warm and smoking. From this I was sure that the Indians who had killed it had been gone only a few minutes, and though I was never much in favor of one hunter stealing from another, yet meat was so scarce in camp, I just took up the deer on my horse before me and carried it on till night.

I could have sold it for almost any price I would have asked, but this wasn't my rule either in peace or war. Whenever I had anything and saw a fellow-being suffering, I was more anxious to relieve him than to benefit myself; and this is one of the true secrets of my being a poor man to this day. I gave all my deer away except a small part I kept for myself and just sufficient to make a good supper for my mess. We had to live mostly on parched corn.

The next night I told my mess I would again try for some meat; so I took my rifle and cut out, but hadn't gone far when I discovered a large gang of hogs. I shot one of them down in his tracks, and the rest broke directly toward the camp. In a few minutes the guns began to roar as bad as if the whole army had been in an Indian battle, and the hogs to squeal as bad as the pig did when the devil turned barber. I shouldered my hog and went on to camp, and when I got there I found they had killed a good many hogs and a fine fat cow into the bargain. The next morning we marched on to a Cherokee town and gave the inhabitants an order on Uncle Sam for the cow and the hogs we had killed.

The next day we met the main army and all went on to Radcliff's. There we found he had hid all his provisions, and learned that, when I was out as a spy, he had sent a runner to the Indian camp with the news that the Red Sticks were crossing at Ten Islands in order to scare me and my men away with a false alarm. To make some atonement for this, we took the old scoundrel's two big sons with us, and made them serve through the war.

We marched to the Ten Islands on the Coosa River, where we established a fort and sent out spy companies. They soon made prisoners of Bob Catala and his warriors, and in a few days brought news of some Indians in a town about eight miles off. So we mounted our horses, and put out for that town under the direction of two friendly Creeks.

When we got near the town, we divided, one of our pilots going with each division. Thus we passed on each side of the town, keeping near to it until our lines met at both sides. We then closed up at both ends so as to surround it completely, and sent Captain Hammond to bring on the affray. When he came near the town, the Indians saw him, raised a yell and came running at him like so many red devils. The main army was now formed in a hollow square around the town, to which Hammond retreated till the Indians came within reach. We then gave them a fire and they returned it, after which they ran back into their town, when we began to close on it. The Indians soon saw they were on our property, and wanted us to take them prisoners. Their squaws and children would run and take hold of us as they could, and give themselves up. I saw seven squaws at a time holding on to the hunting-shirt of one man. We took all prisoners that came out to us in this way. I saw some warriors, however, run into a house until I counted forty-six of them. We pursued them until we got near the house, when we saw a squaw sitting in the door. She placed her feet against the bow she had in her hand, took an arrow, raised her feet, drew with all her might and let the arrow fly at us, killing Lieutenant Moore, I believe. His death so enraged us all that she was fired on, and at least twenty balls were blown through her. This was the first man I ever saw killed with a bow and arrow. We now shot them down like dogs, and then set the house on fire, burning it with the forty-six warriors inside.

I remember seeing an Indian boy, who was shot down near the house. His arm and thigh were broken, and he was so near the burning house that his flesh was fairly cooking. In this situation he was still trying to crawl along, but not a murmur escaped him, though he was only twelve years old. When an Indian's dander is up, he would sooner die than make a noise, or ask for quarter.

The number that we took prisoners being added to the number we killed amounted to one hundred and eighty-six, while five of our men were killed.

PILOTED BY FRIENDLY INDIANS

We then returned to our fort, but no provisions had yet reached us, and we had been for some time on half rations. For several days we remained there almost starving, as all our beef was gone. Then we commenced eating beef hides, and consumed every scrap we could lay our hands on, before we received orders for marching.

We crossed the Coosa River, and when we had come near to Fort Taladega, we met eleven hundred painted warriors, the very choice of the Creek nation, who had shut up the friendly Indians in the fort, and threatened that if they did not come out and fight against the whites, they would lose their fort, ammunition and provisions. The friendly Indians had asked three days to consider their answers, and had immediately started a runner to Captain Jackson, and it was the receipt of this message that had caused us to come over.

The Creeks from their spies had discovered us coming, and told the friendly Indians that we had a great many fine horses and blankets and guns and everything else, and if they would come out and help whip Captain Jackson, they should share the plunder. This they promised to do.

About an hour after sunrise in the morning, piloted by some friendly Indians, we came near the fort and divided as we had done in our former battle; so as to form around the Indians, as before, a hollow square. This time we sent Major Russell and Captain Evans with their companies to bring on the battle.

When they got near the fort, they saw that the top of it was lined with friendly Indians crying out as loud as they could roar—"How-de-do, brothers!

How-de-do!" They kept this up till Major Russell
had passed by the fort and was moving on toward
the besiegers.

The Creeks had concealed themselves under the
bank of a branch that run partly around the fort,
in the manner of a half moon. They were all
painted as red as scarlet, and were just as naked
as they were born. Russell could not see them, and
was going right into their circle; although the
friendly Indians on the top of the fort were trying
every plan to show him his danger. He could not
understand them, but at last two of them jumped
from the fort, ran and took his horse by the bridle,
and pointing, told him there were thousands of
Creeks lying under the bank. This brought his
company to a halt.

At the same moment the Creeks fired on them
and came rushing forth from their hiding place like
a cloud of Egyptian locusts, and screaming like
all the young devils had been turned loose with the
old devil at their head. Russell's company jumped
from their horses and hurried into the fort, while
their horses ran up to our line, which by this time
was come into full view.

The warriors came yelling on until they were
within shot of us, when we fired and killed considerable of them. They then broke like a gang of
steers, and ran across to the other line, where they
were again fired on. And so we kept them running from one line to the other, constantly under
a heavy fire, until we had killed upwards of four
hundred of them. They fought with guns and
also with their bows and arrows, but at length they
made their escape through a part of our line, which

was made up of drafted militia. We lost fifteen
of our men, as brave fellows as ever lived or died.
We buried them all in one grave, and started back
to our fort, but before we got there two more of
our men died with wounds they had received.

We now remained at the fort a few days, but as
no provisions came, we were all liable to perish.
The weather also began to get very cold, our clothes
were nearly worn out, and our horses getting very
feeble and poor; so we proposed to General Jackson to let us return home, get fresh horses and fresh
clothing, and so be prepared for another campaign.
The sixty days for which we had enlisted had long
gone out. The General, however, issued his orders
against it. Nevertheless, we began to fix for a start
home, but the General placed his cannon on a
bridge we had to cross, and ordered out his regu-
lars and drafted men to keep us from passing. But
when the militia started to guard the bridge, they
would shout back to us to bring their knapsacks
along when we came, for they wanted to go as bad
as we did. We moved on till we reached the bridge,
where the General's men were all strung along on
both sides, but we all had our flints ready picked,
and our guns ready, so that if we were fired upon,
we might fight our way through or all die together.
When we came still nearer the bridge, we heard
the guards cocking their guns, and we did the same;
but not a gun was fired nor a life lost. When we
had passed the bridge, no further attempt was made
to stop us. The General said we were the worst
volunteers he had ever seen. That we would volunteer and go out and fight, and then that we would
volunteer and go home again in spite of the devil.

After we had procured fresh horses and a more suitable supply of clothing, a few of us pushed on to the army again. I joined Major Russell's company of spies and overtook General Jackson, where we established Fort Williams. Then we pushed on to the Horseshoe bend of the Tallapoosa River, where we began to find Indian signs in plenty.

Here we struck up camp for the night; but about two hours before day we heard our guard firing and were all up in little or no time. We mended up our camp fires and then fell back into the dark, expecting to see the Indians pouring in, and intending, when they should do so, to shoot them by the light of our own fires. It so happened, however, that the Indians did not rush in as we expected, but commenced a fire on us as we were. This we returned and continued to shoot as well as we could in the dark, guided only by the flash of the Indians' guns. When day broke, the Indians disappeared, but they had killed four of our men and wounded several. Whether we killed any of the Indians or not, we could not tell, for it is their custom to carry off their dead whenever they can. We buried ours all in one grave and laid logs over them and set them afire, so that the savages might not find them when they returned, as we knew they would do, to scalp the slain.

We made some horse-litters for our wounded, and took up our retreat. We had to cross a large creek, and when about half our men were over, the Indians commenced firing and kept it up very warmly. They hid themselves behind a large log and could kill one of our men, who were in open ground and exposed, with almost every shot. At this trying moment two of our colonels left their men, and by a *forced march* crossed the creek out of the reach of the fire. Here Governor Carroll distinguished himself by a greater bravery than I ever saw in any other man. In truth, I believe that if it hadn't been for Carroll, we should all have been genteelly licked that time; with part of our men on one side of the creek and part on the other, and the Indians all the time pouring it in on us as hot as fresh mustard is to sore skin. I know I was mighty glad when the savages quit us, for I began to think there was one behind every tree in the woods.

Soon after this, an army was raised to go to Pensacola, and I determined to go again with them, for I wanted a small taste of British fighting and supposed I would find it there. I joined old Major Russell again and followed on after the main army with about a hundred and thirty men in our company. We crossed the river near where I had crossed when I first went out; then we passed through the Choctaw and Chickasaw nations to what is called the Cut-off at the junction of the Tom Bigby with the Alabama River.

This place is near the old Fort Mimms where the Indians committed the great butchery at the commencement of the war. The fort was built right in the middle of a large old field; and before the massacre the people had been there so long and lived so quietly that they didn't apprehend any danger at all, and had therefore become quite careless. A small negro boy, whose business it was to bring up the calves at milking time, had been out for that purpose, and on coming back he said he saw a great many Indians. At this the inhabitants took alarm,

closed their gates and put out guards who continued
to watch for a few days. Finding that no attack
was made, they concluded the little negro had lied,
and again threw their gates open and sent out their
hands to work their fields. The same boy set out
again on the same errand, and returned in great
haste and alarm, and informed them he had seen
the Indians as thick as trees in the woods. He was
not believed, but was tied up to receive a flogging
for the supposed lie. In fact he was actually getting
badly licked at the very moment when the Indians
came in a troop. They were loaded with rails with
which they stopped all the portholes of the fort on
one side, and then they fell to cutting down the
picketing. Those inside the fort had only the bastion to shoot from, and as fast as one Indian would
fall, another would catch up his ax and chop away
until they succeeded in cutting down enough of the
picketing to permit them to enter. Then they
rushed through and immediately commenced scalping without regard to age or sex. Having forced
the inhabitants up to one side of the fort, they carried on the work as a butcher would in a slaughter
pen.

This scene was partly described to me by a young
man who was in the fort when it happened. He said
that he saw his father and mother, his four sisters
and the same number of brothers all butchered in
the most shocking manner, and that he made his
escape by running over the heads of the crowd to
the top of the fort, and then jumped off and ran
into the woods. He was closely pursued by several Indians until he came to a small bayou, across
which there was a log. He knew the log was hol-

THE ATTACK ON THE FORT

low on the under side, so he slipped off and hid himself. He said he heard the Indians walk over him, back and forward several times. Nevertheless he remained quiet there until night, when he came out and finished his escape.

We left our horses at the Cut-off and hurried on foot over the eighty miles to Pensacola, where our arrival was hailed with great applause; though we were a little after the feast, for they had taken the town and fort before we got there. The next morning we started back toward old Fort Mimms, where we remained two or three days until General Jackson and the main army set out for New Orleans; while we, under the command of Major Russell, turned south to attack the Indians on the Scamby River.

At Fort Montgomery, about a mile and a half from old Fort Mimms, we remained for some days, where we supplied ourselves pretty well with beef by killing wild cattle, which had formerly belonged to the people who had perished in the fort. At last we moved out on the Scamby River, near which we camped a thousand men, of whom about two hundred were Chickasaw and Choctaw Indians. The Indians had all along proposed to cross the river, and thinking it might be well for them to do so, Major Russell and I with fifteen other men went with them, and early the next morning set out from the river bank. We soon came to a place where the whole country was covered with water, and it looked like a sea. We didn't stop for this, but just put in like so many spaniels and waded on, sometimes up to our armpits, until we reached the pine hills about a mile and a half away. Here we struck up a fire to warm ourselves, for it was cold and we were chilled through. Again we moved on, keeping our spies out; two to our left near the bank of the river, two straight before us, and five others on our right.

We had gone in this way about six miles up the river, when our spies on the left came to us, leaping about like so many old bucks, and informed us that they had discovered a camp of Creek Indians and that we must kill them. Here we paused for a few minutes, and the prophets pow-wowed over their men awhile and then got out their paint and painted them all according to their custom when going into battle. Then they brought their paint to old Major Russell and said to him, that as he was an officer he must be painted too. He agreed, and they painted him just as themselves. We let the Indians understand that we white men would first fire on the camp and then fall back so as to give the Indians a chance to rush on them and scalp them. The Chickasaws marched on our left hand and the Choctaws on our right, and thus we moved on till we came in hearing of the camp. On nearer approach we found they were on an island, and we could not get to them.

While we were chatting about this matter we heard some guns fired, and in a very short time after a keen whoop. With that we all broke like a quarter-horses for the firing. There we met our two front spies, who said they had met two Creeks who were out hunting their horses, and as there was a large cluster of green bay bushes exactly between them, they were within a few feet of meeting before either was discovered. Our spies, speaking in the

Shawnee tongue, said they were escaping from
General Jackson, who was at Pensacola, and that
they wanted to know where they could get something to eat. The Creeks told them that nine miles
up the Conaker River was a large camp of Creeks
where they had cattle and plenty to eat; and that
their own camp was on an island about a mile off,
just below the mouth of the Conaker. Then the
four struck up a fire, smoked together, shook hands
and parted. One of the Creeks had a gun, but the
other had none. As soon as they had parted, our
Choctaws turned around and shot down the one that
had the gun. When the other started to run off,
they snapped at him several times, but as the gun
missed fire, they ran after him and one of them
clubbed him to death with the gun. In doing so
they broke the gun, but they fired off the one the
Creek had had, and raised a whoop of victory.
When we reached them they had cut off the heads
of both the Indians and stood ready to scalp them.

Moving on, we came to where a Spaniard, together with a woman whom we supposed to be his
wife, and four children, had all been killed and
scalped. It was now late evening, and we came
down to the river bank opposite the Indian camp,
where some friendly Creeks who were with us said
they would decoy the Indians from the island. Although they could not call the Indians over, they
did succeed in learning that a canoe belonging to
the Indians was on our side of the river. Soon we
found it, and forty of our warriors crossed over to
take the camp. When they arrived they found only
one man in the camp, and he escaped; but they captured two squaws and ten children.

For some time after this we marched about, and had several skirmishes with the Indians, in which we killed several of them. We suffered most from lack of food, and were very hard put to it to keep soul and body together; but by hunting a great deal, we managed to live till we met some East Tennessee troops who were on the road to Mobile, and my youngest brother was with them. They had plenty of corn and provisions, and I remained with them until next morning.

Nothing more that is worthy of the reader's attention transpired till I was safely landed at home once more with my wife and children. I found them, however, doing well, and though I was only a rough sort of a backwoodsman, they seemed mighty glad to see me, however little the quality folks might suppose it. For I do reckon we love as hard in the backwoods country as any people in creation.

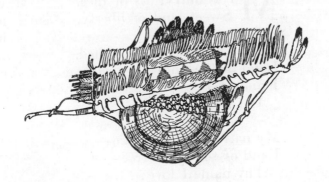

AMERICA

By SAMUEL FRANCIS SMITH

NOTE.—This poem, which is now considered by many to be the great national hymn of the United States, was sung first at a Fourth of July celebration for children in the Park Street Church, Boston.

The author was born in Boston in 1808, and graduated from Harvard University in the same class with Oliver Wendell Holmes. When Smith wrote *America* he was a student in the Andover Theological Seminary. Many years after they had left college, Dr. Holmes at a reunion of his class read his famous poem *The Boys*. In it he alludes to Samuel Francis Smith as follows:

"He chanted a song for the brave and the free;
Just read on his medal 'My country, of thee.'"

MY country, 'tis of thee,
Sweet land of liberty,
Of thee I sing;
Land where my fathers died,
Land of the pilgrims' pride,
From every mountain side
Let freedom ring.

My native country, thee—
Land of the noble free—
Thy name I love;
I love thy rocks and rills,
Thy woods and templed hills,
My heart with rapture thrills
Like that above.

Let music swell the breeze,
And ring from all the trees
　　Sweet freedom's song;
Let mortal tongues awake;
Let all that breathe partake;
Let rocks their silence break—
　　The sound prolong.

Our fathers' God, to thee,
Author of liberty,
　　To thee we sing:
Long may our land be bright,
With freedom's holy light;
Protect us by thy might,
　　Great God, our King.

Perhaps few who know *America* and who sing it well understand it thoroughly.

There are a few historical allusions in it. Who were the pilgrims? Why did the pilgrims take pride in the land? Does the author mean Puritans when he says pilgrims?

The first stanza turned into prose might read something as follows: I sing of thee, my own country, the sweet land of liberty. Let all the people who live in this land where our fathers died, in this land which was the pilgrims' pride, sing songs of freedom till they ring from every mountain side.

In the second stanza the poet in his religious fervor thinks of the hills as being like temples. He calls America the land of the noble free, meaning the noble freemen. Sometimes this line is printed with a comma after the word *noble*. Then the line means land of the noble man, the free man. The stanza as a whole might be rendered into prose after this manner: I love thee, my country, thou land of the noble free, and I love thy name; I love, too, thy rocks, rills, woods and templed hills, and my heart thrills with rapture like that which is felt by the angels above.

The meaning of the third stanza is clearer if we put it into prose as follows: Let music swell grandly on the breeze, and let the sweet song of freedom ring from all the trees; let every human being sing the song; let all living things join in the chorus. Let even the rocks break the silence and prolong the music with their echoes.

The last stanza means this: O Thou great God, who protected our fathers in the wilderness and who created for them and their descendants the liberty we enjoy, to Thee we offer this devout song and prayer: "Through all the coming centuries may our land be free, and do Thou, great God our King, protect us by Thy far-reaching power."

We should learn to think of a song like this as a unit, a perfect whole, and the following summary will aid us in so doing:

First stanza—I sing this song about my country, and may such songs of freedom ring everywhere within it.

Second stanza.—I love my country and every good thing in it devotedly.

Third stanza.—Let every one join in songs of freedom.

Fourth stanza.—We sing praises to God, and ask Him to protect us, and keep freedom forever ours.

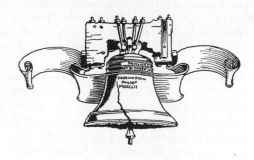

THE RETREAT OF CORTES*

By WILLIAM H. PRESCOTT

HERE was no longer any question as to the expediency of evacuating the capital. The only doubt was as to the time of doing so, and the route. The Spanish commander called a council of officers to deliberate on these matters. It was his purpose to retreat on Tlascala, and in that capital to decide according to circumstances on his future operations. After some discussion, they agreed on the causeway of Tlacopan as the avenue by which to leave the city. It would, indeed, take them back by a circuitous route, considerably longer than either of those by

---

*NOTE.—Hernando Cortes, the conqueror of Mexico, sailed from Cuba, which he had assisted in subduing, for the mainland, where he landed in the spring of 1519. After tarrying on the coast for a time, and founding the city of Vera Cruz, he started inland, passing first through the country of the Tlascalans, who were easily induced to submit to him, and who became his most faithful native allies. By November, 1519, the Spaniards had reached the city of Mexico, the capital of the Aztecs, and here they established themselves.

The chief of the Aztecs, Montezuma, determined not to offer serious opposition to the Spaniards, but Cortes was distrustful of the Aztecs, and managed to secure possession of Montezuma, whom he kept as a hostage. Called from the city of Mexico by an expedition which had been sent against him from Cuba, Cortes returned as soon as possible, only to find that the Aztecs had adopted a more aggressive policy. His men were surrounded and attacked as soon as they entered the city, and the attacks were kept up from day to day. Finally, when Montezuma died, it became clear to Cortes that a longer stay in the city would be impossible. This extract from Prescott's *The Conquest of Mexico* tells the story of the retreat.

63

which they had approached the capital. But, for that reason, it would be less likely to be guarded, as least suspected; and the causeway itself, being shorter than either of the other entrances, would sooner place the army in comparative security on the mainland.

There was some difference of opinion in respect to the hour of departure. The daytime, it was argued by some, would be preferable, since it would enable them to see the nature and extent of their danger, and to provide against it. Darkness would be much more likely to embarrass their own movements than those of the enemy, who were familiar with the ground. A thousand impediments would occur in the night, which might prevent them acting in concert, or obeying, or even ascertaining, the orders of the commander. But, on the other hand, it was urged that the night presented many obvious advantages in dealing with a foe who rarely carried his hostilities beyond the day. The late active operations of the Spaniards had thrown the Mexicans off their guard, and it was improbable they would anticipate so speedy a departure of their enemies. With celerity and caution, they might succeed, therefore, in making their escape from the town, possibly over the causeway, before their retreat should be discovered; and, could they once get beyond that pass of peril, they felt little apprehension for the rest.

The general had already superintended the construction of a portable bridge to be laid over the open canals in the causeway. This was given in charge to an officer named Magarino, with forty soldiers under his orders, all pledged to defend the bridge to the last extremity. The bridge was to be taken up when the entire army had crossed one of the breaches, and transported to the next. There were three of these openings in the causeway, and most fortunate would it have been for the expedition, if the foresight of the commander had provided the same number of bridges. But the labor would have been great, and the time was short.

At midnight the troops were under arms, in readiness for the march. Mass was performed by Father Olmedo, who invoked the protection of the Almighty through the awful perils of the night. The gates were thrown open, and, on the first of July, 1520, the Spaniards for the last time sallied forth from the walls of the ancient fortress, the scene of so much suffering and such indomitable courage.

The night was cloudy, and a drizzling rain, which fell without intermission, added to the obscurity. The great square before the palace was deserted, as, indeed, it had been since the fall of Montezuma. Steadily, and as noiselessly as possible, the Spaniards held their way along the great street of Tlacopan, which so lately had resounded to the tumult of battle. All was now hushed in silence; and they were only reminded of the past by the occasional presence of some solitary corpse, or a dark heap of the slain, which too plainly told where the strife had been hottest. As they passed along the lanes and alleys which opened into the great street, or looked down the canals, whose polished surface gleamed with a sort of ebon lustre through the obscurity of the night, they easily fancied they discerned the shadowy forms of their foe lurking in ambush, and ready to spring on them. But it was only fancy; and the city slept undisturbed even by the prolonged echoes of the tramp of horses, and the hoarse rumbling of the artillery and baggage trains. At length, a lighter space beyond the dusky line of buildings showed the van of the army that it was emerging on the open causeway. They might well have congratulated themselves on having thus escaped the dangers of assault in the city itself, and that a brief time would place them in comparative safety on the opposite shore. But the Mexicans were not all asleep.

As the Spaniards drew near the spot where the street opened on the causeway, and were preparing to lay the portable bridge across the uncovered breach which now met their eyes, several Indian sentinels, who had been stationed at this, as at the other approaches to the city, took alarm and fled, rousing their countrymen by their cries. The priests, keeping their night watch on the summit of the *teocallis,* instantly caught the tidings and sounded their shells, while the huge drum in the desolate temple of the war-god sent forth those solemn tones, which, heard only in seasons of calamity, vibrated through every corner of the capital. The Spaniards saw that no time was to be lost. The bridge was brought forward and fitted with all possible expedition. Sandoval was the first to try its strength, and, riding across, was followed by his little body of cavalry, his infantry, and Tlascalan allies, who formed the first divisions of the army. Then came Cortes and his squadrons, with the baggage, ammunition wagons, and a part of the artillery. But before they had time to defile across the

narrow passage, a gathering sound was heard, like
that of a mighty forest agitated by the winds. It
grew louder and louder, while on the dark waters of
the lake was heard a plashing noise, as of many
oars. Then came a few stones and arrows striking
at random among the troops. They fell every
moment faster and more furious, till they thickened into a terrible tempest, while the very heavens
were rent with the yells and war cries of myriads
of combatants, who seemed all at once to be swarm-
ing over land and lake!

The Spaniards pushed steadily on through this
arrowy sleet, though the barbarians, dashing their
canoes against the sides of the causeway, clambered
up and broke in upon their ranks. But the Christians, anxious only to make their escape, declined
all combat except for self-preservation. The cavaliers, spurring forward their steeds, shook off their
assailants, and rode over their prostrate bodies,
while the men on foot with their good swords or the
butts of their pieces drove them headlong again
down the sides of the dike.

But the advance of several thousand men, marching, probably, on a front of not more than fifteen
or twenty abreast, necessarily required much time,
and the leading files had already reached the second
breach in the causeway before those in the rear had
entirely traversed the first. Here they halted, as
they had no means of effecting a passage, smarting
all the while under unintermitting volleys from the
enemy, who were clustered thick on the waters
around this second opening. Sorely distressed, the
vanguard sent repeated messages to the rear to
demand the portable bridge. At length the last

of the army had crossed, and Magarino and his sturdy followers endeavoured to raise the ponderous frame-work. But it stuck fast in the sides of the dike. In vain they strained every nerve. The weight of so many men and horses, and above all of the heavy artillery, had wedged the timbers so firmly in the stones and earth, that it was beyond their power to dislodge them. Still they laboured amidst a torrent of missiles, until, many of them slain, and all wounded, they were obliged to abandon the attempt.

The tidings soon spread from man to man, and no sooner was their dreadful import comprehended, than a cry of despair arose, which for a moment drowned all the noise of conflict. All means of retreat were cut off. Scarcely hope was left. The only hope was in such desperate exertions as each could make for himself. Order and subordination were at an end. Intense danger produced intense selfishness. Each thought only of his own life. Pressing forward, he trampled down the weak and the wounded, heedless whether it were friend or foe. The leading files, urged on by the rear, were crowded on the brink of the gulf. Sandoval, Ordaz, and the other cavaliers dashed into the water. Some succeeded in swimming their horses across. Others failed, and some, who reached the opposite bank, being overturned in the ascent, rolled headlong with their steeds into the lake. The infantry followed pell-mell, heaped promiscuously on one another, or struck down by the war clubs of the Aztecs; while many an unfortunate victim was dragged half-stunned on board their canoes, to be reserved for a protracted, but more dreadful death.

The carnage raged fearfully along the length of
the causeway. Its shadowy bulk presented a mark
of sufficient distinctness for the enemy's missiles,

BATTLE ON THE CAUSEWAY

which often prostrated their own countrymen in the
blind fury of the tempest. Those nearest the dike,
running their canoes alongside, with a force that
shattered them to pieces, leaped on the land, and

grappled with the Christians, until both came rolling down the side of the causeway together. But the Aztec fell among his friends, while his antagonist was borne away in triumph to the sacrifice. The struggle was long and deadly. The Mexicans were recognized by their white cotton tunics, which showed faint through the darkness. Above the combatants rose a wild and discordant clamor, in which horrid shouts of vengeance were mingled with groans of agony, with invocations of the saints and the Blessed Virgin, and with the screams of women; for there were several women, both natives and Spaniards, who had accompanied the Christian camp. Among these, one named Maria de Estrada is particularly noticed for the courage she displayed, battling with broadsword and target like the staunchest of the warriors.

The opening in the causeway, meanwhile, was filled up with the wreck of matter which had been forced into it, ammunition wagons, heavy guns, bales of rich stuffs scattered over the waters, chests of solid ingots, and bodies of men and horses, till over this dismal ruin a passage was gradually formed, by which those in the rear were enabled to clamber to the other side. Cortes, it is said, found a place that was fordable, where, halting, with the water up to his saddle girths, he endeavoured to check the confusion, and lead his followers by a safer path to the opposite bank. But his voice was lost in the wild uproar, and finally, hurrying on with the tide, he pressed forward with a few trusty cavaliers, who remained near his person, to the van; but not before he had seen his favorite page, Juan de Salazar, struck down, a corpse, by his

side. Here he found Sandoval and his companions,
halting before the third and last breach, endeavouring to cheer on their followers to surmount it. But
their resolution faltered. It was wide and deep;
though the passage was not so closely beset by
the enemy as the preceding ones. The cavaliers
again set the example by plunging into the water.
Horse and foot followed as they could, some swimming, others with dying grasp clinging to the
manes and tails of the struggling animals. Those
fared best, as the general had predicted, who traveled lightest; and many were the unfortunate
wretches, who, weighed down by the fatal gold
which they loved so well, were buried with it in the
salt floods of the lake. Cortes, with his gallant
comrades, Olid, Morla, Sandoval, and some few
others, still kept in the advance, leading his broken
remnant off the fatal causeway. The din of battle lessened in the distance; when the rumor reached
them, that the rearguard would be wholly overwhelmed without speedy relief. It seemed almost
an act of desperation; but the generous hearts of
the Spanish cavaliers did not stop to calculate danger, when the cry for succour reached them. Turning their horses' bridles, they galloped back to the
theatre of action, worked their way through the
press, swam the canal, and placed themselves in
the thick of the mêlée on the opposite bank.

The first grey of the morning was now coming
over the waters. It showed the hideous confusion
of the scene which had been shrouded in the obscurity of night. The dark masses of combatants,
stretching along the dike, were seen struggling for
mastery, until the very causeway on which they

stood appeared to tremble, and reel to and fro, as if shaken by an earthquake; while the bosom of the lake, as far as the eye could reach, was darkened by canoes crowded with warriors, whose spears and bludgeons, armed with blades of "volcanic glass," gleamed in the morning light.

The cavaliers found Alvarado unhorsed, and defending himself with a poor handful of followers against an overwhelming tide of the enemy. His good steed, which had borne him through many a hard fight, had fallen under him. He was himself wounded in several places, and was striving in vain to rally his scattered column, which was driven to the verge of the canal by the fury of the enemy, then in possession of the whole rear of the causeway, where they were reinforced every hour by fresh combatants from the city. The artillery in the earlier part of the engagement had not been idle, and its iron shower, sweeping along the dike, had mowed down the assailants by hundreds. But nothing could resist their impetuosity. The front ranks, pushed on by those behind, were at length forced up to the pieces, and, pouring over them like a torrent, overthrew men and guns in one general ruin. The resolute charge of the Spanish cavaliers, who had now arrived, created a temporary check, and gave time for their countrymen to make a feeble rally. But they were speedily borne down by the returning flood. Cortes and his companions were compelled to plunge again into the lake, though all did not escape. Alvarado stood on the brink for a moment, hesitating what to do. Unhorsed as he was, to throw himself into the water, in the face of the hostile canoes that now swarmed

around the opening, afforded but a desperate
chance of safety. He had but a second for thought.
He was a man of powerful frame, and despair
gave him unnatural energy. Setting his long lance
firmly on the wreck which strewed the bottom of
the lake, he sprung forward with all his might,
and cleared the wide gap at a leap! Aztecs and
Tlascalans gazed in stupid amazement, exclaiming,
as they beheld the incredible feat, "This is truly the
Tonatiuh,—the child of the Sun!"—The breadth of
the opening is not given. But it was so great, that
the valorous Captain Diaz, who well remembered
the place, says the leap was impossible to any man.
Other contemporaries, however, do not discredit the
story. It was, beyond doubt, a matter of popular belief at the time; it is to this day familiarly
known to every inhabitant of the capital; and the
name of the *Salto de Alvarado,* "Alvarado's Leap,"
given to the spot, still commemorates an exploit
which rivaled those of the demi-gods of Grecian
fable.

Cortes and his companions now rode forward to
the front, where the troops, in a loose, disorderly
manner, were marching off the fatal causeway. A
few only of the enemy hung on their rear, or annoyed them by occasional flights of arrows from
the lake. The attention of the Aztecs was diverted
by the rich spoil that strewed the battle-ground;
fortunately for the Spaniards, who, had their
enemy pursued with the same ferocity with which
he had fought, would, in their crippled condition,
have been cut off, probably, to a man. But little
molested, therefore, they were allowed to defile
through the adjacent village of Popotla.

The Spanish commander there dismounted from
his jaded steed, and sitting down on the steps of
an Indian temple, gazed mournfully on the broken

THEY DRAGGED THEIR FEEBLE LIMBS WITH DIFFICULTY

files as they passed before him. What a spectacle
did they present! The cavalry, most of them dismounted, were mingled with the infantry, who
dragged their feeble limbs along with difficulty;

their shattered mail and tattered garments dripping
with the salt ooze, showing through their rents
many a bruise and ghastly wound; their bright arms
soiled, their proud crests and banners gone, the baggage, artillery, all, in short, that constitutes the
pride and panoply of glorious war, forever lost.
Cortes, as he looked wistfully on their thinned and
disordered ranks, sought in vain for many a familiar face, and missed more than one dear companion
who had stood side by side with him through all the
perils of the Conquest. Though accustomed to control his emotions, or, at least, to conceal them, the
sight was too much for him. He covered his face
with his hands, and the tears which trickled down
revealed too plainly the anguish of his soul.

BATTLE OF IVRY

By Lord Macaulay

NOTE.—When Henry of Navarre became king of France as Henry IV, he found that a part of his subjects, under the duke of Mayenne, refused to submit to him. On March 14, 1590, he won over his enemies a splendid victory at Ivry. In his speech to his soldiers before the battle he called upon them to rally to his white plume, if at any time they lost sight of the standard.

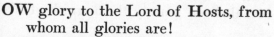OW glory to the Lord of Hosts, from
    whom all glories are!
And glory to our Sovereign Liege,
    King Henry of Navarre!
Now let there be the merry sound
    of music and the dance,
    Through thy cornfields green and
sunny vines, oh! pleasant land of France.
And thou, Rochelle, our own Rochelle, proud city
    of the waters,
Again let rapture light the eyes of all thy mourn-
    ing daughters.
As thou wert constant in our ills, be joyous in our
    joy,
For cold, and stiff, and still are they who wrought
    thy walls annoy.
Hurrah! hurrah! a single field hath turned the
    chance of war;
Hurrah! hurrah! for Ivry and King Henry of
    Navarre.

Oh! how our hearts were beating, when, at the dawn
　　of day,
We saw the army of the League drawn out in long
　　array;
With all its priest-led citizens, and all its rebel
　　peers,
And Appenzel's stout infantry, and Egmont's
　　Flemish spears,
There rode the brood of false Lorraine, the curses
　　of our land,
And dark Mayenne was in the midst, a truncheon
　　in his hand;
And as we looked on them, we thought of Seine's
　　empurpled flood,
And good Coligni's hoary hair all dabbled with
　　his blood;
And we cried unto the living God, who rules the
　　fate of war,
To fight for his own holy name and Henry of
　　Navarre.

The King is come to marshal us, in all his armor
　　drest,
And he has bound a snow-white plume upon his
　　gallant crest;
He looked upon his people, and a tear was in his
　　eye,
He looked upon the traitors, and his glance was
　　stern and high.
Right graciously he smiled on us, as rolled from
　　wing to wing,
Down all our line, in deafening shout, "God save
　　our lord, the King."
"And if my standard-bearer fall, as fall full well
　　he may—

For never saw I promise yet of such a bloody
  fray—
Press where ye see my white plume shine, amidst
  the ranks of war,
And be your oriflamme to-day the helmet of
  Navarre."

Hurrah! the foes are moving. Hark to the mingled
  din
Of fife, and steed, and trump, and drum, and roar-
  ing culverin!
The fiery Duke is pricking fast across St. Andre's
  plain,
With all the hireling chivalry of Guelders and
  Almayne.
Now by the lips of those ye love, fair gentlemen of
  France,
Charge for the golden lilies now, upon them with
  the lance!
A thousand spurs are striking deep, a thousand
  spears in rest,
A thousand knights are pressing close behind the
  snow-white crest;
And in they burst, and on they rushed, while like
  a guiding star,
Amidst the thickest carnage blazed the helmet of
  Navarre.

Now, God be praised, the day is ours! Mayenne
  hath turned his rein,
D'Aumale hath cried for quarter, the Flemish
  Count is slain,
Their ranks are breaking like thin clouds before a
  Biscay gale;

The field is heaped with bleeding steeds, and flags
and cloven mail;
And then we thought on vengeance, and all along
our van,

"CHARGE FOR THE GOLDEN LILIES NOW"

"Remember St. Bartholomew," was passed from
man to man;
But out spake gentle Henry then, "No Frenchman
is my foe;

Down, down with every foreigner, but let your
    brethren go."
Oh! was there ever such a knight in friendship or
    in war,
As our sovereign lord, King Henry, the soldier of
    Navarre.

Ho! maidens of Vienna,—ho! matrons of Luzerne,
Weep, weep, and rend your hair for those who
    never shall return.
Ho! Philip, send for charity, thy Mexican pistoles,
That Antwerp monks may sing a mass for thy poor
    spearmen's souls.
Ho! gallant nobles of the League, look that your
    arms be bright;
Ho! burghers of St. Généviève, keep watch and
    ward to-night;
For our God hath crushed the tyrant, our God hath
    raised the slave,
And mocked the counsel of the wise and the valor
    of the brave.
Then glory to his holy name from whom all glories
    are;
And glory to our sovereign lord, King Henry of
    Navarre.

THE BATTLE OF THERMOPYLAE

OR some time the Greeks had known that danger was threatening them, and in 480 B. C. they learned that it was well-nigh at their gates. Xerxes, the "Great King," whose heralds when announcing a decree began with the words, "All people and nations and languages," whose resources both of men and of treasures were more than could be estimated, was gathering his forces to proceed against Greece; and many were the rumors as to the size of his army.

"There were twelve hundred and seven great ships; and in each ship there were two hundred rowers and thirty fighting men. Also he had of smaller ships, having fifty oars or under, three thousand, and in each of these, taking one with another, there were eighty men. Therefore the whole number of the men that served on the ships was five hundred and seventeen thousand and six hundred. Of foot soldiers there were seventeen hundred thousand, and of horsemen eighty thousand, and of Arabs riding on camels and of Libyans that fought from chariots twenty thousand. There were also one hundred and twenty ships of Greeks that dwelt in Thrace and in the islands thereof, and in these twenty and four thousand men. To these must be added foot soldiers of the Thracians, the Pæonians, the Macedonians, and others. And the sum of the whole was two million six hundred and forty-one thousand six hundred and ten. And of all this great host there was none fitter to be the ruler for beauty and great stature than King Xerxes himself. Of those that followed the camp, and of the crews of the provision ships and other vessels of transport, the number was more rather than less than the number of the fighting men. As for the women that ground the corn, and others that came with the army, and the horses and beasts of burden, and dogs, their number can not be told."

What could the Greeks do against so many? And yet when the envoys of King Xerxes came to the Greek states, demanding from each earth and water, as a sign that Xerxes was lord of land and sea, all the states but Thessaly, which Xerxes would enter first, refused. The Greek states were not always on friendly terms one with another; but the great danger that threatened them now united them in one common object—to repel the Persian invader and to save their temples and their idols from desecration. A council, at which were present deputies from all the Greek states, was held on the Isthmus of Corinth, and plans for defense were considered.

There were two narrow passes through which Xerxes would have to come before he should find himself in Greece proper, and it was evident that it was at such places as these that the few Greeks could best withstand the numerous Persians. To Tempe, therefore, the northernmost of these passes, a body of troops was hastily despatched, but they soon returned declaring that the defense of the pass was out of the question. All agreed then that the best plan would be to guard Thermopylae, which led from Thessaly into Locris. To-day a swampy

plain almost three miles broad lies between Mount
Œta and the Maliac Gulf, but in ancient times
there was but a stretch of sand not more than fifty
feet wide at its broadest part, and in some places so
narrow that a single wagon could scarce pass along
it. The Greek fleet was posted off the coast to prevent the Persians from landing men beyond the
pass, and a company was at once gathered for the
defense of Thermopylae and put under the command of Leonidas, King of Sparta.

"Now, the Greeks that abode the coming of the
Persians in this place were these—three hundred
Spartans, heavy-armed men; and men of Tegea
and Matinea a thousand, from each five hundred,
and from Orchomenus one hundred and twenty,
and from the rest of Arcadia a thousand. From
Corinth there came four hundred, and from Phlius
two hundred, and from Mycenae eighty. So many
came from the Peloponnesus; of the Bœotians there
came seven hundred from Thespiae and four hundred from Thebes. Besides these there had come
at the summons the Locrians of Opus with all the
men that they had, and a thousand Phocians."

All of the Greeks knew that they were setting out
on a dangerous enterprise, but to the Spartans it
meant more than that. Leonidas himself felt that
he was going to his death, for the oracle at Delphi
had foretold that Sparta should be saved if one of
her kings should perish, and Leonidas was more
than willing to make this sacrifice for his state. His
three hundred followers, trained from childhood
to look upon death as infinitely preferable to defeat,
had, with that courage which has made their name
an epithet indicating the highest sort of bravery,

celebrated their funeral games before setting out. When they came to the pass of Thermopylae, they found a new cause for fear. This was the path which led over the mountains, and which made possible a descent of the enemy to the rear of those stationed in the pass. However, Leonidas was assured that this mountain track was practically unknown, and that the entrance to it was very difficult to find; so when he had sent a band of Phocians to guard it, he thought little more about it. Many of the soldiers, however, felt that they were being subjected to danger unnecessarily, and insisted that they be allowed to retreat to the Isthmus of Corinth. As this would have guarded only the Peloponnesus and have left the other states at the mercy of the Persians, Leonidas determined that they should remain where they were and await the onset of the enemy.

While they lay encamped in the pass, a scout sent by Xerxes rode up to see how strong the enemy were, and how they were employing their time. In front of and on the walls were a number of the Greeks engaging in games and combing out their long hair. Surprised to see so few men, and to see those few busying themselves in such an apparently unnecessary way, the scout rode back and made his report to the Persian king. Now there was in the camp of Xerxes one Demaratus, who had formerly been King of Sparta, but who had been driven out and had joined himself to the Persian court. Xerxes sent for him and, describing to him what he considered the foolishness of the Greeks, asked what it might mean. In reply Demaratus said, "Thou hast heard from me, O King, the truth concerning these men before this, even when we were first beginning this war; but when thou heardest it thou didst laugh at me, though I told thee that which I knew would surely come to pass. For indeed, O King, I strive always with my whole heart to tell thee the truth. Hear, therefore, yet again what I say. These men are come hither to contend with us for the pass; and this they now prepare to do; and they have this custom among them, that when they are about to put their lives in peril they adorn their heads with exceeding care. Know, also, O King, that if thou canst subdue these men, and such others of their nation as have been left behind in Sparta, there is no nation upon the earth that will abide thy coming or lift up a hand against thee; for this city that thou now fightest against is the most honorable in all Greece, and these men are the bravest."

Incredulously Xerxes asked, "In what manner will these men, being so few, as we know them to be, fight with my great army?"

Demaratus replied, "O King, deal with me as with a liar if everything fall not out even as I have said."

After this, Xerxes allowed four days to pass, thinking that perhaps the Greeks would come to their senses and flee. "But on the fifth day, seeing that they were not departed, but as it seemed to him, were full of impudence and folly, he grew angry, and sent against them the Medes and the Cissians, giving them a command that they should take these Greeks alive and bring them before him. But when these men came up and fell upon the Greeks, many of them were slain. Then others came up into their places and ceased not from fighting, though indeed they suffered a very grievous slaughter, so that it was manifest to all men, and more especially to the King, that though he had very many that bore arms, yet had he but few men of war. And this battle endured throughout the whole day."

For two days the troops of Xerxes, even his great Ten Thousand, who were known as the Immortals, hurled themselves upon the Greeks, but they accomplished nothing, for they fought in a narrow place, where their greater numbers were of no help to them; and their spears were shorter than those of the Greeks, so that they were easily thrust through before they could come close enough to harm an enemy. Three times, it is said, while his troops were being driven backward, did Xerxes spring in despair from his throne at the sight of the peril of his army.

But on the evening of the second day there came to the camp of the Persian King a man named Ephialtes. On being ushered into the presence of Xerxes, this man admitted that he was a Greek, and proposed that for a great reward he should lead the Persian army over the hidden mountain path, and bring them to the rear of the Greek defenders. Of course Xerxes accepted the offer, and sent off one of his generals with a detachment to follow Ephialtes over the mountain path. In the morning the Phocians who had been set to guard this path were awakened by the sound of rustling in the underbrush and rushed from their camp only to see a detachment of Persian soldiers close upon them. Resolving to sell their lives dearly, they fled to the top of the mountain, where they thought that they might have the advantage of position over their enemies; but the Persians, paying no attention to them, passed on down the mountain to fall upon the brave defenders of Thermopylae.

The Greeks in the pass knew when morning dawned of the danger that awaited them, for Megistias the soothsayer told of it, and certain messengers running before the Persians confirmed his prophecy. "Then the Greeks held a council, considering what they should do; and they were divided; for some would not leave the post where they had been set, and others were very eager to depart. And when the council was broken up, some departed, going each to their own cities, and others made ready to abide in the pass with Leonidas. Some say, indeed, that Leonidas sent away them that departed, having a care for their safety; but it did not become him and the Spartans that were with him, he said, to leave their post that they had come to keep at the first. And indeed it seems fit to be believed that Leonidas, seeing that the others were faint-hearted and would not willingly abide the peril, bade them go, but that he himself held it to be a shameful thing to depart. For he knew that he should get for himself great glory by abiding at his post, and that the prosperity of Sparta should not be destroyed."

The allies, therefore, with the exception of the Thespians and the Thebans, departed, and the brave remainder prepared themselves for their death. Hitherto, Leonidas had stood on the defensive in order to spare the lives of his men, but now, knowing that death must come, he desired only to work as great havoc among the Persians as possible, and he therefore marched his men out before the wall and fell upon the vanguard of the Persian army. It does not seem strange that the hired soldiers should have feared to meet this little band of Greeks, and indeed it is told that the Persian captains were obliged to go behind their troops and with whips scourge them to the fight. Many of the Persians were forced into the sea and so died; some were trodden under foot, and thousands fell by the hands of the Greeks. But it was not only the Persians who fell in this fierce struggle; Leonidas was one of the first who was slain, and many other Spartans fell with him.

But the death of their leader did not demoralize the Greeks—it only made them more reckless and more desperate. At length they saw that the end was close at hand; the "Immortals," who had come in the night over the mountain, had arrived, and were ready to fall upon their rear. Closely pressed by the Persians, they drew back to the narrowest part of the pass, where they had fought on the preceding days, and there made their last stand. Their spears were broken, their swords were dulled; but even had their weapons been still of the best, it would have availed them little, for the Persians, all too well acquainted now with the Greek daring, refused to close with their enemies. In their wellnigh useless armour, which had been hacked from their limbs during their earlier encounters, the Greeks stood on a little hillock and braved the shower of Persian arrows and javelins. By the time the sun went down there remained not one of all the Grecian band, but before their death they

THEIR LAST ENCOUNTER

had succeeded in slaying twenty thousand of the
enemy. Xerxes inquired of Demaratus, in whose
word he had come to have more confidence since
witnessing the events of the last three days,
whether there were many more men at Sparta like
these; and when he was told that there were thousands, he realized that perhaps even his mighty
army might not be a match for them. That all
Greeks were not like the Spartans who had fallen

at Thermopylae; that all Greek leaders were not as brave and as devoted as Leonidas—these facts Xerxes did not realize. The struggle which had proved so fatal to so many of his men had shown him that he was not so irresistible, and had thereby done much for the Greeks.

Where the Greeks fell they were buried, and in after years pillars were set up to commemorate their bravery. One, in honor of those who fell before the allies were sent away, bore the words:

"Four times a thousand men from Pelops' land
Three thousand times a thousand did withstand."

While over the Spartans by themselves there stood another column which bore the words,

"Go tell the Spartans, thou that passeth by,
That here, obedient to their law, we lie."

MARCO BOZZARIS

By FITZ-GREENE HALLECK

NOTE.—Marco Bozzaris, a Greek patriot of Suli, threw himself heart and soul into the Greek struggle for freedom. On August 20, 1823, he led a night attack against the Turks, who were encamped on the site of ancient Plataea. The Greek army was but a handful in comparison with that of the Turks, but the Turks were thrown into utter confusion, and the attacking party won a complete victory. Bozzaris, however, was killed in the final attack.

AT midnight, in his guarded tent,
　The Turk was dreaming of the hour
When Greece, her knee in suppliance bent, .
　Should tremble at his power.
In dreams, through camp and court, he bore
The trophies of a conqueror;
　In dreams his song of triumph heard;

Then wore his monarch's signet-ring,
Then pressed that monarch's throne—a king;
As wild his thoughts, and gay of wing,
    As Eden's garden bird.

At midnight, in the forest shades,
    Bozzaris ranged his Suliote band,—
True as the steel of their tried blades,
    Heroes in heart and hand.
There had the Persian's thousands stood,
There had the glad earth drunk their blood,
    On old Plataea's day;
And now there breathed that haunted air
The sons of sires who conquered there,
With arms to strike, and soul to dare,
    As quick, as far, as they.

An hour passed on, the Turk awoke;
    That bright dream was his last;
He woke—to hear his sentries shriek,
"To arms! they come! the Greek! the Greek!"
He woke—to die midst flame, and smoke,
And shout and groan, and sabre-stroke,
    And death-shots falling thick and fast
As lightning from the mountain-cloud;
And heard, with voice as trumpet loud,
    Bozzaris cheer his band:
"Strike—till the last armed foe expires;
Strike—for your altars and your fires;
Strike—for the green graves of your sires,
    God, and your native land!"

They fought—like brave men, long and well;
    They piled that ground with Moslem slain:
They conquered—but Bozzaris fell,
    Bleeding at every vein.

His few surviving comrades saw
His smile when rang their proud hurrah,

THE TURK AWOKE

And the red field was won;
Then saw in death his eyelids close
Calmly, as to a night's repose,
    Like flowers at set of sun.

Come to the bridal chamber, death,
  Come to the mother's, when she feels,
For the first time, her first-born's breath;
  Come when the blessed seals
That close the pestilence are broke,
And crowded cities wail its stroke;
Come in consumption's ghastly form,
The earthquake shock, the ocean storm;
Come when the heart beats high and warm,
With banquet song and dance and wine,—
And thou art terrible; the tear,
The groan, the knell, the pall, the bier,
And all we know, or dream, or fear
  Of agony, are thine.

But to the hero, when his sword
  Has won the battle for the free,
Thy voice sounds like a prophet's word,
And in its hollow tones are heard
  The thanks of millions yet to be.
Come when his task of fame is wrought;
Come with her laurel-leaf, blood-bought;
  Come in her crowning hour,—and then
Thy sunken eye's unearthly light
To him is welcome as the sight
  Of sky and stars to prisoned men;
Thy grasp is welcome as the hand
Of brother in a foreign land;
Thy summons welcome as the cry
That told the Indian isles were nigh
  To the world-seeking Genoese,
When the land-wind, from woods of palm,
And orange-groves, and fields of balm,
  Blew o'er the Haytian seas.

Bozzaris! with the storied brave
   Greece nurtured in her glory's time,
Rest thee; there is no prouder grave,
   Even in her own proud clime.
She wore no funeral weeds for thee,
   Nor bade the dark hearse wave its plume,
Like torn branch from death's leafless tree,
In sorrow's pomp and pageantry,
   The heartless luxury of the tomb.

But she remembers thee as one
Long loved, and for a season gone.
For thee her poet's lyre is wreathed,
Her marble wrought, her music breathed;
For thee she rings the birthday bells;
Of thee her babes' first lisping tells;
For thine her evening prayer is said
At palace couch and cottage bed.
Her soldier, closing with the foe,
Gives for thy sake a deadlier blow;
His plighted maiden, when she fears
For him, the joy of her young years,
Thinks of thy fate, and checks her tears.
   And she, the mother of thy boys,
Though in her eye and faded cheek
Is read the grief she will not speak,
   The memory of her buried joys,—
And even she who gave thee birth,—
Will, by her pilgrim-circled hearth,
   Talk of thy doom without a sigh;
For thou art freedom's now, and fame's,—
One of the few, the immortal names
   That were not born to die.

A DESCENT INTO THE MAELSTROM

By Edgar Allan Poe

E had now reached the summit of the loftiest crag. For some minutes the old man seemed too much exhausted to speak.

"Not long ago," said he at length, "and I could have guided you on this route as well as the youngest of my sons; but, about three years past, there happened to me an event such as never happened before to mortal man—or at least such as no man ever survived to tell of—and the six hours of deadly terror which I then endured have broken me up body and soul. You suppose me a *very* old man—but I am not. It took less than a single day to change these hairs from a jetty black to white, to weaken my limbs, and to unstring my nerves, so that I tremble at the least exertion, and am frightened at a shadow. Do you know I can scarcely look over this little cliff without getting giddy?"

The "little cliff," upon whose edge he had so carelessly thrown himself down to rest that the weightier portion of his body hung over it, while he was only kept from falling by the tenure of his elbow on its extreme and slippery edge—this "little cliff" arose, a sheer, unobstructed precipice of black shining rock, some fifteen or sixteen hun-

dred feet from the world of crags beneath us.
Nothing would have tempted me to within half
a dozen yards of its brink. In truth, so deeply
was I excited by the perilous position of my companion, that I fell at full length upon the ground,
clung to the shrubs around me, and dared not even
glance upward at the sky—while I struggled in
vain to divest myself of the idea that the very foundations of the mountain were in danger from the
fury of the winds. It was long before I could
reason myself into sufficient courage to sit up and
look out into the distance.

"You must get over these fancies," said the
guide, "for I have brought you here that you
might have the best possible view of the scene of
that event I mentioned—and to tell you the whole
story with the spot just under your eye.

"We are now," he continued in that particu-
larizing manner which distinguished him—"we
are now close upon the Norwegian coast—in the
sixty-eighth degree of latitude—in the great province of Nordland—and in the dreary district of
Lofoden. The mountain upon whose top we sit
is Helseggen, the Cloudy. Now raise yourself up
a little higher—hold on to the grass if you feel
giddy—so—and look out, beyond the belt of vapor
beneath us, into the sea."

I looked dizzily, and beheld a wide expanse of
ocean, whose waters wore so inky a hue as to bring
at once to my mind the Nubian geographer's account of the *Mare Tenebrarum*. A panorama
more deplorably desolate no human imagination
can conceive. To the right and left, as far as the
eye could reach, there lay outstretched, like ram-

parts of the world, lines of horridly black and beetling cliff, whose character of gloom was but the
more forcibly illustrated by the surf which reared
high up against it its white and ghastly crest, howling and shrieking forever. Just opposite the promontory upon whose apex we were placed, and at a
distance of some five or six miles out at sea, there
was visible a small, bleak-looking island; or, more
properly, its position was discernible through the
wilderness of surge in which it was enveloped.
About two miles nearer the land arose another of
smaller size, hideously craggy and barren and en-
compassed at various intervals by a cluster of dark
rocks.

The appearance of the ocean, in the space between the more distant island and the shore, had
something very unusual about it. Although at the
time so strong a gale was blowing landward that a
brig in the remote offing lay to under a double-
reefed trysail, and constantly plunged her whole
hull out of sight, still there was here nothing like
a regular swell, but only a short, quick, angry cross
dashing of water in every direction—as well in the
teeth of the wind as otherwise. Of foam there was
little except in the immediate vicinity of the rocks.

"The island in the distance," resumed the old
man, "is called by the Norwegians Vurrgh. The
one midway is Moskoe. That a mile to the northward is Ambaaren. Yonder are Islesen, Hotholm,
Keildhelm, Suarven, and Buckholm. Farther off
—between Moskoe and Vurrgh—are Otterholm,
Flimen, Sandflesen, and Stockholm. These are the
true names of the places—but why it has been
thought necessary to name them at all, is more than

either you or I can understand. Do you hear anything? Do you see any change in the water?"

We had now been about ten minutes upon the
top of Helseggen, to which we had ascended from
the interior of Lofoden, so that we had caught no
glimpse of the sea until it had burst upon us from
the summit. As the old man spoke, I became aware
of a loud and gradually increasing sound, like the
moaning of a vast herd of buffaloes upon an American prairie; and at the same moment I perceived
that what seamen term the *chopping* character of
the ocean beneath us, was rapidly changing into
a current which set to the eastward. Even while I
gazed this current acquired a monstrous velocity.
Each moment added to its speed—to its headlong
impetuosity. In five minutes the whole sea as far
as Vurrgh was lashed into ungovernable fury; but
it was between Moskoe and the coast that the main
uproar held its sway. Here the vast bed of the
waters, seamed and scarred into a thousand conflicting channels, burst suddenly into frenzied convul-
sion—heaving, boiling, hissing—gyrating in gigantic and innumerable vortices, and all whirling and
plunging on to the eastward with a rapidity which
water never elsewhere assumes except in precipi-
tous descents.

In a few minutes more, there came over the
scene another radical alteration. The general
surface grew somewhat more smooth, and the whirlpools one by one disappeared, while prodigious
streaks of foam became apparent where none had
been seen before. These streaks, at length, spreading out to a great distance, and entering into combination, took unto themselves the gyratory motion

of the subsided vortices, and seemed to form the
germ of another more vast. Suddenly—very suddenly—this assumed a distinct and definite existence in a circle of more than a mile in diameter.
The edge of the whirl was represented by a broad
belt of gleaming spray; but no particle of this slipped into the mouth of the terrific funnel, whose interior, as far as the eye could fathom it, was a
smooth, shining and jet-black wall of water, inclined to the horizon at an angle of some forty-five
degrees, speeding dizzily round and round with a
swaying and sweltering motion, and sending forth
to the wind an appalling voice, half-shriek, half-
roar, such as not even the mighty cataract of Niag-
ara ever lifts up in its agony to Heaven.

The mountain trembled to its very base, and the
rock rocked. I threw myself upon my face, and
clung to the scant herbage in an excess of nervous
agitation.

"This," said I at length, to the old man—"this
can be nothing else than the great whirlpool of the
Maelstrom."

"So it is sometimes termed," said he. "We Norwegians call it the Moskoe-strom, from the island of
Moskoe in the midway."

The ordinary accounts of this vortex had by no
means prepared me for what I saw. That of Jonas
Ramus, which is perhaps the most circumstantial
of any, cannot impart the faintest conception of
either the magnificence, or of the horror of the
scene—or of the wild, bewildering sense of *the novel*
which confounds the beholder. I am not sure from
what point of view the writer in question surveyed
it, nor at what time; but it could neither have been

from the summit of Helseggen, nor during a storm. There are some passages of this description, nevertheless, which may be quoted for their details, although their effect is exceedingly feeble in conveying an impression of the spectacle.

"Between Lofoden and Moskoe," he says, "the depth of the water is between thirty-five and forty fathoms; but on the other side, toward Ver (Vurrgh) this depth decreases so as not to afford a convenient passage for a vessel, without the risk of splitting on the rocks, which happens even in the calmest weather. When it is flood, the stream runs up the country between Lofoden and Moskoe with a boisterous rapidity, but the roar of its impetuous ebb to the sea is scarce equaled by the loudest and most dreadful cataracts—the noise being heard several leagues off, and the vortices or pits are of such an extent and depth, that if a ship comes within its attraction it is inevitably absorbed and carried down to the bottom and there beat to pieces against the rocks, and when the water relaxes the fragments thereof are thrown up again. But these intervals of tranquillity are only at the turn of the ebb and flood, and in calm weather, and last but a quarter of an hour, its violence gradually returning. When the stream is most boisterous, and its fury heightened by a storm, it is dangerous to come within a Norway mile of it. Boats, yachts, and ships have been carried away by not guarding against it before they were within its reach. It likewise happens frequently that whales come too near the stream, and are overpowered by its violence, and then it is impossible to describe their howlings and bellowings in their fruitless struggles to disengage themselves. A bear once, attempting to swim from Lofoden to Moskoe, was caught by the stream and borne down, while he roared terribly, so as to be heard on shore. Large stocks of firs and pine trees, after being absorbed by the current, rise again broken and torn to such a degree as if bristles grew upon them. This plainly shows the bottom to consist of craggy rocks, among which they are whirled to and fro. This stream is regulated by the flux and reflux of the sea—it being constantly high and low water every six hours. One morning, in the year 1645, it raged with such noise and impetuosity that the very stones of the houses on the coast fell to the ground."

In regard to the depth of the water, I could not see how this could have been ascertained at all in the immediate vicinity of the vortex. The "forty fathoms" must have reference only to portions of the channel close upon the shore either of Moskoe or Lofoden. The depth in the center of the Moskoe-strom must be immeasurably greater; and no better proof of this fact is necessary than can be obtained from even the sidelong glance into the abyss of the whirl which may be had from the highest crag of Helseggen. Looking down from this pinnacle upon the howling Phlegethon below, I could not help smiling at the simplicity with which the honest Jonas Ramus records, as a matter difficult of belief, the anecdotes of the whales and the bears; for it appeared to me, in fact, a self-evident thing that the largest ship of the line in existence coming within the influence of that deadly attraction could resist it as little as a feather the hurricane, and must disappear bodily and at once.

The attempts to account for the phenomenon now wore a very different and unsatisfactory aspect. The idea generally received is that this, as well as three smaller vortices among the Ferroe Islands, "have no other cause than the collision of waves rising and falling at flux and reflux against a ridge of rocks and shelves, which confines the water so that it precipitates itself like a cataract; and thus the higher the flood rises the deeper must the fall be, and the natural result of all is a whirlpool or vortex, the prodigious suction of which is sufficiently known by lesser experiments." These are the words of the Encyclopædia Britannica. Kircher and others imagine that in the center of the channel of the Maelstrom is an abyss penetrating the globe, and issuing in some very remote part—the Gulf of Bothnia being somewhat decidedly named in one instance. This opinion, idle in itself, was the one to which, as I gazed, my imagination most readily assented; and, mentioning it to the guide, I was rather surprised to hear him say that, although it was the view almost universally entertained of the subject by the Norwegians, it nevertheless was not his own. As to the former notion, he confessed his inability to comprehend it; and here I agreed with him—for, however conclusive on paper, it becomes altogether unintelligible, and even absurd, amid the thunder of the abyss.

"You have had a good look at the whirl now," said the old man, "and if you will creep round this crag so as to get in its lee, and deaden the roar of the water, I will tell you a story that will convince you I ought to know something of the Moskoe-strom."

I placed myself as desired, and he proceeded.

"Myself and my two brothers once owned a schooner-rigged smack of about seventy tons burthen, with which we were in the habit of fishing among the islands beyond Moskoe, nearly to Vurrgh. In all violent eddies at sea there is good fishing at proper opportunities if one has only the courage to attempt it, but among the whole of the Lofoden coastmen, we three were the only ones who made a regular business of going out to the islands, as I tell you. The usual grounds are a great way lower down to the southward. There fish can be got at all hours, without much risk, and therefore these places are preferred. The choice spots over here among the rocks, however, not only yield the finest variety, but in far greater abundance, so that we often got in a single day what the more timid of the craft could not scrape together in a week. In fact, we made it a matter of desperate speculation—the risk of life standing instead of labor, and courage answering for capital.

"We kept the smack in a cove about five miles higher up the coast than this; and it was our practice, in fine weather, to take advantage of the fifteen minutes' slack to push across the main channel of the Moskoe-strom, far above the pool, and then drop down upon anchorage somewhere near Otterholm, or Sandflesen, where the eddies are not so violent as elsewhere. Here we used to remain until nearly time for slack water again, when we weighed and made for home. We never set out upon this expedition without a steady side wind for going and coming—one that we felt sure would not fail us before our return—and we seldom made a miscal-

culation upon this point. Twice during six years
we were forced to stay all night at anchor on account of a dead calm, which is a rare thing indeed
just about here; and once we had to remain on the
grounds nearly a week, starving to death, owing to
a gale which blew up shortly after our arrival, and
made the channel too boisterous to be thought of.
Upon this occasion we should have been driven out
to sea in spite of everything (for the whirlpools
threw us round and round so violently that at
length we fouled our anchor and dragged it) if it
had not been that we drifted into one of the innumerable cross currents—here to-day and gone to-
morrow—which drove us under the lee of Flimen,
where, by good luck, we brought up.

"I could not tell you the twentieth part of the
difficulties we encountered 'on the grounds'—it is
a bad spot to be in, even in good weather—but we
made shift always to run the gauntlet of the Moskoe-strom itself without accident; although at times
my heart has been in my mouth when we happened
to be a minute or so behind or before the slack. The
wind sometimes was not as strong as we thought
it at starting, and then we made rather less way
than we could wish, while the current rendered the
smack unmanageable. My eldest brother had a son
eighteen years old, and I had two stout boys of my
own. These would have been of great assistance
at such times in using the sweeps, as well as afterward in fishing, but somehow, although we ran the
risk ourselves, we had not the heart to let the young
ones get into the danger—for, after all is said and
done, it *was* a horrible danger, and that is the
truth.

"It is now within a few days of three years since what I am going to tell you occurred. It was on the tenth day of July, 18—, a day which the people of this part of the world will never forget—for it was one in which blew the most terrible hurricane that ever came out of the heavens; and yet all the morning, and indeed until late in the afternoon, there was a gentle and steady breeze from the southwest, while the sun shone brightly, so that the oldest seaman among us could not have foreseen what was to follow.

"The three of us—my two brothers and myself —had crossed over to the islands about 2 o'clock p. m., and had soon nearly loaded the smack with fine fish, which, we all remarked, were more plentiful that day than we had ever known them. It was just seven *by my watch* when we weighed and started for home, so as to make the worst of the Strom at slack water, which we knew would be at eight.

"We set out with a fresh wind on our starboard quarter, and for some time spanked along at a great rate, never dreaming of danger, for indeed we saw not the slightest reason to apprehend it. All at once we were taken aback by a breeze from over Helseggen. This was most unusual—something that had never happened to us before—and I began to feel a little uneasy without exactly knowing why. We put the boat on the wind, but could make no headway at all for the eddies, and I was put upon the point of proposing to return to the anchorage, when, looking astern, we saw the whole horizon covered with a singular copper-colored cloud that rose with the most amazing velocity.

"In the meantime the breeze that had headed us off fell away, and we were dead becalmed, drifting about in every direction. This state of things, however, did not last long enough to give us time to think about it. In less than a minute the storm was upon us—in less than two the sky was entirely overcast—and what with this and the driving spray it became suddenly so dark that we could not see each other in the smack.

"Such a hurricane as then blew it is folly to attempt describing. The oldest seaman in Norway never experienced anything like it. We had let our sails go by the run before it cleverly took us; but, at the first puff both our masts went by the board as if they had been sawed off—the mainmast taking with it my youngest brother, who had lashed himself to it for safety.

"Our boat was the lightest feather of a thing that ever sat upon water. It had a complete flushed deck, with only a small hatch near the bow, and this hatch it had always been our custom to batten down when about to cross the Strom, by way of precaution against the chopping seas. But for this circumstance we should have foundered at once—for we lay entirely buried for some moments. How my elder brother escaped destruction I cannot say, for I never had an opportunity of ascertaining. For my part, as soon as I had let the foresail run, I threw myself flat on deck, with my feet against the narrow gunwale of the bow, and with my hands grasping a ring-bolt near the foot of the fore-mast. It was mere instinct that prompted me to do this—which was undoubtedly the very best thing I could have done—for I was too much flurried to think.

"For some moments we were completely deluged, as I say, and all this time I held my breath, and clung to the bolt. When I could stand it no longer I raised myself upon my knees, still keeping hold with my hands, and thus got my head clear. Presently our little boat gave herself a shake, just as a dog does in coming out of the water, and thus rid herself in some measure of the seas. I was now trying to get the better of the stupor that had come over me, and to collect my senses so as to see what was to be done, when I felt somebody grasp my arm. It was my elder brother, and my heart leaped for joy, for I had made sure that he was overboard —but the next moment all this joy was turned to horror—for he put his mouth close to my ear, and screamed out the word '*Moskoestrom!*'

"No one will ever know what my feelings were at that moment. I shook from head to foot, as if I had had the most violent fit of the ague. I knew what he meant by that one word well enough—I knew what he wished to make me understand. With the wind that now drove us on we were bound for the whirl of the Strom, and nothing could save us!

"You perceive that in crossing the Strom *channel,* we always went a long way up above the whirl, even in the calmest weather, and then had to wait and watch carefully for the slack—but now we were driving right upon the pool itself, and in such a hurricane as this! 'To be sure,' I thought, 'we shall get there just about the slack—there is some little hope in that'—but in the next moment I cursed myself for being so great a fool as to dream of hope at all. I knew very well that we were doomed had we been ten times a ninety-gun ship.

"By this time the first fury of the tempest had spent itself, or perhaps we did not feel it so much as we scudded before it, but at all events the seas, which at first had been kept down by the wind and lay flat and frothing, now got up into absolute mountains. A singular change, too, had come over the heavens. Around in every direction it was still as black as pitch, but nearly overhead there burst out, all at once, a circular rift of clear sky—as clear as I ever saw, and of a deep bright blue—and through it there blazed forth the full moon with a luster that I never before knew her to wear. She lit up everything about us with the greatest distinctness—but, O God, what a scene it was to light up!

"I now made one or two attempts to speak to my brother—but, in some manner which I could not understand, the din had so increased that I could not make him hear a single word, although I screamed at the top of my voice in his ear. Presently he shook his head, looking as pale as death, and held up one of his fingers as if to say '*listen!*'

"At first I could not make out what he meant—but soon a hideous thought flashed upon me. I dragged my watch from its fob. It was not going. I glanced at its face by the moonlight, and then burst into tears as I flung it far away into the ocean. *It had run down at seven o'clock! We were behind the time of the slack, and the whirl of the Strom was in full fury!*

"When a boat is well built, properly trimmed, and not deep laden, the waves in a strong gale, when she is going large, seem always to slip from beneath her—which appears very strange to a

landsman—and this is what is called *riding,* in sea-
phrase. Well, so far we had ridden the swells very
cleverly, but presently a gigantic sea happened to
take us right under the counter, and bore us with
it as it rose—up—up—as if into the sky. I would
not have believed that any wave could rise so high.
And then down we came with a sweep, a slide, and a
plunge, that made me feel sick and dizzy, as if I
was falling from some lofty mountain-top in a
dream. But while we were up I had thrown a quick
glance around—and that one glance was all sufficient. I saw our exact position in an instant. The
Moskoe-strom whirlpool was about a quarter of a
mile dead ahead—but no more like the everyday
Moskoe-strom, than the whirl as you now see it is
like a mill-race. If I had not known where we
were, and what we had to expect, I should not have
recognized the place at all. As it was, I involun-
tarily closed my eyes in horror. The lids clenched
themselves together as if in a spasm.

"It could not have been more than two minutes
afterward until we suddenly felt the waves sub-
side, and were enveloped in foam. The boat made
a sharp half turn to larboard, and then shot off in
its new direction like a thunderbolt. At the same
moment the roaring noise of the water was completely drowned in a kind of shrill shriek—such a
sound as you might imagine given out by the waste-
pipes of many thousand steam-vessels letting off
their steam all together. We were now in the belt
of surf that always surrounds the whirl; and I
thought of course that another moment would
plunge us into the abyss—down which we could
only see indistinctly on account of the amazing vel-

ocity with which we were borne along. The boat
did not seem to sink into the water at all, but to
skim like an air-bubble upon the surface of the
surge. Her starboard side was next the whirl, and
on the larboard arose the world of ocean we had
left. It stood like a huge writhing wall between us
and the horizon.

"It may appear strange, but now, when we were
in the very jaws of the gulf, I felt more composed
than when we were only approaching it. Having
made up my mind to hope no more, I got rid of a
great deal of that terror which unmanned me at
first. I suppose it was despair that strung my
nerves.

"It may look like boasting—but what I tell you
is truth—I began to reflect how magnificent a thing
it was to die in such a manner, and how foolish it
was in me to think of so paltry a consideration as
my own individual life in view of so wonderful a
manifestation of God's power. I do believe that I
blushed with shame when this idea crossed my
mind. After a little while I became possessed with
the keenest curiosity about the whirl itself. I positively felt a *wish* to explore its depths, even at the
sacrifice I was going to make; and my principal
grief was that I should never be able to tell my old
companions on shore about the mysteries I should
see. These, no doubt, were singular fancies to oc-
cupy a man's mind in such extremity, and I have
often thought since that the revolutions of the boat
around the pool might have rendered me a little
light-headed.

"There was another circumstance which tended
to restore my self-possession, and this was the ces-

sation of the wind, which could not reach us in
our present situation—for, as you saw yourself, the
belt of surf is considerably lower than the general
bed of the ocean, and this latter now towered above
us, a high, black, mountainous ridge. If you have
never been at sea in a heavy gale you can form no
idea of the confusion of mind occasioned by the
wind and spray together. They blind, deafen, and
strangle you, and take away all power of action
or reflection. But we were now, in a great measure,
rid of these annoyances—just as death-condemned
felons in prison are allowed petty indulgences, forbidden them while their doom is yet uncertain.

"How often we made the circuit of the belt it
is impossible to say. We careered round and round
for perhaps an hour, flying rather than floating,
getting gradually more and more into the middle of
the surge, and then nearer and nearer to its horrible inner edge. All this time I had never let go
of the ring-bolt. My brother was at the stern,
holding on to a small empty water-cask which had
been securely lashed under the coop of the counter,
and was the only thing on deck that had not been
swept overboard when the gale first took us. As
we approached the brink of the pit he let go his
hold upon this, and made for the ring, from which,
in the agony of his terror, he endeavored to force
my hands, as it was not large enough to afford us
both a secure grasp. I never felt deeper grief than
when I saw him attempt this act—although I knew
he was a madman when he did it—a raving maniac
through sheer fright. I did not care, however, to
contest the point with him. I knew it could make
no difference whether either of us held on at all, so

I let him have the bolt, and went astern to the cask. This there was no great difficulty in doing, for the smack flew round steadily enough, and upon an even keel, only swaying to and fro with the immense sweeps and swelters of the whirl. Scarcely had I secured myself in my new position when we gave a wild lurch to starboard, and rushed headlong into the abyss. I muttered a hurried prayer to God, and thought all was over.

"As I felt the sickening sweep of the descent I had instinctively tightened my hold upon the barrel, and closed my eyes. For some seconds I dared not open them, while I expected instant destruction, and wondered that I was not already in my death-struggles with the water. But moment after moment elapsed. I still lived. The sense of falling had ceased; and the motion of the vessel seemed much as it had been before while in the belt of foam, with the exception that she now lay more along. I took courage, and looked once again upon the scene.

"Never shall I forget the sensations of awe, horror, and admiration with which I gazed about me. The boat appeared to be hanging, as if by magic, midway down, upon the interior surface of a funnel vast in circumference, prodigious in depth, and whose perfectly smooth sides might have been mistaken for ebony but for the bewildering rapidity with which they spun around, and for the gleaming and ghastly radiance they shot forth, as the rays of the full moon, from that circular rift amid the clouds which I have already described, streamed in a flood of golden glory along the black walls, and far away down into the inmost recesses of the abyss.

"At first I was too much confused to observe anything accurately. The general burst of terrific grandeur was all that I beheld. When I recovered myself a little, however, my gaze fell instinctively downward. In this direction I was able to obtain an unobstructed view from the manner in which the smack hung on the inclined surface of the pool. She was quite upon an even keel—that is to say, her deck lay in a plane parallel with that of the water—but this latter sloped at an angle of more than forty-five degrees, so that we seemed to be lying upon our beam-ends. I could not help observing, nevertheless, that I had scarcely more difficulty in maintaining my hold and footing in this situation than if we had been upon a dead level, and this, I suppose, was owing to the speed at which we revolved.

"The rays of the moon seemed to search the very bottom of the profound gulf; but still I could make out nothing distinctly, on account of a thick mist in which everything there was enveloped, and over which there hung a magnificent rainbow, like that narrow and tottering bridge which Mussulmen say is the only pathway between Time and Eternity. This mist or spray was no doubt occasioned by the clashing of the great walls of the funnel as they all met together at the bottom, but the yell that went up to the heavens from out of that mist I dare not attempt to describe.

"Our first slide into the abyss itself, from the belt of foam above, had carried us a great distance down the slope, but our farther descent was by no means proportionate. Round and round we swept —not with any uniform movement—but in dizzy-

ing swings and jerks, that sent us sometimes only
a few hundred yards—sometimes nearly the complete circuit of the whirl. Our progress downward
at each revolution was slow but very perceptible.

"Looking about me upon the wide waste of liquid
ebony on which we were thus borne, I perceived
that our boat was not the only object in the embrace of the whirl. Both above and below us were
visible fragments of vessels, large masses of building timber and trunks of trees, with many smaller
articles, such as pieces of house furniture, broken
boxes, barrels, and staves. I have already described the unnatural curiosity which had taken the
place of my original terrors. It appeared to grow
upon me as I drew nearer and nearer to my dreadful doom. I now began to watch, with a strange
interest, the numerous things that floated in our
company. I *must* have been delirious, for I even
sought *amusement* in speculating upon the relative
velocities of their several descents toward the foam
below. 'This fir tree,' I found myself at one time
saying, 'will certainly be the next thing that takes
the awful plunge and disappears'—and then I was
disappointed to find that the wreck of a Dutch
merchant ship overtook it and went down before.
At length, after making several guesses of this nature, and being deceived in all, this fact—the fact
of my invariable miscalculation—set me upon a
train of reflection that made my limbs again tremble, and my heart beat heavily once more.

"It was not a new terror that thus affected me,
but the dawn of a more exciting *hope*. This hope
arose partly from memory, and partly from present observation. I called to mind the great variety

of buoyant matter that strewed the coast of Lofoden, having been absorbed and then thrown forth by the Moskoe-strom. By far the greater number of the articles were shattered in the most extraordinary way—so chafed and roughened as to have the appearance of being stuck full of splinters—but then I distinctly recollected that there were *some* of them which were not disfigured at all. Now I could not account for this difference except by supposing that the roughened fragments were the only ones which had been *completely absorbed*—that the others had entered the whirl at so late a period of the tide, or, for some reason, had descended so slowly after entering, that they did not reach the bottom before the turn of the flood came, or of the ebb, as the case might be. I conceived it possible, in either instance, that they might thus be whirled up again to the level of the ocean, without undergoing the fate of those which had been drawn in more early, or absorbed more rapidly. I made also three important observations. The first was that, as a general rule, the larger the bodies were, the more rapid their descent; the second, that, between two masses of equal extent, the one spherical and the other *of any other shape,* the superiority in speed of descent was with the sphere; the third, that between two masses of equal size, the one cylindrical and the other of any other shape, the cylinder was absorbed the more slowly. Since my escape I have had several conversations on this subject with an old schoolmaster of the district, and it was from him that I learned the use of the words 'cylinder' and 'sphere.' He explained to me —although I have forgotten the explanation—how

what I observed was in fact the natural consequence of the forms of the floating fragments, and
showed me how it happened that a cylinder swimming in a vortex offered more resistance to its suction, and was drawn in with greater difficulty than
an equally bulky body of any form whatever.

"There was one startling circumstance which
went a great way in enforcing these observations
and rendering me anxious to turn them to account, and this was that at every revolution we
passed something like a barrel, or else the yard or
the mast of a vessel, while many of these things
which had been on our level when I first opened
my eyes upon the wonders of the whirlpool were
now high up above us, and seemed to have moved
but little from their original station.

"I no longer hesitated what to do. I resolved
to lash myself securely to the water-cask upon
which I now held, to cut it loose from the counter,
and to throw myself with it into the water. I attracted my brother's attention by signs, pointed to
the floating barrels that came near us, and did
everything in my power to make him understand
what I was about to do. I thought at length that
he comprehended my design, but, whether this was
the case or not, he shook his head despairingly,
and refused to move from his station by the ring-
bolt. It was impossible to reach him, the emer-
gency admitted of no delay, and so, with a bitter
struggle, I resigned him to his fate, fastened myself to the cask by means of the lashings which
secured it to the counter, and precipitated myself
with it into the sea without another moment's
hesitation.

"The result was precisely what I had hoped it might be. As it is myself who now tell you this tale—as you see that I *did* escape—and as you are already in possession of the mode in which this escape was effected, and must therefore anticipate all that I have further to say, I will bring my story quickly to conclusion. It might have been an hour or thereabout after my quitting the smack, when, having descended to a vast distance beneath me, it made three or four wild gyrations in rapid succession, and bearing my loved brother with it, plunged headlong at once and forever into the chaos of foam below. The barrel to which I was attached sunk very little farther than half the distance between the bottom of the gulf and the spot at which I leaped overboard, before a great change took place in the character of the whirlpool. The slope of the sides of the vast funnel became momently less and less steep. The gyrations of the whirl grew gradually less and less violent. By degrees the froth and the rainbow disappeared, and the bottom of the gulf seemed slowly to uprise. The sky was clear, the winds had gone down, and the full moon was setting radiantly in the west, when I found myself on the surface of the ocean, in full view of the shores of Lofoden, and above the spot where the pool of the Moskoe-strom *had been*. It was the hour of the slack—but the sea still heaved in mountainous waves from the effects of the hurricane. I was borne violently into the channel of the Strom, and in a few minutes was hurried down the coast into the 'grounds' of the fishermen. A boat picked me up, exhausted from fatigue and (now that the danger was removed) speechless from the memory of its horror. Those who drew me on board were my old mates and daily companions, but they knew me no more than they would have known a traveler from the spirit-land. My hair, which had been raven-black the day before, was as white as you see it now. They say, too, that the whole expression of my countenance had changed. I told them my story—they did not believe it. I now tell it to *you,* and I can scarcely expect you to put more faith in it than did the merry fishermen of Lofoden."

A Descent into the Maelstrom is a remarkable example of forcible description as well as of artistic skill in the setting.

I.   The first third of the story is an introduction to the main tale. The story itself might seem to be sufficiently exciting, but it would have much less power if it began where the old man commences to tell the tale. Notice what Poe throws into his introduction:

1.   He represents the tale as told to himself by an old man with white hair, weakened limbs and unstrung nerves that tremble at the least exertion. The old man claims to be frightened at a shadow, yet he is able to throw himself down to rest with the weightier portion of his body hanging over a precipice and held back from the slippery edge of the cliff of black shining rock, some sixteen hundred feet high, merely by the power of his elbows thrust into the earth. The position is so perilous that the hearer throws himself at full length upon the ground, clinging to the shrubs around him and scarcely daring to glance upward at the sky. Besides the precarious position in which the men are placed, fierce winds that seem to shake the very foundations of the mountain cause thrills of terror to the onlooker.

2.   The guide points out the scene of his terrible experience.

3. The author describes the sea, the islands and the location of the whirlpool.

4. Then follows a description of the water in the conflicting channels.

5. Suddenly the circular whirlpool appears, and from the awful height the observers are able to look down into the mouth of the terrific funnel.

6. More description follows, showing what happens to objects caught within the fierce grasp of the revolving waters.

7. Reference is made to ancient accounts of the whirlpool.

8. He makes some effort to explain the causes which would produce such fearful currents so furiously in action, but finds himself unable to arrive at a satisfactory explanation.

Such sights, such a discussion, such a perilous position in which to listen, make the hearer susceptible to the slightest impression.

II. The story proper is told in the most convincing, matter-of-fact way, yet we are conscious all the time that the language of the old man is rather that of a trained writer than of an ignorant fisherman, and here Poe sacrifices the personality of his hero to vividness of incident. What he wishes to accomplish is to impress us with a terrible experience. He does not care to make us see the narrator as a man, yet the story is not devoid of touches of strong human interest; if it were it would be less powerful. The fisherman and his brothers will not take with them their sons on their perilous fishing trip. The youngest brother is carried away in the first blast of the tempest with the mainmast to which he had bound himself. The oldest brother selfishly drives our hero from the ring in the deck.

There are remarkable touches of realism in the story. It was just seven by the old man's watch when they started for home; later, when the tempest is upon them, it is discovered that the watch had run down at seven o'clock, and they are behind the time of the slack water in the whirlpool.

III.   Vividly descriptive phrases abound in the narration, and figures of speech give powerful interest to the imagination.

"We came with a sweep, a slide, and a plunge, that made me feel sick and dizzy, as if I was falling from some lofty mountain-top in a dream."

"The roaring noise of the water was completely drowned in a kind of shrill shriek—such a sound as you might imagine given out by the waste-pipes of many thousand steam-vessels letting off their steam all together."

"How foolish it was in me to think of so paltry a consideration as my own individual life in view of so wonderful a manifestation of God's power."

"We were now, in a great measure, rid of these annoyances—just as death-condemned felons in prison are allowed petty indulgences, forbidden them while their doom is yet uncertain."

IV.   It is meant that our interest should center in the story itself.   Accordingly, when the narrator has finished his tale the story is finished.   We are not further interested in the listener, or in the old man.

V.   It is almost unnecessary to say that the tale is pure fiction, and an example of brilliant exaggeration.   As a matter of fact the maelstrom is a whirlpool lying where Poe places it, and it has been made noted by many other accounts than this of Poe, most of which are exaggerated, but none of them so brilliant in execution as Poe's.   The difference between high tide and low tide in this vicinity is very great, and every twelve hours vast masses of water must be moved into the fiord and out again through narrow channels and rough rocks.   The currents resulting are dangerous to navigation, and there are numerous whirlpools and eddies besides the great maelstrom itself.   Ordinarily, however, ships traverse the passage without danger; but when in conjunction with high tide the winds blow fiercely, the sea for miles around becomes highly perilous to small vessels.

PERE MARQUETTE

By JARED SPARKS[1]

T is generally believed that the Mississippi River was first discovered by Ferdinand de Soto, as early as 1541. The accounts of his expedition in Florida are so highly exaggerated, so indefinite, and in many parts so obviously false, that little more can be inferred from them, than that he passed far into the country, had many combats with the natives, and finally died in the interior. The probability is so strong, however, that he and his party actually crossed the Mississippi, that it has usually been assumed as a historical fact.

The first Europeans, however, who are certainly known to have discovered and explored this river, were two Frenchmen, Father Marquette[2] and M. Joliet, in the year 1673. Marquette was a native of Picardy, and Charlevoix calls him "one of the

1. Jared Sparks was born in 1789, and was one of the most industrious of our early historians, for he collected documents, edited them, and wrote untiringly on American biography. Some of his work is not considered very reliable, but he contributed a great deal of valuable information in rather a pleasing way. This sketch of Marquette's expedition is particularly interesting, as he followed so closely the report of the great missionary.

2. Father Marquette, the famous Jesuit explorer and missionary, was born in France in 1637. He was sent as a missionary to Canada, and in 1668 founded the mission of Sault Sainte Marie. In 1673, when he was ordered by Count Frontenac to join Joliet and find and explore the Mississippi, he was in charge of a new mission at Mackinaw.

most illustrious missionaries of New France," adding, that he travelled widely, and made many discoveries besides that of the Mississippi. He had resided some time in Canada, and attained a proficiency in the languages of the principal native tribes who resided in the regions bordering on the Upper Lakes. The first settlement of the old town of Michillimackinac, in 1671, is ascribed to his exertions and influence.

The Indians had given many accounts of a great river at the west, which flowed southwardly, and which they called *Mississipy,* as the word is written by Marquette. It became a matter of curious speculation, what course this river pursued, and at what place it disembogued itself into the sea. There were three opinions on this subject. First, that it ran towards the southwest, and entered the Gulf of California; secondly, that it flowed into the Gulf of Mexico; and thirdly, that it found its way in a more easterly direction, and discharged itself into the Atlantic Ocean somewhere on the coast of Virginia. The question was not less important in a commercial and political view, than interesting as a geographical problem.

To establish the point, and to make such other discoveries as opportunities would admit, M. de Frontenac, the governor of Canada, encouraged an expedition to be undertaken. The persons to whom it was intrusted, were M. Joliet, then residing at Quebec, and Father Marquette, who was at Michillimackinac, or in the vicinity of that place. Marquette wrote an account of his tour, and voyage down the Mississippi, which was sent to France, and published eight years afterwards in Paris. From this account the following particulars are chiefly taken. In some parts the translation is nearly literal, and all the prominent facts are retained.

On the 13th of May, 1673, Father Marquette and M. Joliet, with five other Frenchmen, embarked in two canoes, with a small provision of Indian corn and smoked meat, having previously acquired from the Indians all the intelligence they could afford respecting their proposed route.[3]

The first nation[4] through which they passed, was the *Folles Avoines* (Wild Rice),[5] so called from the grain of that name, which abounds in the rivers and marshy lands. This plant is described as growing about two feet above the water, resembling European oats, and is gathered by the savages during the month of September. The ears are dried, separated from the chaff, and prepared for food either by pounding into meal, or simply boiling the grain in water.

The natives, having been made acquainted by Father Marquette with his design of visiting the most remote nations, and preaching to them the Gospel, did their utmost to dissuade him from it, representing the cruelty of some of the tribes, and

3. "The joy that we felt at being selected for This Expedition animated our Courage, and rendered the labor of paddling from morning to night agreeable to us."—MARQUETTE.

4. The wild rice people were the Menominees, who lived on the river that now bears that name and which forms part of the boundary between Wisconsin and Michigan. Father Marquette went out of his way to see these friendly Indians, whose name Menominee means simply *wild rice*.

5. This wild rice still grows in the streams and lakes of northern Wisconsin and Michigan, still clogs the courses of the rivers and is still gathered by the scattered Indians of that vicinity.

their warlike state, the dangerous navigation of the river, the dreadful monsters that were found in it, and, finally, the excessive heat of the climate.

He thanked them for their good advice, but declined following it; assuring them, that, to secure the success of his undertaking, he would gladly give his life; that he felt no fear of the monsters they described; and that their information would only oblige him to keep more on his guard against surprise. After having prayed, and given them some instructions, he parted from them, and arrived at the *Bay of Puans,*[6] now called Green Bay, where considerable progress had been made by the French priests in the conversion of the Indians.

The name of this bay has a less unpleasant meaning in the Indian, than in the French language, signifying also *salt bay,* which induced Father Marquette to make strict researches for salt springs in this vicinity, but without success. He concluded, therefore, that the name was given to it in consequence of the ooze and mud deposited there, from whence, as he thought, arise vapors, that produce frequent and violent thunder storms. He speaks of this bay as about thirty leagues long and eight leagues wide at its entrance, gradually contracting towards its head, where the flux and reflux of the tides, much like those of the sea, may be easily observed.

Leaving this bay, they ascended the river, since known as Fox River, that empties into it. At its mouth, he says, the river is broad and deep, and flows gently; but, as you advance, its course is interrupted by rapids and rocks; which he passed,

6. The name *puans* in French signifies *ill-smelling.*

however, in safety. It abounds with bustards,[7] ducks, and teal, attracted by the wild rice, which grows there.

Approaching the village of *Maskoutins,*[8] or *nation of fire,* he had the curiosity to taste the mineral water of a stream in its vicinity. The village consisted of three several nations, namely, *Miamis, Maskoutins,* and *Kikabeaux.* The first were the most friendly and liberal, and the finest looking men. Their hair was long over their ears. They were good warriors, successful in their expeditions, docile, and fond of instruction. They were so eager to listen to Father Allouez,[9] when he was among them, that they allowed him no repose, even in the night. The Maskoutins and Kikabeaux were coarser, and less civilized; their wigwams were constructed of rushes (birch bark being scarce in this country), and might be rolled up in bundles and carried where they pleased.

In visiting these people, Father Marquette was much gratified at seeing a large cross erected in the center of the village, decorated with thank-offerings to the Great Spirit, for their success during the last winter. The situation of the village was striking and beautiful, it being built on an eminence, whence the eye overlooked on all sides a boundless extent of prairie, interspersed with groves and forests. The soil was good, producing abundantly Indian corn, grapes, and plums.

7. There are no bustards in North America. The writer probably saw wild geese with the ducks.

8. It is not known certainly where this village was located, but it may have been near the present city of Berlin or Princeton.

9. Father Allouez arrived at the Sault Sainte Marie in 1668, and was engaged in missionary work between lakes Superior and Michigan. It is probable that he had visited the Indians the year before.

Immediately on their arrival, Father Marquette and M. Joliet assembled the chiefs, and explained to them the objects of their expedition, expressing their determination to proceed at all risks, and making them some presents. They requested the assistance of two guides, to put them in their way; which request the natives readily granted, returning for their presents a mat, which served them as a bed during the voyage. The next day, being the 10th of June, the two Miamis, their guides, embarked with them in sight of all the inhabitants of the village who looked with astonishment on the hardihood of seven Frenchmen in undertaking such an expedition.

They knew that within three leagues of the Maskoutins was a river, which discharged itself into the Mississippi; and further, that their course must be west southwest; but so many marshes and small lakes intervened, that the route was intricate; the more so, as the river was overgrown with wild rice, which obstructed the channel to such a degree, that it was difficult to follow it. On this account their guides were necessary, who conducted them safely to a portage, which was about two thousand seven hundred paces across.[10] The guides aided them in transporting their canoes over the portage to the river, which ran towards the west, and then they left them and returned.

The travellers quitted the waters, which flow towards Quebec, five or six hundred leagues from

10. The Fox and Wisconsin river systems approach within a mile and a half of each other at Portage, Wisconsin. The land is low and swampy, and in flood times the current sometimes sets from one river into the other. The government constructed a canal across this narrow divide, which, you see, Marquette described and measured quite accurately.

that place, and embarked on an unknown stream.[11]
This river was called *Mescousin* (Wisconsin). It
was very broad, but its bottom was sandy, and the
navigation was rendered difficult by the shoals.[12]
It was full of islands, overgrown with vines; and
the fertile banks through which it flowed were interspersed with woods, prairies, and groves of nut,
oak, and other trees. Numbers of bucks and buffaloes were seen, but no other animals. Within
thirty leagues of their place of embarkation, they
found iron mines, which appeared abundant and
of a good quality. After continuing their route
for forty leagues, they arrived at the mouth of the
river, in forty-two degrees and a half of latitude;[13]
and on the 17th of June, they entered with great
joy the waters of the Mississippi.

This river derives its source from several lakes in
the north. At the mouth of the Mescousin its
channel was narrow, and it flowed onwards with a
gentle current. On the right was seen a chain of
high mountains,[14] and on the left fertile fields in-

11. Marquette writes: "Thus we left the Waters flowing to
Quebec, four or five hundred leagues from here, to float on those that
would thenceforth take us through strange lands. Before embark-
ing thereon, we began all together a new devotion to the blessed
Virgin Immaculate, which we practiced daily, addressing to her
special prayers to place under her protection, both our persons
and the success of our voyage; and, after mutually encouraging one
another, we entered our Canoes."

12. Now, as then, the shifting sand bars make navigation of the
Wisconsin difficult and impracticable, although the government has
spent large sums of money in trying to improve it.

13. The latitude Marquette gives is about right. 43° is practically correct.

14. "High mountains," as we now understand the phrase, is an
exaggerated term to apply to the bold bluffs about three or four
hundred feet high on the Iowa side of the Mississippi, south of
McGregor.

terrupted by islands in many places. They slowly followed the course of the stream to the south and southwest, until, in forty-two degrees of latitude,[15] they perceived a sensible change in the surrounding country. There were but few hills and forests. The islands were covered with beautiful trees.[16]

From the time of leaving their guides, they descended the two rivers more than one hundred leagues, without discovering any other inhabitants of the forest, than birds and beasts. They were always on their guard, kindling a fire on the shore towards evening, to cook their food, and afterwards anchoring their canoes in the middle of the stream during the night. They proceeded thus for more than sixty leagues[17] from the place where they entered the Mississippi, when, on the 25th of June, they perceived on the bank of the river the footsteps of men, and a well-beaten path leading into a beautiful prairie. They landed, and, leaving the canoes under the guard of their boatmen, Father Marquette and M. Joliet set forth to make discoveries. After silently following the path for about two leagues, they perceived a village, situate on the margin of a river, and two others on a hill, within

15. This is a little south of Savanna, Ill., if Marquette's latitude is right.

16. Sparks has not given us the whole of the famous journal. Among other interesting things in this connection Marquette writes: "When we cast our nets into the water we caught sturgeon, and a very extraordinary kind of fish. It resembles the trout, with this difference, that its mouth is larger. Near its nose—which is smaller, as are also the eyes—is a large bone, shaped like a woman's corset-bone, three fingers wide and a cubit long, at the end of which is a disk as wide as one's hand. This frequently causes it to fall backward when it leaps out of the water." This was the paddle fish, or spoonbill sturgeon.

17. This was in about 41° latitude.

half a league of the first. As they approached
nearer, they gave notice of their arrival by a loud
call. Hearing the noise, the Indians came out of

THE GIFT OF THE CALUMET

their cabins, and, having looked at the strangers for
a while, they deputed four of their elders to talk
with them, who slowly advanced. Two of them
brought pipes ornamented with feathers, which,

without speaking, they elevated towards the sun,
as a token of friendship. Gaining assurance from
this ceremony, Father Marquette addressed them,
inquiring of what nation they were. They answered,
that they were Illinois, and, offering their pipes,
invited the strangers to enter the village; where
they were received with every mark of attention,
conducted to the cabin of the chief, and compli-
mented on their arrival by the natives, who gathered
round them, gazing in silence.

After they were seated, the calumet[18] was presented to them, and while the old men were smoking for their entertainment, the chief of all the
Illinois tribes sent them an invitation to attend a
council at his village. They were treated by him
with great kindness, and Father Marquette, having
explained to him the motives of this voyage, enforcing each part of his speech with a present, the chief
in reply expressed his approbation; but urged him,
in the name of the whole nation, not to incur the
risks of a further voyage, and rewarded his presents
by the gift of a calumet.

The council was followed by a feast, consisting
of four courses, from each of which they were fed
with much ceremony; and afterwards they were
conducted in state through the village, receiving
many presents of girdles and garters from the
natives. The following day, they took leave of the
chief, promising to return in four moons, and were
accompanied to their canoes, with every demonstra-
tion of joy, by more than six hundred savages.

18. The *calumet* was a pipe that usually consisted of a bowl of
red stone and a long reed stem. In this the Indians smoked
tobacco, passing the pipe from one to another in token of peace and
friendship. To hold up the calumet was a signal of peace.

Before leaving this nation, Father Marquette remarked some of their peculiarities. The name *Illinois,* in the native language, signifies *men,* as if implying thereby, that other tribes are brutes in comparison, which in some sense Father Marquette thought to be true, as they were more civilized than most of the tribes. Their language, on the borders of the river, was a dialect of the *Algonquin,* and was understood by Father Marquette. In the form of their bodies the Illinois were light and active. They were skilful in the use of arms, brave, but mild and tractable in disposition. They were entirely ignorant of the use of leather, and iron tools, their weapons being made of stone, and their clothing of the skins of wild beasts. The soil was rich and productive, and game abundant.

After this peaceful interview with the natives, the voyagers embarked again, and passed down the stream, looking out for the river *Pekitanoni* (Missouri), which empties into the Mississippi from the northwest.

They observed high and steep rocks, on the face of which were the figures of two monsters, which appeared as if painted in green, red, and blue colors; frightful in appearance, but so well executed, as to leave Father Marquette in doubt, whether they could be the work of savages, they being also at so great a height on the rocks as to be inaccessible to a painter.[19]

19. These monsters Marquette further described thus: "They are as large as a Calf, they have Horns on their heads like those of deer, a horrible look, red eyes, a beard like a tiger's, a face somewhat like a man's, a body covered with scales, and so long a tail that it winds all around the body, passing above the head and going back between the legs, ending in a fish's tail." These figures were on the face of a bluff near Alton, Ill.

As they floated quietly down a clear and placid stream, conversing about the figures they had just passed, they were interrupted by the sound of rapids before them; and a mass of floating timber, trunks and branches of trees, was swept from the mouth of the Pekitanoni with such a degree of violence, as to render the passage dangerous. So great was the agitation, that the water was thereby made very muddy, and it did not again become clear.[20] The Pekitanoni is described as a large river flowing into the Mississippi from the northwest, with several villages on its banks.

At this place Father Marquette decided, that, unless the Mississippi altered its previous course, it must empty its waters into the Gulf of Mexico; and he conjectured from the accounts of the natives, that, by following the stream of the Pekitanoni, a river would be discovered, which flowed into the Gulf of California.[21]

About twenty leagues south of the Pekitanoni, and a little more to the southeast, they discovered the mouth of another river, called *Ouabouskigou* (Ohio), in the latitude of thirty-six degrees; a short distance above which, they came to a place formidable to the savages, who, believing it the residence of a demon, had warned Father Marquette of its dangers. It proved nothing more than a ledge of

20. What Father Marquette did not understand was, that the Missouri brought the mud from far to the northwest and poured it into the clearer waters of the Mississippi. The character of the rivers has not changed in this respect.

21. To us this seems a curious supposition, and Father Marquette had little idea what it would mean to the hardy explorer who should go up the Missouri, cross the mountains and find the head waters of the Colorado. Trace such a route on a map of the United States, and read an account of the Lewis and Clark Expedition.

rocks, thirty feet high, against which the waves, being contracted by an island, ran with violence, and, being thrown back with a loud noise, flowed rapidly on through a narrow and unsafe channel.

The Ouabouskigou came from the eastward, where the country was thickly inhabited by the tribe of *Chuouanons,* a harmless and peaceful people, much annoyed by the Iroquois, who were said to capture them as slaves, and kill and torture them cruelly.

A little above the entrance of this river were steep banks, in which the boatmen discovered iron ore, several veins of which were visible, about a foot in thickness, portions of it adhering to the flint-stones; and also a species of rich earth, of three different colors, namely, purple, violet and red, and a very heavy red sand, some of which, being laid on an oar, left a stain during fifteen days. They here first saw tall reeds, or canes, growing on the shores, and began to find the *maringouins* (mosquitoes) very troublesome; the attacks of which, with the heat of the weather, obliged the voyagers to construct an awning of the sails of their canoes.

Shortly afterwards they saw savages armed with muskets, waiting their approach on the bank of the river. While the boatmen prepared for a defence, Father Marquette presented his calumet and addressed them in Huron, to which they gave no answer, but made signals to them to land, and accept some food. They consequently disembarked, and, entering their cabins, were presented with buffalo's meat, bear's oil, and fine plums. These savages had guns, hatchets, knives, hoes and glass bottles for their gunpowder. They informed Father

Marquette, that he was within ten days' journey
of the sea; that they purchased their goods of Europeans, who came from the east, that these Europeans had images and beads, played on many instruments, and were dressed like himself; and that
they had treated them with much kindness. As they
had no knowledge of Christianity, the worthy
Father gave them what instruction he could, and
made them a present of some medals. Encouraged
by the information received from these savages, the
party proceeded with renewed ardor on their voyage, between banks covered with thick forests, that
intercepted their view of the prairies; in which,
however, they heard at no great distance the bellowing of buffaloes. They also saw quails upon the
shores, and shot a small parrot.

They had nearly reached the thirty-third degree
of latitude,[22] steering toward the south, when they
discovered a village on the river's side, called
Metchigamea. The natives, armed with bows and
arrows, clubs, and tomahawks, prepared to attack
them; some in canoes, trying to intercept their
course, others remaining on shore. Father Marquette in vain presented his calumet of peace. They
were ready to attack, when the elders, perceiving at
last the calumet, commanded the young warriors to
stop, and, throwing their arms at the feet of the
strangers, as a sign of peace, entered their canoes,
and constrained them to land, though not without
some uneasiness.

As the savages were not acquainted with any of
the six languages spoken by Father Marquette, he

22. This was near the mouth of the Saint Francis River, in
Arkansas.

addressed them by signs, until an old man was found, who understood a little Illinois. Through this interpreter, he explained their intention of going to the borders of the sea, and gave the natives some religious instruction. In reply they answered that whatever information he desired might be obtained at *Akamsca* (Arkansas), a village ten leagues lower down the river; and presented them with food. After passing a night of some anxiety, they embarked the following morning with their interpreter; a canoe with ten savages preceding them. About half a league from Akamsca, they were met by two canoes full of Indians, the chief of whom presented his calumet, and conducted them to the shore, where they were hospitably received and supplied with provisions. Here they found a young man well acquainted with the Illinois language, and through him Father Marquette addressed the natives, making them the usual presents, and requesting information from them respecting the sea. They answered, that it was within five days' journey of Akamsca, that they knew nothing of the inhabitants on its borders, being prevented by their enemies from holding intercourse with these Europeans; that their knives and other weapons were purchased partly from the eastern nations, and partly from a tribe of Illinois, to the westward; that the armed savages whom the travellers had met, were their enemies; that they were continually on the river between that place and the sea; and that, if the voyagers proceeded further, great danger might be apprehended from them. After this communication, food was offered, and the rest of the day was spent in feasting.

These people were friendly and hospitable, but poor, although their Indian corn produced three abundant crops in a year, which Father Marquette saw in its different stages of growth. It was prepared for food in pots, which, with plates and other utensils, were neatly made of baked earth by the Indians. Their language was so very difficult, that Father Marquette despaired of being able to pronounce a word of it. Their climate in winter was rainy, but they had no snow, and the soil was extremely fertile.

During the evening the old men held a secret council. Some of them proposed to murder the strangers, and seize their effects. The chief, however, overruled this advice, and, sending for Father Marquette and M. Joliet, invited them to attend a dance of the calumet, which he afterwards presented to them as a sign of peace.

The good Father and his companions began now to consider what further course they should pursue. As it was supposed that the Gulf of Mexico extended as far north as thirty-one degrees and forty minutes, they believed themselves not to be more than two or three days' journey from it,[23] and it appeared to them certain, that the Mississippi must empty itself into that gulf, and not into the sea through Virginia, at the eastward, because the coast of Virginia was in the latitude of thirty-four degrees, at which they had already arrived; nor yet into the Gulf of California, at the southwest, because they had found the course of the river to be invariably south. Being thus persuaded

23. As a matter of fact, they were more than seven hundred miles from the gulf.

that the main object of their expedition was attained; and considering, moreover, that they were unable to resist the armed savages, who infested

AT THE PORTAGE

the lower parts of the river, and that, should they fall into the hands of the Spaniards, the fruits of their voyage and discoveries would be lost, they resolved to proceed no further, and, having informed the natives of their determination and rested another day, they prepared for their return.

After a month's navigation on the Mississippi, having followed its course from the forty-second to the thirty-fourth degree of latitude, they left the village of Akamsca, on the 17th of July, to return up the river. They retraced their way, slowly ascending the stream, until, in about the thirty-eighth degree of latitude, they turned into another river (Illinois), which abridged their route and brought them directly to Lake *Illinois* (Michigan). They were struck with the fertility of the country through which that river flowed, the beauty of the forests and prairies, the variety of the game, and the numerous small lakes and streams which they saw. The river was broad and deep, and navigable for sixty-five leagues, there being, in the season of spring and part of the summer, only half a league of portage between its waters and those flowing into Lake Illinois. On its banks they found a village, the inhabitants of which received them kindly, and, on their departure, extorted a promise from Father Marquette to return and instruct them.[24] One of the chiefs, accompanied by the young men, conducted them as far as the lake; whence they proceeded to the Bay of Puans, where they arrived near the end of September, having been absent about four months.[25]

24. This village was called Kaskaskia, and was situated about seven miles below the present city of Ottawa. There was another Kaskaskia to the south and west that became more famous.

25. This journey must have been about twenty-five hundred miles long, and when we consider the smallness of the party, the frailty of their two boats and the savage wildness of both the country and its inhabitants, the accomplishment seems one of the greatest in the history of American exploration.

On the Mississippi

Such is the substance of Father Marquette's narrative; and the whole of it accords so remarkably with the descriptions of subsequent travellers, and with the actual features of the country through which he passed, as to remove every doubt of its genuineness. The melancholy fate of the author, which followed soon afterwards, was probably the reason why his expedition was not in a more conspicuous manner brought before the public.[26] In addition to this narrative, nothing is known of Marquette, except what is said of him by Charlevoix. After returning from this last expedition, he took up his residence, and pursued the vocation of a missionary, among the Miamis in the neighborhood of Chicago.[27] While passing by water along the eastern shore of Lake Michigan towards Michillimackinac, he entered a small river, on the 18th of May, 1675.[28] Having landed, he constructed an altar, performed mass, and then retired a short distance into the wood, requesting the two men,

26. In this connection it is interesting to know that Joliet, who was really the explorer in charge of the expedition, spent the winter preparing a full report of his journey, which he illustrated with carefully drawn maps, and in the spring started for Quebec with them. In passing through La Chine Rapids his canoe was wrecked, and Joliet barely escaped with his life. His precious reports and maps were lost in the rushing waters. Father Marquette's comparatively brief journal and his map form the only original records of the expedition, and they are preserved at St. Mary's College, Montreal. The humble priest who sought only to carry his religion to the savages becomes the historian, while the ambitious explorer is hardly remembered in connection with the wonderful journey.

27. Always delicate, his health was grievously broken by his severe labors and privation, and his efforts to keep his promise to the Illinois were attended by terrible sufferings. The winter was passed in a bleak hut, and on his return journey he was not able to walk much of the time.

28. This river was the one on which the city of Ludington, Michigan, is now built.

who had charge of his canoe, to leave him alone for half an hour. When the time had elapsed, the men went to seek for him and found him dead. They were greatly surprised, as they had not discovered any symptoms of illness; but they remembered, that, when he was entering the river, he expressed a presentiment that his voyage would end there. To this day the river retains the name of *Marquette*. The place of his grave, near its bank, is still pointed out to the traveller; but his remains were removed the year after his death to Michilli-mackinac.[29]

29. The final resting place of the bones of Marquette is the little village of Saint Agnace, in the mainland of the northern peninsula of Michigan, west of Mackinac Island. A simple monument in the midst of a little park marks his grave.

THE FALL OF THE ALAMO

EXAS began its struggle for independence from Mexico in September, 1835, driven to it by the fact that under the rule of the new republic their treatment was little better than it had been while Mexico herself was under the Spanish control. No sooner, however, had the Texans declared their independence than General Cos led a large detachment into the state and determined to drive out of it those Americans who had settled there. The Mexican general met with so fierce a resistance that he was compelled to take refuge behind the walls of the Alamo in San Antonio de Bexar.[1] He had seventeen hundred men, but in spite of this fact the two hundred and sixteen Texans under General Burlison stormed the place, captured the Mexican general and sent him under parole to his brother-in-law, the famous Santa Ana.[2]

1. At this time San Antonio had a population of about seven thousand Mexicans, a small proportion of whom were favorable to the Texan cause. The majority had no particular leaning toward either side, but were willing to make the best terms they could. The San Antonio River separated the town from the Alamo village and fort, or mission, as it was originally called. The Alamo proper was a stone structure built during the first settlement of that locality by the Spaniards, who intended it as a refuge for the colonists in case of attacks by the hostile Indians. A wall two and a half feet thick and eight feet high surrounded the stone structure and enclosed an area of two or three acres. It was so large that it could not have been properly garrisoned by less than a thousand men, and the walls were not thick enough to make it a strong fortification.

2. Santa Ana was one of the most famous of Mexican soldiers and politicians. He was prominent as a leader in the expulsion of

A garrison of about a hundred and sixty men under the joint command of Colonel Travis[3] and Colonel Bowie[4] was in the Alamo in February of 1836. About this time there came to the Alamo David Crockett[5] of Tennessee, a famous hunter, warrior and politician, who had already represented his district in Congress, where he distinguished himself by his rough and powerful oratory.

On the afternoon of February 22nd, a large force of Mexicans under General Santa Ana arrived at San Antonio, and the next morning demanded an

the Spaniards, and finally became president of the republic. When Texas seceded, he advanced into that territory, but after his victory at the Alamo was decisively defeated and captured at San Jacinto by General Houston. After he had recognized the independence of Texas, he was released, and twice afterwards he served as president of Mexico.

During our war with that country, the Mexicans under his command were several times defeated, and Santa Ana resigned his commission. In 1853 he was for the last time made president, but before his term expired he was for a third time driven from his country in disgrace.

3. William B. Travis, after serving as a scout, had been appointed lieutenant-colonel and sent by the Texan governor to relieve Colonel Neill at the Alamo. The volunteers there were not willing to accept Travis as higher than second in command, but wished to elect their own colonel. In response to this feeling, Neill issued an order for the election of a lieutenant-colonel, and was about to make his departure, but the Texans seeing his purpose resented it and threatened Neill's life unless he yielded to their demands. Accordingly, under his direction James Bowie was elected full colonel, and when Travis reached the garrison he found Bowie in full command. Travis brought with him a company of regular recruits, but it was evident that trouble might soon arise between the rival commanders.

4. This Colonel Jas. Bowie had been a popular leader of the Texans, and had already defeated a large Mexican force. It is said that in one of his battles he broke his sword, but fought so desperately and successfully with the stump that afterwards he designed from the broken blade the terrible knife, which was known during the Mexican War and the Rebellion as the "Bowie knife."

5. David Crockett is so interesting a character that a longer account of him is given on page 29 of this volume.

unconditional surrender of the fort and its garrison. Although the Texans were taken almost completely by surprise, Travis answered the demand with a cannon shot, and the Mexicans raised the red flag which signified "no quarter."

The next morning the following proclamation was issued by Colonel Travis:

"To the people of Texas and
  all Americans of the world.

"Commandancy of the Alamo, Bexar,
"February 24, 1836.

"Fellow Citizens and Compatriots,—I am besieged by a thousand or more of the Mexicans under Santa Ana. I have sustained a continued bombardment and cannonade for twenty-four hours and have not lost a man. The enemy have demanded a surrender at discretion; otherwise the garrison is to be put to the sword if the fort is taken. I have answered the summons with a cannon shot, and our flag still waves proudly from the walls. I shall never surrender or retreat. Then I call on you in the name of liberty, patriotism, and everything dear to the American character, to come to our aid with all despatch. The enemy are receiving reënforcements daily, and will no doubt increase to three or four thousand in four or five days. Though this call may be neglected, I am determined to sustain myself as long as possible, and die like a soldier who never forgets what is due to his own honour and that of his country. Victory or death!

"(Signed)   W. BARRETT TRAVIS,
"Lieut.-Col. Com't."

When the Mexicans were first seen in San Antonio the defenders of the Alamo were thrown into a panic, for no one dreamed that enemies were in the vicinity; yet no one of the hardy garrison thought of flight, and after the first surprise was over, order was quickly restored and everything put in readiness for a bitter contest. The possible conflict of authority between Colonel Bowie and Colonel Travis was prevented by the fact that the former had been stricken with pneumonia and was lying in the hospital, a very sick man.

It was soon found that the siege lines of the enemy were not so close but that messengers might be sent through. One or two privates were despatched to bring assistance, but none succeeded in doing so. On the twenty-ninth of February it was resolved to send Captain Seguin, who spoke Spanish fluently, and who might by his own personal influence accomplish what the simple messages alone seemed unable to do. Seguin had no horse of his own, so he went to Colonel Bowie and borrowed his equipment, though the latter was so ill that he scarcely recognized the man who made the request. After a perilous ride, in which they were fired upon by the Mexicans, Seguin and his single aid succeeded in reaching the camp of volunteers which was forming at Gonzales. Here he induced thirty-six men to leave the camp and proceed to the Alamo, which they entered, thus raising the number of defenders to about a hundred and ninety. On the third of March,[6] Travis sent another courier with a letter

6. The people of Texas assembled in a general convention at Washington on the Brazos River, and issued their declaration of independence from Mexico on the second of March, 1836. That same day, General Sam Houston called attention to the perilous position

to his governor. In this he stated the situation
calmly, urged him to assist him, and closed with the
following words: "The bearer of this will give your
honorable body a statement more in detail, should
he escape through the enemies' lines. *God and
Texas! Victory or death.*"

For about ten days Travis held the little fort
under a storm of cannon balls, which really were
more alarming than destructive, for few, if any, of
the defenders were killed or wounded. Travis felt
that they had been almost miraculously preserved,
and in all the hardy company was born a feeling
that they could not lose in this terribly one-sided
contest. Every day they looked to the northward,
hoping to see relief coming, and every night turned
in disappointment to the little rest that was allowed
them. They fought manfully, wasting no ammunition and making every shot count. Until the
final assault, the execution done by the guns was
overwhelmingly in favor of the Texans.

The Mexicans had fixed on the morning of the
sixth of March for the final assault. Their infantry met, between midnight and dawn, at convenient distances from the fort, in four columns.
To each column was assigned a commanding officer
with a second to take his place in case the first was
disabled. Some of the columns were provided with
scaling ladders, axes and other implements by
which they might mount the wall or open breaches
in it. The cavalry was stationed at different points
surrounding the fort, so that they would be able

of the garrison at the Alamo, saying, "Independence is declared; it
must be maintained. Immediate action united with valor alone
can achieve the great work." This "immediate action" was too late
for the brave men in the Alamo.

to cut off any fugitives who might escape from the
fort. The attack was probably led by General
Castrillon, a Spaniard, who had already had a
brilliant military career.

THE MEXICANS STORM THE FORT

It is not thought that Santa Ana engaged per-
sonally in the assault, as it is known that before
the advance was made, he was stationed with several bands of music and a battery about five hun-

dred yards south of the Alamo, and that from this point he gave the bugle-signal for the advance. At double-quick time the columns advanced simultaneously against the little fort, one rushing through a breach which had already been made in the walls at the north, a second storming the chapel and a third scaling the west barrier.

General Cos, who had been captured by the Texans the year before and who was released on parole, broke his word of honor and led the storming column against the chapel. All this had been so planned that the several columns should reach the walls of the fort just as the coming dawn gave light enough to guide their movements. When the hour came, the bugle sounded, and the Mexicans, maddened by their losses and determined to avenge themselves on this courageous little troop, rushed forward to the walls while their bands played the assassin music that signified "no quarter."

It is difficult to give an orderly account of the conflict which followed, but some incidents stand out boldly. General Cos was repulsed from the chapel, and the column which attacked the north wall was badly cut before it succeeded in making an entrance. Here at the breach they met Colonel Travis in person, and here after the action he was found dead with a bullet hole through his head, and by his side a Mexican officer pierced to the heart by a sword still held in the hand of the dead Texan. On the west side the walls were scaled, and after bitter fighting the garrison, driven from the outer defenses, took refuge in the low barracks and other buildings, where, being more united, they could

fight to better advantage. However, there was no
easy means of communication between the buildings, and thus the surviving Texans soon were

THE DEFENDERS FIRING FROM WINDOWS

broken up into small groups, fighting desperately
against the overwhelming numbers of the Mexicans. There was no need of leadership, however,
or of direction from officers. The Mexicans pur-

posed to allow no quarter, and nothing remained for the Texans except that each man should fight to the last, doing as great execution as he could before finally falling under the weight of numbers.

Again and again the enemy charged upon the little buildings, while from the windows and loopholes the crack of rifles and the whiz of bullets showed that the living defenders were still active. It is not exaggerating to say that the assailants fell in heaps, for around each little building and before the long barracks the carnage was dreadful. One by one, however, the buildings were carried at the point of the bayonet, and the little groups of Texans broken up and destroyed.

The last point to yield was the chapel, which seems to have been held by a somewhat larger force than any of the other buildings. However, after the parade grounds were cleared and the other companies destroyed, it was possible to burn the most of the fort and thus batter it down and kill its brave defenders.

It is said that toward the close of the struggle in the chapel, Lieutenant Dickinson was seen to leap from one of the windows with a small child in his arms, and that both were shot as they leaped. This was perhaps the last act in the great tragedy, for if any were alive in the chapel after the lieutenant made his attempted escape, they were quickly bayonetted where they stood.

With the dead and dying strewn around, Santa Ana entered the fort. What he saw there, we cannot attempt to describe, but a few things we must mention. In his own room they found Colonel Bowie dead in his bed, where he had lain too sick to rise; but he had had strength to use his weapons, for four Mexicans had fallen, shot to death in the room, while a fifth lay across the bed with the Colonel's terrible knife sticking in his heart. Near the door of the magazine it is said that they found Major Evans, the master of ordnance, shot down

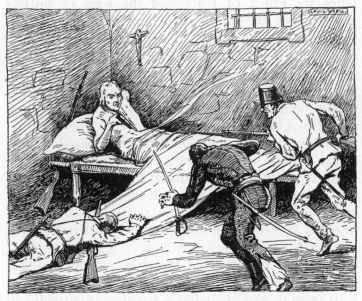

COLONEL BOWIE USED HIS WEAPONS TO THE LAST

with a burning match in his hand, before he could fire the powder and blow the fort and his enemies into the air.

Upon a high platform in one corner, there was a small cannon which was turned upon the Mexicans in the fort and did terrible execution. Who handled it is not exactly known, but near it were found the bodies of David Crockett and five of his companions. It is said, though possibly without much foundation, that when Santa Ana stepped into the courtyard he found Crockett and his companions still fighting.

Concealed in one of the rooms under some mattresses, five men were found, and under a bridge crossing an irrigating ditch another was discovered. All these were immediately shot by the orders of Santa Ana, and so hastily and excitedly was it all done that a Mexican was killed with them by accident. The wife of Lieutenant Dickinson, a negro servant of Travis, and a few Mexican women were the only human beings whose lives were spared.

Thus fell the Alamo. In thinking of this bloody tragedy, we must remember that these were simple citizens, bound together by no tie save their affection for one another and their loyalty to a state of whose independence they were as yet ignorant, for though Texas was then the "Lone Star State," no intimation of the Texas declaration of independence had reached Travis or his devoted followers. According to the report of General Santa Ana, the action lasted but thirty minutes from the time the enemy entered the walls till the resistance was completely quelled.

So many false reports have been made of the number engaged in this struggle that it is impossible even now to tell definitely. We do know that the number of Texans was less than two hundred, and it is probable that about twenty-five hundred Mexicans were engaged in the assault. All the Texans were killed, and from the various accounts we are led to infer that about five hundred Mexicans fell, a number which shows that the defense of the Texans was indeed fierce and bloody.

The history of our country does not show any incident of greater bravery or more heroic self-sacrifice, and it is hardly to be conceived that such a defense will ever be excelled. This was no disciplined force fighting under trained officers, but a group of simple, manly men, not agreeing in all things, but united with the one idea of fighting against cruelty and oppression.

On the Capitol grounds at Austin, Texas, a monument was erected in 1891 to the heroes of the Alamo. On it is this inscription:

"Thermopylæ had her messenger of defeat:
The Alamo had none."

THE ALHAMBRA

By WASHINGTON IRVING

NOTE.—The Alhambra is now a beautiful ruin, but at one time it was the great fortified palace of the Moors and the place where they made their last stand against the Christian Spaniards. From its beautiful courts the Moorish defenders were at last driven, and with their departure the Mohammedan faith ceased as a power in Europe.

The palace occupied but a portion of the space within the walls of the fortress, which in the time of the Moors was capable of containing an army of forty thousand men.

After the kingdom had passed into the hands of the Christians, the castle was occasionally inhabited by the Castilian monarchs. Early in the eighteenth century, however, it was abandoned as a court residence, its beautiful walls became desolate, and some of them fell to ruin, the gardens were destroyed, and the fountains ceased to play.

In 1829 Washington Irving lived for some time within the walls of the Alhambra and studied its history and the legends of Spain. These he has embodied in a charming book, from which we draw a description of the Alhambra.

E now found ourselves in a deep, narrow ravine, filled with beautiful groves, with a steep avenue and various footpaths winding through it, bordered with stone seats and ornamented with fountains. To our left, we beheld the towers of the Alhambra beetling above us; to our right, on the opposite side of the ravine, we were equally dominated by rival towers on a rocky eminence. These, we were told,

153

were the Torres Vermejos, or Vermilion towers, so
called from their ruddy hue. No one knows their
origin. They are of a date much anterior to the

THE GATE OF JUSTICE

Alhambra. Some suppose them to have been built
by the Romans; others, by some wandering colony
of Phœnicians. Ascending the steep and shady
avenue, we arrived at the foot of a huge square

Moorish tower, forming a kind of barbican, through which passed the main entrance to the fortress. This portal is called the Gate of Justice, from the tribunal held within its porch during the Moslem domination, for the immediate trial of petty causes; a custom common to the Oriental nations, and occasionally alluded to in the sacred Scriptures.

The great vestibule, or porch of the gate, is formed by an immense Arabian arch of the horseshoe form, which springs to half the height of the tower. On the keystone of this arch is engraven a gigantic hand. Within the vestibule, on the keystone of the portal, is engraven, in like manner, a gigantic key. Those who pretend to some knowledge of Mohammedan symbols affirm that the hand is the emblem of doctrine, and the key of faith; the latter, they add, was emblazoned on the standard of the Moslems when they subdued Andalusia, in opposition to the Christian emblem of the cross.

It was a tradition handed down from the oldest inhabitants, and which our informant had from his grandfather, that the hand and key were magical devices on which the fate of the Alhambra depended. The Moorish king who built it was a great magician, and, as some believed, had sold himself to the devil, and had laid the whole fortress under a magic spell. By this means it had remained standing for several hundred years, in defiance of storms and earthquakes, while almost all the other buildings of the Moors had fallen to ruin and disappeared. The spell, the tradition went on to say, would last until the hand on the outer arch should reach down and grasp the key, when the whole pile would tumble to pieces, and all the treasures buried beneath it by the Moors would be revealed.

After passing through the barbican we ascended a narrow lane, winding between walls, and came on an open esplanade within the fortress, called the Plaza de los Algibes, or Place of the Cisterns, from great reservoirs which undermine it, cut in the living rock by the Moors, for the supply of the fortress. Here, also, is a well of immense depth, furnishing the purest and coldest of water, another monument of the delicate taste of the Moors, who were indefatigable in their exertions to obtain that element in its crystal purity.

In front of the esplanade is the splendid pile commenced by Charles V, intended, it is said, to eclipse the residence of the Moslem kings. With all its grandeur and architectural merit, it appeared to us like an arrogant intrusion, and passing by it we entered a simple, unostentatious portal, opening into the interior of the Moorish palace.

The transition was almost magical; it seemed as if we were at once transported into other times and another realm, and were treading the scenes of Arabian story. We found ourselves in a great court paved with white marble and decorated at each end with light Moorish peristyles. It is called the court of the Alberca. In the center was an immense basin, or fish-pool, a hundred and thirty feet in length by thirty in breadth, stocked with goldfish, and bordered by hedges of roses. At the upper end of this court rose the great tower of Comares.

From the lower end, we passed through a Moorish archway into the renowned Court of Lions. There is no part of the edifice that gives us a more complete idea of its original beauty and magnificence than this; for none has suffered so little from the ravages of time. In the center stands the

THE COURT OF LIONS

fountain famous in song and story. The alabaster basins still shed their diamond drops, and the twelve lions which support them cast forth their crystal streams as in the days of Boabdil. The court is laid out in flower-beds, and surrounded by light Arabian arcades of open filigree work, supported by slender pillars of white marble.

The architecture, like that of all the other parts of the palace, is characterized by elegance rather than grandeur, bespeaking a delicate and graceful taste, and a disposition to indolent enjoyment. When we look upon the fairy tracery of the peristyles and the apparently fragile fretwork of the walls, it is difficult to believe that so much has survived the wear and tear of centuries, the shocks of earthquakes, the violence of war, and the quiet, though no less baneful, pilferings of the tasteful traveler. It is almost sufficient to excuse the popular tradition that the whole is protected by a magic charm.

On one side of the court a portal richly adorned opens into a lofty hall paved with white marble, and called the Hall of the Two Sisters. A cupola or lantern admits a tempered light from above, and a free circulation of air. The lower part of the walls is incrusted with beautiful Moorish tiles, on some of which are emblazoned the escutcheons of the Moorish monarchs: the upper part is faced with the fine stucco work invented at Damascus, consisting of large plates cast in molds and artfully joined, so as to have the appearance of having been laboriously sculptured by the hand into light relievos and fanciful arabesques, intermingled with texts of the Koran, and poetical inscriptions in Arabian and Celtic characters. These decorations of the walls and cupolas are richly gilded, and the interstices paneled with lapis lazuli and other brilliant and enduring colors. Above an inner porch is a balcony which communicated with the women's apartment. The latticed balconies still remain, from whence the dark-eyed beauties of the harem might gaze unseen upon the entertainments of the hall below.

It is impossible to contemplate this once favorite abode of Oriental manners without feeling the early associations of Arabian romance, and almost expecting to see the white arm of some mysterious princess beckoning from the balcony, or some dark eye sparkling through the lattice. The abode of beauty is here, as if it had been inhabited but yesterday—but where are the Zoraydas and Linderaxas!

On the opposite side of the Court of Lions is the hall of the Abencerrages, so called from the gallant cavaliers of that illustrious line, who were here perfidiously massacred. There are some who doubt the whole truth of this story, but our humble attendant, Mateo, pointed out the very wicket of the portal through which they are said to have been introduced, one by one, and the white marble fountain in the center of the hall, where they were beheaded. He showed us also certain broad, ruddy stains in the pavement, traces of their blood, which, according to popular belief, can never be effaced. Finding we listened to him with easy faith, he added that there was often heard at night, in the Court of the Lions, a low, confused sound, resembling the murmurings of a multitude; with now and then a faint tinkling, like the distant clank of chains. These noises are probably produced by the bubbling currents and tinkling falls of water, conducted under the pavement through the pipes and channels to supply the fountains; but according to the legend of the son of the Alhambra, they are made by the spirits of the murdered Abencerrages, who nightly haunt the scene of their suffering, and invoke the vengeance of Heaven on their destroyer.

From the Court of Lions we retraced our steps through the court of the Alberca, or great fish-pool, crossing which, we proceeded to the tower

THE HALL OF ABENCERRAGES

of Comares, so called from the name of the Arabian architect. It is of massive strength and lofty height, domineering over the rest of the edifice and overhanging the steep hillside, which descends abruptly to the banks of the Darro. A Moorish archway admitted us into a vast and lofty hall, which occupies the interior of the tower and was the grand audience chamber of the Moslem monarchs, thence called the hall of Ambassadors. It still bears the traces of past magnificence. The walls are richly stuccoed and decorated with arabesques, the vaulted ceilings of cedar wood, almost lost in obscurity from its height, still gleam with rich gilding and the brilliant tints of the Arabian pencil. On three sides of the saloon are deep windows, cut through the immense thickness of the walls, the balconies of which look down upon the verdant valley of the Darro, the streets and convents of the Albaycin, and command a prospect of the distant Vega. I might go on to describe the other delightful apartments of this side of the palace; the Tocador or toilet of the Queen, an open belvedere on the summit of the tower, where the Moorish sultanas enjoyed the pure breezes from the mountain and the prospect of the surrounding paradise; the secluded little patio or garden of Lindaraxa, with its alabaster fountain, its thickets of roses and myrtles, of citrons and oranges; the cool halls and grottoes of the baths, where the glare and heat of the day are tempered into a self-mysterious light and a pervading freshness.

An abundant supply of water, brought from the mountains by old Moorish aqueducts, circulates throughout the palace, supplying its baths and fish-pools, sparkling in jets within its halls, or murmuring in channels along the marble pavements. When it has paid its tribute to the royal pile, and visited its gardens and pastures, it flows down the long avenue leading to the city, trinkling in rills, gushing in fountains, and maintaining a perpetual verdure in those groves that embower and beautify the whole hill of the Alhambra.

While the city below pants with the noon-tide heat, and the parched Vega trembles to the eye, the delicate airs from the Sierra Nevada play through the lofty halls, bringing with them the sweetness of the surrounding gardens. Everything invites to that indolent repose, the bliss of Southern climes; and while the half-shut eyes look out from shaded balconies upon the glittering landscape, the ear is lulled by the rustling of groves and the murmur of running streams.

The reader has had a sketch of the interior of the Alhambra, and may be desirous of a general idea of its vicinity. The morning is serene and lovely; the sun has not gained sufficient power to destroy the freshness of the night; we will mount to the summit of the tower of Comares, and take a bird's-eye view of Granada and its environs.

Come, then, worthy reader and comrade, follow my steps into this vestibule ornamented with rich tracery, which opens to the hall of Ambassadors. We will not enter the hall, however, but turn to the left, to this small door, opening in the wall. Have a care! here are steep winding steps and but scanty light. Yet, up this narrow, obscure and winding staircase the proud monarchs of Granada and their queens have often ascended to the battlements of the tower to watch the approach of Christian armies or to gaze on the battles in the Vega. At length we are upon the terraced roof, and may take breath for a moment, while we cast

a general eye over the splendid panorama of city
and country, of rocky mountain, verdant valley
and fertile plain; of castle, cathedral, Moorish towers and Gothic domes, crumbling ruins and blooming groves.

Let us approach the battlements and cast our
eyes immediately below. See—on this side we have
the whole plan of the Alhambra laid open to us, and
can look down into its courts and gardens. At the
foot of the tower is the Court of the Alberca with
its great tank or fish-pool bordered with flowers;
and yonder is the Court of Lions, with its famous fountain, and its light Moorish arcades; and
in the center of the pile is the little garden of Lindaraxa, buried in the heart of the building, with
its roses and citrons and shrubbery of emerald
green.

That belt of battlements studded with square
towers, straggling round the whole brow of the hill,
is the outer boundary of the fortress. Some of the
towers, you may perceive, are in ruins, and their
massive fragments are buried among vines, fig-trees
and aloes.

Let us look on this northern side of the tower.
It is a giddy height; the very foundations of the
tower rise above the groves of the steep hillside.
And see, a long fissure in the massive walls shows
that the tower has been rent by some of the earthquakes which from time to time have thrown Granada into consternation; and which, sooner or later,
must reduce this crumbling pile to a mere mass of
ruin. The deep, narrow glen below us, which gradually widens as it opens from the mountains, is the
valley of the Darro; you see the little river wind-

ing its way under embowered terraces and among orchards and flower gardens. It is a stream famous in old times for yielding gold, and its sands are still sifted occasionally in search of the precious ore. Some of those white pavilions which here and there gleam from among groves and vineyards were rustic retreats of the Moors, to enjoy the refreshment of their gardens.

The airy palace with its tall white towers and long arcades, which breast yon mountain, among pompous groves and hanging gardens, is the Generaliffe, a summer palace of the Moorish kings, to which they resorted during the sultry months, to enjoy a still more breezy region than that of the Alhambra. The naked summit of the height above it, where you behold some shapeless ruins, is the Silla del Moro, or seat of the Moor; so called from having been a retreat of the unfortunate Boabdil during the time of an insurrection, where he seated himself and looked down mournfully upon his rebellious city.

A murmuring sound of water now and then rises from the valley. It is from the aqueduct of yon Moorish mill nearly at the foot of the hill. The avenue of trees beyond is the Alameda along the bank of the Darro, a favorite resort in evenings, and a rendezvous of lovers in the summer nights, when the guitar may be heard at a late hour from the benches along its walks. At present there are but a few loitering monks to be seen there, and a group of water carriers from the fountain of Avellanos.

You start! 'Tis nothing but a hawk we have frightened from his nest. This old tower is a complete brooding-place for vagrant birds. The swallow and martlet abound in every chink and cranny, and circle about it the whole day long; while at night, when all other birds have gone to rest, the moping owl comes out of its lurking place and utters its boding cry from the battlements. See how the hawk we have dislodged sweeps away below us, skimming over the tops of the trees, and sailing up to ruins above the Generaliffe.

Let us leave this side of the tower and turn our eyes to the west. Here you behold in the distance a range of mountains bounding the Vega, the ancient barrier between Moslem Granada and the land of the Christians. Among the heights you may still discern warrior towns, whose gray walls and battlements seem of a piece with the rocks on which they are built; while here and there is a solitary atalaya or watch-tower, mounted on some lofty point, and looking down as if it were from the sky, into the valleys on either side. It was down the defiles of these mountains, by the pass of Lope, that the Christian armies descended into the Vega. It was round the base of yon gray and naked mountain, almost insulated from the rest, and stretching its bald, rocky promontory into the bosom of the plain, that the invading squadrons would come bursting into view, with flaunting banners and the clangor of drums and trumpets. How changed is the scene! Instead of the glittering line of mailed warriors, we behold the patient train of the toilful muleteer, slowly moving along the skirts of the mountain.

Behind that promontory is the eventful bridge of Pinos, renowned for many a bloody strife be-

tween Moors and Christians; but still more renowned as being the place where Columbus was
overtaken and called back by the messenger of
Queen Isabella just as he was departing in despair
to carry his project of discovery to the court of
France.

Behold another place famous in the history of
the discoverer; yon line of walls and towers, gleaming in the morning sun in the very center of the
Vega; the city of Santa Fe, built by the Catholic
sovereigns during the siege of Granada, after a
conflagration had destroyed their camp. It was
to these walls that Columbus was called back by the
heroic queen, and within them the treaty was concluded that led to the discovery of the Western
World.

Here, toward the south, the eye revels on the
luxuriant beauties of the Vega, a blooming wilderness of grove and garden, and teeming orchards,
with the Xenil winding through it in silver links
and feeding innumerable rills, conducted through
ancient Moorish channels, which maintain the landscape in perpetual verdure. Here are the beloved
bowers and gardens and rural retreats for which
the Moors fought with such desperate valor.

Beyond the embowered region of the Vega you
behold, to the south, a line of arid hills down which
a long train of mules is slowly moving. It was
from the summit of one of those hills that the unfortunate Boabdil cast back his last look upon
Granada and gave vent to the agony of his soul.
It is the spot famous in song and story, "The last
sigh of the Moor."

Now raise your eyes to the snowy summit of yon pile of mountains, shining like a white summer cloud on the blue sky. It is the Sierra Nevada, the pride and delight of Granada; the source of her cooling breezes and perpetual verdure, of her gushing fountains and perennial streams. It is this glorious pile of mountains that gives to Granada that combination of delights so rare in a southern city: the fresh vegetation and the temperate airs of a northern climate, with the vivifying ardor of a tropical sun, and the cloudless azure of a southern sky. It is this aërial treasury of snow, which, melting in proportion to the increase of the summer heat, sends down rivulets and streams through every glen and gorge of the Alpuxarras, diffusing emerald verdure and fertility throughout a chain of happy and sequestered valleys.

These mountains may well be called the glory of Granada. They dominate the whole extent of Andalusia, and may be seen from its most distant parts. The muleteer hails them as he views their frosty peaks from the sultry level of the plain; and the Spanish mariner on the deck of his bark, far, far off on the bosom of the blue Mediterranean, watches them with a pensive eye, thinks of delightful Granada, and chants in low voice some old romance about the Moors.

But enough, the sun is high above the mountains, and is pouring his full fervor upon our heads. Already the terraced roof of the town is hot beneath our feet; let us abandon it, and descend and refresh ourselves under the arcades by the fountain of the Lions.

HERVÉ RIEL

By Robert Browning

NOTE.—This poem of Browning's furnishes its own historical setting; it gives date and places and names. All, in fact, that it does not tell us is that the battle at Cape la Hogue was a part of the struggle between England and France undertaken because Louis XIV of France would not acknowledge William III as king of England.

The poem is written in characteristic Browning style. You have read in the earlier volumes *An Incident of the French Camp*, *How They Brought the Good News from Ghent to Aix*, and *the Pied Piper of Hamelin*, and are therefore familiar with Browning's custom of leaving out words, using odd, informal words which another man might think out of place in poetry, and employing strange, sometimes jerky, meters.

N the sea and at the Hogue, sixteen
  hundred ninety-two,
 Did the English fight the French—
  woe to France!
 And, the thirty-first of May, helter-
  skelter thro' the blue,
  Like a crowd of frightened porpoises
a shoal of sharks pursue,
 Came crowding ship on ship to Saint Malo on
  the Rance,
With the English fleet in view.

'Twas the squadron that escaped, with the victor
 in full chase;
 First and foremost of the drove, in his great ship,
 Damfreville;
 Close on him fled, great and small,
 Twenty-two good ships in all;
And they signalled to the place,
 "Help the winners of a race!
 Get us guidance, give us harbor, take us quick
 —or, quicker still,
 Here's the English can and will!"

Then the pilots of the place put out brisk and leapt
 on board;
 "Why, what hope or chance have ships like these
 to pass?" laughed they:
"Rocks to starboard, rocks to port, all the passage
 scarred and scored,
 Shall the 'Formidable' here with her twelve and
 eighty guns
 Think to make the river-mouth by the single
 narrow way,
 Trust to enter where 'tis ticklish for a craft of
 twenty tons,
 And with flow at full beside?
 Now, 'tis slackest ebb of tide.
 Reach the mooring? Rather say,
While rock stands or water runs,
 Not a ship will leave the bay!"

Then was called a council straight.
 Brief and bitter the debate:
 "Here's the English at our heels; would you have
 them take in tow

All that's left us of the fleet, linked together stern
    and bow,
For a prize to Plymouth Sound?
. Better run the ships aground!"
    (Ended Damfreville his speech).
Not a minute more to wait!
    "Let the Captains all and each
    Shove ashore, then blow up, burn the vessels on
    the beach!
France must undergo her fate.

Give the word!" But no such word
Was ever spoke or heard;
    For up stood, for out stepped, for in struck amid
    all these—
A captain? A lieutenant? A mate—first, sec-
    ond, third?
    No such man of mark, and meet
    With his betters to compete!
    But a simple Breton sailor pressed by Tourville
    for the fleet,
A poor coasting-pilot he, Hervé Riel the Croi-
    sickese.

And, "What mockery or malice have we here?"
    cries Hervé Riel:
    "Are you mad, you Malouins? Are you cowards,
    fools, or rogues?
Talk to me of rocks and shoals, me who took the
    soundings, tell
On my fingers every bank, every shallow, every
    swell
    'Twixt the offing here and Grève where the river
    disembogues?

Are you bought by English gold? Is it love the
        lying's for?
    Morn and eve, night and day,
    Have I piloted your bay,
Entered free and anchored fast at the foot of
        Solidor.
    Burn the fleet and ruin France? That were
        worse than fifty Hogues!
    Sirs, they know I speak the truth! Sirs, believe
        me there's a way!
Only let me lead the line,
    Have the biggest ship to steer,
    Get this 'Formidable' clear,
Make the others follow mine,
And I lead them, most and least, by a passage I
        know well,
    Right to Solidor past Grève,
    And there lay them safe and sound;
    And if one ship misbehave,
    Keel so much as grate the ground,
Why, I've nothing but my life—here's my head!"
        cries Hervé Riel.

Not a minute more to wait.
"Steer us in, then, small and great!
    Take the helm, lead the line, save the squadron!"
        cried its chief.
Captains, give the sailor place!
    He is Admiral, in brief.
Still the north-wind, by God's grace!
See the noble fellow's face,
As the big ship with a bound,
Clears the entry like a hound,

Keeps the passage as its inch of way were the
    wide sea's profound!
  See, safe thro' shoal and rock,

THEY FOLLOW IN A FLOCK

  How they follow in a flock,
Not a ship that misbehaves, not a keel that grates
    the ground.

Not a spar that comes to grief!
The peril, see, is past,
All are harbored to the last,
And just as Hervé Riel hollas "Anchor!"—sure as
  fate
Up the English come, too late!

So, the storm subsides to calm:
  They see the green trees wave
  On the heights o'erlooking Grève.
Hearts that bled are stanched with balm.
"Just our rapture to enhance,
  Let the English rake the bay,
Gnash their teeth and glare askance,
  As they cannonade away!
'Neath rampired Solidor pleasant riding on the
  Rance!"
How hope succeeds despair on each captain's
  countenance!
Out burst all with one accord,
  "This is Paradise for Hell!
  Let France, let France's King
  Thank the man that did the thing!"
What a shout, and all one word,
  "Hervé Riel!"
As he stepped in front once more,
  Not a symptom of surprise
  In the frank blue Breton eyes,
Just the same man as before.

Then said Damfreville, "My friend,
I must speak out at the end,
  Though I find the speaking hard.
Praise is deeper than the lips:

You have saved the King his ships,
  You must name your own reward.
'Faith our sun was near eclipse!
Demand whate'er you will,
France remains your debtor still.
Ask to heart's content and have! or my name's not
    Damfreville."

Then a beam of fun outbroke
On the bearded mouth that spoke,
As the honest heart laughed through
Those frank eyes of Breton blue:
"Since I needs must say my say,
  Since on board the duty's done,
  And from Malo Roads to Croisic Point, what is
    it but a run?—
Since 'tis ask and have, I may—
  Since the others go ashore—
Come! A good whole holiday!
  Leave to go and see my wife, whom I call the
    Belle Aurore!"
That he asked and that he got—nothing more.

Name and deed alike are lost:
Not a pillar nor a post
  In his Croisic keeps alive the feat as it befell;
Not a head in white and black
On a single fishing smack,
In memory of the man but for whom had gone
    to wrack
  All that France saved from the fight whence
    England bore the bell.
Go to Paris: rank on rank
  Search the heroes flung pell-mell

On the Louvre, face and flank!
    You shall look long enough ere you come to
        Hervé Riel.
So, for better and for worse,
Hervé Riel, accept my verse!
In my verse, Hervé Riel, do thou once more
Save the squadron, honor France, love thy wife,
    the Belle Aurore!

THE BATTLE OF WATERLOO

By LORD BYRON

HERE was a sound of revelry by
    night,
  And Belgium's capital had gathered
    then
  Her Beauty and her Chivalry, and
    bright
    The lamps shone o'er fair women and
brave men;
A thousand hearts beat happily; and when
Music arose with its voluptuous swell,
Soft eyes looked love to eyes which spake again,
And all went merry as a marriage bell;
But hush! hark! a deep sound strikes like a rising
    knell!

  Did ye not hear it?—No; 'twas but the wind,
  Or the car rattling o'er the stony street;
  On with the dance! let joy be unconfined;
No sleep till morn, when Youth and Pleasure
    meet
  To chase the glowing Hours with flying feet—
  But, hark!—that heavy sound breaks in once
    more
  As if the clouds its echo would repeat;
  And nearer, clearer, deadlier that before!
Arm! Arm! it is—it is—the cannon's opening
    roar!

Within a windowed niche of that high hall
Sate Brunswick's fated chieftain; he did hear
That sound the first amidst the festival,
And caught its tone with Death's prophetic ear.
And when they smiled because he deemed it near,

BUT, HARK!

His heart more truly knew that peal too well
Which stretched his father on a bloody bier,
And roused the vengeance blood alone could
    quell:
He rushed into the field, and, foremost, fighting,
    fell.

Ah! then and there was hurrying to and fro,
And gathering tears, and tremblings of distress,
And cheeks all pale, which but an hour ago
Blushed at the praise of their own loveliness;
And there were sudden partings, such as press
The life from out young hearts, and choking
    sighs
Which ne'er might be repeated; who could guess
If ever more should meet those mutual eyes,
Since upon night so sweet such awful morn could
    rise!

And there was mounting in hot haste: the steed,
The mustering squadron, and the clattering car,
Went pouring forward with impetuous speed,
And swiftly forming in the ranks of war;
And the deep thunder peal on peal afar;
And near, the beat of the alarming drum
Roused up the soldier ere the morning star;
While thronged the citizens with terror dumb,
Or whispering, with white lips—"The foe! They
    come! They come!"

And wild and high the "Cameron's gathering"
    rose!
The war-note of Lochiel, which Albyn's hills
Have heard, and heard, too, have her Saxon
    foes:—
How in the noon of night that pibroch thrills,
Savage and shrill! But with the breath which
    fills
Their mountain-pipe, so fill the mountaineers

With the fierce native daring which instills
The stirring memory of a thousand years,
And Evan's, Donald's fame rings in each clans-
    man's ears!

And Ardennes waves above them her green
    leaves,
  Dewy with nature's tear-drops, as they pass,
Grieving, if aught inanimate e'er grieves,
  Over the unreturning brave,—alas!
Ere evening to be trodden like the grass
  Which now beneath them, but above shall grow
In its next verdure, when this fiery mass
  Of living valor, rolling on the foe
And burning with high hope, shall moulder cold
    and low.

Last noon beheld them full of lusty life,
  Last eve in Beauty's circle proudly gay,
The midnight brought the signal-sound of strife,
  The morn the marshalling in arms,—the day
Battle's magnificently-stern array!
  The thunder-clouds close o'er it, which when rent
The earth is covered thick with other clay,
  Which her own clay shall cover, heaped and pent,
Rider and horse,—friend, foe,—in one red burial
    blent.

HOW THEY TOOK THE GOLD-TRAIN[1]

By CHARLES KINGSLEY[2]

 FORTNIGHT or more has passed in severe toil;[3] but not more severe than they have endured many a time before. Bidding farewell once and forever to the green ocean of the eastern plains, they have crossed the Cordillera; they have taken a longing glance at the city of Santa Fé, lying in the midst of rich gardens on its lofty mountain plateau, and have

1. This selection is abridged from the twenty-fifth chapter in *Westward Ho!* Charles Kingsley's great novel of adventure.

In the story are related the adventures of Amyas Leigh, a large, powerful and exceedingly vigorous man from Devonshire, who follows the life of the sea during the days of Queen Elizabeth. Like many of the men of his age, he becomes absorbed with the notion that in South America is the great city of Manoa, whose wealth in gold and jewels far exceeds that of Mexico and Peru.

After an exciting voyage, enlivened by conflicts with Spanish ships, the survivors land on the coast of South America and proceed inward in search of Manoa. Besides the dangers from Spaniards and natives, they meet with all the perils of the wilderness; disease and death at the hands of the Spaniards, Indians and wild animals thinning their ranks to less than half; yet the spirits of Amyas never falter, and the remnant of his force follow him with a devotion that is wonderful.

2. Charles Kingsley, an English clergyman, was born in 1819 and entered Cambridge University in 1838. Ten years later he published the first of his stories, and in 1855, *Westward Ho!* Next to this book probably ranks his *Hypatia*, which he published in 1855, and which tells a thrilling tale of the struggles of Christianity with the Greek faith in the fifth century. He was a successful clergyman and became Canon of Westminster. He visited the United States in 1874, but his health was even then failing, and a year later he died.

seen, as was to be expected, that it was far too large
a place for any attempt of theirs. But they had not
altogether thrown away their time. Their Indian
lad[4] has discovered that a gold-train is going down
from Santa Fé toward the Magdalena; and they
are waiting for it beside the miserable rut which
serves for a road, encamped in a forest of oaks
which would make them almost fancy themselves
back again in Europe, were it not for the tree-ferns
which form the undergrowth; and were it not, too,
for the deep gorges opening at their very feet; in
which, while their brows are swept by the cool
breezes of a temperate zone, they can see far below,
dim through their everlasting vapor-bath of rank
hot steam, the mighty forms and gorgeous colors
of the tropic forest.

They have pitched their camp among the tree-
ferns, above a spot where the path winds along
a steep hill-side, with a sheer cliff below of many
a hundred feet. There was a road there once, perhaps, when Cundinamarca[5] was a civilized and cul-
tivated kingdom; but all which Spanish misrule
has left of it are a few steps slipping from their

3. The party landed on the coast of South America, and in the
preceding chapter is told the story of their stay in a hospitable
Indian village where they rested and prepared themselves for two
weeks of hard travel.

4. This Indian lad was rescued from the Spaniards by Amyas
and is devoted to the latter. He acts as interpreter, and his keen
sight and familiarity with the southern wilderness make him of
great value to the wanderers.

5. Cundinamarca was the central province in what is now the
Republic of Colombia. Its streams are tributary to the Orinoco,
though it extends westward into the Andes. It derived its name
from a native American goddess, and before the Spaniards dev-
astated the region it was one of the chief centers of Indian civilization in South America.

places at the bottom of a narrow ditch of mud. It
has gone the way of the aqueducts, and bridges, and
post-houses, the gardens and the llama-flocks of
that strange empire. In the mad search for gold,
every art of civilization has fallen to decay, save
architecture alone; and that survives only in the
splendid cathedrals which have risen upon the ruins
of the temples of the Sun.

And now, the rapid tropic vegetation has re-
claimed its old domains, and Amyas and his crew
are as utterly alone, within a few miles of an important Spanish settlement, as they would be in the
solitudes of the Orinoco or the Amazon.

In the meanwhile, all their attempts to find sul-
phur and nitre have been unavailing; and they have
been forced to depend after all (much to Yeo's[6] dis-
gust) upon their swords and arrows. Be it so:
Drake[7] took Nombre de Dios and the gold-train
there with no better weapons; and they may do as
much.

So, having blocked up the road above by felling
a large tree across it, they sit there among the flowers chewing coca, in default of food and drink, and
meditating among themselves the cause of a mysterious roar, which has been heard nightly in their
wake ever since they left the banks of the Meta.

6. Salvation Yeo is a big white-haired man, older than Amyas,
who spent his early life in wild adventure with Drake and other
sailors in the Southern Seas. After incredible sufferings while in
the hands of the Spaniards, Salvation becomes a most ardent and
devoted Christian, but with a fierce hatred of the Spaniards and all
things Spanish that makes his acts strangely inconsistent.

7. This is Sir Francis Drake, the discoverer of the Pacific Ocean,
a leader in many thrilling expeditions and exciting conflicts with
the Spaniards.

Jaguar it is not, nor monkey: it is unlike any sound they know; and why should it follow them? However, they are in the land of wonders; and, moreover, the gold-train is far more important than any noise.

At last, up from beneath there was a sharp crack and a loud cry. The crack was neither the snapping of a branch, nor the tapping of a woodpecker; the cry was neither the scream of the parrot, nor the howl of the monkey,—

"That was a whip's crack," said Yeo, "and a woman's wail. They are close here, lads!"

"A woman's? Do they drive women in their gangs?" asked Amyas.

"Why not, the brutes? There they are, sir. Did you see their basnets glitter?"

"Men!" said Amyas in a low voice, "I trust you all not to shoot till I do. Then give them one arrow, out swords, and at them! Pass the word along."

Up they came, slowly, and all hearts beat loud at their coming.

First, about twenty soldiers, only one-half of whom were on foot; the other half being borne, incredible as it may seem, each in a chair on the back of a single Indian, while those who marched had consigned their heavier armor and their arquebuses into the hands of attendant slaves, who were each pricked on at will by the pikes of the soldier behind them.

"The men are made to let their ordnance out of their hands."

"Oh, sir, an Indian will pray to an arquebus not to shoot him; be sure their artillery is safe enough," said Yeo.

"Look at the proud villains," whispered another, "to make dumb beasts of human creatures like that!"

"Ten shot," counted the businesslike Amyas, "and ten pikes."

Last of this troop came some inferior officer, also in his chair, who, as he went slowly up the hill, with his face turned toward the gang which followed, drew every other second the cigar from his lips, to inspirit them with those ejaculations which earned for the Spaniards of the sixteenth century the uncharitable imputation of being the most abominable swearers of all Europeans.

"The blasphemous dog!" said Yeo, fumbling at his bowstring, as if he longed to send an arrow through him. But Amyas had hardly laid his finger on the impatient veteran's arm, when another procession followed, which made them forget all else.

A line of Indians, Negroes, and Zambos, naked, emaciated, scarred with whips and fetters, and chained together by their left wrists, toiled upwards, panting and perspiring under the burden of a basket held up by a strap which passed across their foreheads. Yeo's sneer was but too just; there were not only old men and youths among them, but women; slender young girls, mothers with children running at their knee; and, at the sight, a low murmur of indignation rose from the ambushed Englishmen, worthy of the free and righteous hearts of those days, when Raleigh could appeal to man and God, on the ground of a common humanity, in behalf of the outraged heathens of the New World; when Englishmen still knew that man was man, and that the instinct of freedom was the righteous voice of

God; ere the hapless seventeenth century had
brutalized them also, by bestowing on them, amid
a hundred other bad legacies, the fatal gift of negro-
slaves.

But the first forty, so Amyas counted, bore on
their backs a burden which made all, perhaps, but
him and Yeo, forget even the wretches who bore
it. Each basket contained a square package of
carefully corded hide; the look whereof friend Amyas knew full well.

"What's in they, captain?"

"Gold!" And at that magic word all eyes were
strained greedily forward, and such a rustle followed, that Amyas, in the very face of detection,
had to whisper—

"Be men, be men, or you will spoil all yet!"

The last twenty, or so, of the Indians bore larger
baskets, but more lightly freighted, seemingly with
manioc, and maize-bread, and other food for the
party; and after them came, with their bearers and
attendants, just twenty soldiers more, followed by
the officer in charge, who smiled away in his chair,
and twirled two huge mustachios, thinking of nothing less than of the English arrows which were itching to be away and through his ribs. The ambush
was complete; the only question how and when to
begin?

Amyas had a shrinking, which all will understand, from drawing bow in cold blood on men so
utterly unsuspicious and defenseless, even though
in the very act of devilish cruelty— for devilish
cruelty it was, as three or four drivers armed with
whips, lingered up and down the slowly staggering
file of Indians, and avenged every moment's lag-

ging, even every stumble, by a blow of the cruel manati-hide, which cracked like a pistol-shot against the naked limbs of the silent and uncomplaining victim.

Suddenly the casus belli,[8] as usually happens, arose of its own accord.

The last but one of the chained line was an old gray-headed man, followed by a slender graceful girl of some eighteen years old, and Amyas' heart yearned over them as they came up. Just as they passed, the foremost of the file had rounded the corner above; there was a bustle, and a voice shouted, "Halt, Señors! there is a tree across the path!"

"A tree across the path?" bellowed the officer, while the line of trembling Indians, told to halt above, and driven on by blows below, surged up and down upon the ruinous steps of the Indian road, until the poor old man fell groveling on his face.

The officer leaped down, and hurried upward to see what had happened. Of course, he came across the old man.

"Grandfather of Beelzebub, is this a place to lie worshiping your fiends?" and he pricked the prostrate wretch with the point of his sword.

The old man tried to rise; but the weight of his head was too much for him; he fell again, and lay motionless.

The driver applied the manati-hide across his loins, once, twice, with fearful force; but even that specific was useless.

"Gastado, Señor Capitan," said he, with a shrug. "Used up. He has been failing these three months!"

8. *Casus belli* means *cause of war.*

"What does the intendant mean by sending me out with worn-out cattle like these? Forward there!" shouted he. "Clear away the tree, Señors, and I'll soon clear the chain. Hold it up, Pedrillo!"

The driver held up the chain, which was fastened to the old man's wrist. The officer stepped back, and flourished round his head a Toledo blade, whose beauty made Amyas break the Tenth Commandment on the spot.

The man was a tall, handsome, broad-shouldered, high-bred man; and Amyas thought that he was going to display the strength of his arm, and the temper of his blade, in severing the chain at one stroke.

Even he was not prepared for the recondite fancies of a Spanish adventurer, worthy son or nephew of those first conquerors, who used to try the keenness of their swords upon the living bodies of Indians, and regale themselves at meals with the odor of roasting caciques.

The blade gleamed in the air, once, twice, and fell: not on the chain, but on the wrist which it fettered. There was a shriek, a crimson flash—and the chain and its prisoner were parted indeed.

One moment more, and Amyas's arrow would have been through the throat of the murderer, who paused, regarding his workmanship with a satisfied smile; but vengeance was not to come from him.

Quick and fierce as a tiger-cat, the girl sprang on the ruffian, and with the intense strength of passion, clasped him in her arms and leaped with him from the narrow ledge into the abyss below.

There was a rush, a shout; all faces were bent over the precipice. The girl hung by her chained wrist: the officer was gone.   There was a moment's awful silence; and then Amyas heard his body crashing through the tree-tops far below.

"DO NOT SHOOT TILL I DO"

"Haul her up! Hew her to pieces! Burn the witch!" and the driver, seizing the chain, pulled at it with all his might, while all springing from their chairs, stooped over the brink.

Now was the time for Amyas! Heaven had delivered them into his hands. Swift and sure, at ten yards off, his arrow rushed through the body of the driver, and then, with a roar as of a leaping lion, he sprang like an avenging angel into the midst of the astonished ruffians.

His first thought was for the girl. In a moment, by sheer strength, he had jerked her safely up into the road; while the Spaniards recoiled right and left, fancying him for the moment some mountain giant or supernatural foe. His hurrah undeceived them in an instant, and a cry of "English! Dogs!" arose, but arose too late. The men of Devon had followed their captain's lead: a storm of arrows left five Spaniards dead, and a dozen more wounded, and down leapt Salvation Yeo, his white hair streaming behind him, with twenty good swords more, and the work of death began.

The Spaniards fought like lions; but they had no time to fix their arquebuses on the crutches; no room, in that narrow path, to use their pikes. The English had the wall of them; and to have the wall there, was to have the foe's life at their mercy. Five desperate minutes, and not a living Spaniard stood upon those steps; and certainly no living one lay in the green abyss below. Two only, who were behind the rest, happening to be in full armor, escaped without mortal wound, and fled down the hill again.

"After them! Michael Evans and Simon Heard; and catch them, if they run a league."

The two long and lean Clovelly men, active as deer from forest training, ran two feet for the Spaniard's one; and in ten minutes returned, having done their work; while Amyas and his men hurried past the Indians, to help Cary and the party forward, where shouts and musket shots announced a sharp affray.

Their arrival settled the matter. All the Spaniards fell but three or four, who scrambled down the crannies of the cliff.

"Let not one of them escape! Slay them as Israel slew Amalek!" cried Yeo, as he bent over; and ere the wretches could reach a place of shelter, an arrow was quivering in each body, as it rolled lifeless down the rocks.

"Now then! Loose the Indians!"

They found armorers' tools on one of the dead bodies, and it was done.

"We are friends," said Amyas. "All we ask is, that you shall help us carry this gold down to the Magdalena, and then you are free."

Some few of the younger groveled at his knees, and kissed his feet, hailing him as the child of the Sun: but the most part kept a stolid indifference, and when freed from their fetters, sat quietly down where they stood, staring into vacancy. The iron had entered too deeply into their soul. They seemed past hope, enjoyment, even understanding.

But the young girl, who was last of all in the line, as soon as she was loosed, sprang to her father's body, speaking no word, lifted it in her thin arms, laid it across her knees, kissed the fallen lips, stroked the furrowed cheeks, murmured inarticulate sounds like the cooing of a woodland dove, of which none knew the meaning but she, and he who heard not, for his soul had long since fled. Suddenly the truth flashed on her; silent as ever, she drew one long heavy breath, and rose erect, the body in her arms.

Another moment, and she had leaped into the abyss. They watched her dark and slender limbs, twined closely round the old man's corpse, turn over, and over, and over, till a crash among the leaves, and a scream among the birds, told that she had reached the trees; and the green roof hid her from their view.

"Brave lass!" shouted a sailor.

"The Lord forgive her!" said Yeo. "But, your worship, we must have these rascals' ordnance."

"And their clothes, too, Yeo, if we wish to get down the Magdalena unchallenged. Now listen, my masters all! We have won, by God's good grace, gold enough to serve us the rest of our lives, and that without losing a single man; and may yet win more, if we be wise, and He thinks good. But oh, my friends, do not make God's gift our ruin, by faithlessness, or greediness, or any mutinous haste."

"You shall find none in us!" cried several men. "We know your worship. We can trust our general."

"Thank God!" said Amyas. "Now then, it will be no shame or sin to make the Indians carry it, saving the women, whom God forbid we should burden. But we must pass through the very heart of the Spanish settlements, and by the town of Saint Martha itself. So the clothes and weapons of these Spaniards we must have, let it cost us what labor it may. How many lie in the road?"

"Thirteen here, and about ten up above," said Cary.[9]

9. Will Cary is the lieutenant and right-hand man of Amyas.

"Then there are near twenty missing. Who will volunteer to go down over the cliff, and bring up the spoil of them?"

"I, and I, and I"; and a dozen stepped out, as they did always when Amyas wanted anything done; for the simple reason, that they knew that he meant to help at the doing of it himself.

"Very well, then, follow me. Sir John,[10] take the Indian lad for your interpreter, and try and comfort the souls of these poor heathens. Tell them that they shall all be free."

"Why, who is that comes up the road?"

All eyes were turned in the direction of which he spoke. And, wonder of wonders! up came none other than Ayacanora[11] herself, blow-gun in hand, bow on back, and bedecked in all her feather garments, which last were rather the worse for a fortnight's woodland travel.

All stood mute with astonishment, as, seeing Amyas, she uttered a cry of joy, quickened her pace into a run, and at last fell panting and exhausted at his feet.

"I have found you!" she said; "you ran away from me, but you could not escape me!" And she fawned round Amyas, like a dog who has found his master, and then sat down on the bank, and burst into wild sobs.

10.   Sir John Brimblecombe is the chaplain of the expedition.

11.   Ayacanora is a beautiful Indian Princess whom the Spaniards met in the Indian village described in the preceding chapter. She seems quite different from others of the tribe, and is thought to be a descendent from one of the light-skinned Peruvian Incas, whom the Spaniards had almost entirely extinguished. Much later in the story she is discovered to be of real white descent, and at the end of the book she becomes the wife of Amyas.

"God help us!" said Amyas, clutching his hair, as he looked down upon the beautiful weeper. "What am I to do with her, over and above all these poor heathens?"

But there was no time to be lost, and over the cliff he scrambled; while the girl, seeing that the main body of the English remained, sat down on a point of rock to watch him.

After half-an-hour's hard work, the weapons, clothes, and armor of the fallen Spaniards were hauled up the cliff, and distributed in bundles among the men; the rest of the corpses were thrown over the precipice, and they started again upon their road toward the Magdalena, while Yeo snorted like a war-horse who smells the battle, at the delight of once more handling powder and ball.

"We can face the world now, sir! Why not go back and try Santa Fé, after all?"

But Amyas thought that enough was as good as a feast, and they held on downwards, while the slaves followed, without a sign of gratitude, but meekly obedient to their new masters, and testifying now and then by a sign or a grunt, their surprise at not being beaten, or made to carry their captors. Some, however, caught sight of the little calabashes of coca which the English carried. That woke them from their torpor, and they began coaxing abjectly (and not in vain), for a taste of that miraculous herb, which would not only make food unnecessary, and enable their panting lungs to endure the keen mountain air, but would rid them, for a while at least, of the fallen Indian's most unpitying foe, the malady of thought.

As the cavalcade turned the corner of the mountain, they paused for one last look at the scene of that fearful triumph. Lines of vultures were already streaming out of infinite space, as if created suddenly for the occasion. A few hours and there would be no trace of that fierce fray, but a few white bones amid untrodden beds of flowers.

And now Amyas had time to ask Ayacanora the meaning of this her strange appearance. He wished her anywhere but where she was: but now that she was here, what heart could be so hard as not to take pity on the poor wild thing? And Amyas as he spoke to her had, perhaps, a tenderness in his tone, from very fear of hurting her, which he had never used before. Passionately she told him how she had followed on their track day and night, and had every evening made sounds, as loud as she dared, in hopes of their hearing her, and either waiting for her, or coming back to see what caused the noise. Amyas now recollected the strange roaring which had followed them.

"Noises? What did you make them with?"

Ayacanora lifted her finger with an air of most self-satisfied mystery; and then drew cautiously from under her feather cloak an object at which Amyas had hard work to keep his countenance.

"Look!" whispered she, as if half afraid that the thing itself should hear her. "I have it—the holy trumpet!"

There it was, a handsome earthen tube some two feet long, neatly glazed, and painted with quaint grecques and figures of animals; a relic evidently of some civilization now extinct.

Brimblecombe rubbed his little fat hands. "Brave maid! you have cheated Satan this time," quoth he; while Yeo advised that the idolatrous relic should be forthwith "hove over cliff."

"Let be," said Amyas. "What is the meaning of this, Ayacanora? And why have you followed us?" She told a long story, from which Amyas picked up, as far as he could understand her, that that trumpet had been for years the torment of her life; the one thing in the tribe superior to her; the one thing which she was not allowed to see, because, forsooth, she was a woman. So she determined to show them that a woman was as good as a man; and hence her hatred of marriage, and her Amazonian exploits. But still the Piache[12] would not show her that trumpet, or tell her where it was: and as for going to seek it, even she feared the superstitious wrath of the tribe at such a profanation. But the day after the English went, the Piache chose to express his joy at their departure; whereon, as was to be expected, a fresh explosion between master and pupil, which ended, she confessed, in her burning the old rogue's hut over his head, from which he escaped with loss of all his conjuring-tackle, and fled raging into the woods, vowing that he would carry off the trumpet to the neighboring tribe. Whereon, by a sudden impulse, the young lady took plenty of coca, her weapons, and her feathers, started on his trail, and ran him to earth just as he was unveiling the precious mystery. At which sight (she confessed), she was horribly afraid, and half inclined to run: but, gathering courage from the thought that the white men used to laugh at the whole matter, she rushed upon the hapless con-

12. The *Piache* is the chief medicine man of the tribe of Indians among whom Ayacanora was regarded as a powerful princess.

jurer, and bore off her prize in triumph; and there
it was!

"I hope you have not killed him?" said Amyas.

"I did beat him a little; but I thought you would
not let me kill him."

Amyas was half amused with her confession of
his authority over her: but she went on,

"And then I dare not go back to the Indians;
so I was forced to come after you."

"And is that, then, your only reason for coming
after us?" asked stupid Amyas.

He had touched some secret chord—though what
it was he was too busy to inquire. The girl drew
herself up proudly, blushing scarlet, and said—

"You never tell lies. Do you think that I would
tell lies?"

On which she fell to the rear, and followed them
steadfastly, speaking to no one, but evidently determined to follow them to the world's end.

They soon left the high road; and for several
days held on downwards, hewing their path slowly
and painfully through the thick underwood. On
the evening of the fourth day, they had reached
the margin of a river, at a point where it seemed
broad and still enough for navigation. For those
three days they had not seen a trace of human beings, and the spot seemed lonely enough for them
to encamp without fear of discovery, and begin the
making of their canoes. They began to spread
themselves along the stream, in search of the soft-
wooded trees proper for their purpose; but hardly
had their search begun, when, in the midst of a
dense thicket, they came upon a sight which filled
them with astonishment. Beneath a honey-combed

cliff, which supported one enormous cotton-tree, was a spot of some thirty yards square sloping down to the stream, planted in rows with magnificent banana-plants, full twelve feet high, and bearing among their huge waxy leaves clusters of ripening fruit; while, under their mellow shade, yams

SOLEMNLY HE APPROACHED, STAFF IN HAND

and cassava plants were flourishing luxuriantly, the whole being surrounded by a hedge of orange and scarlet flowers.   There it lay, streaked with long shadows from the setting sun, while a cool southern air rustled in the cotton-tree, and flapped to and fro the great banana leaves; a tiny paradise of art and care.   But where was its inhabitant?

Aroused by the noise of their approach, a figure issued from a cave in the rocks, and, after gazing at them for a moment, came down the garden towards them. He was a tall and stately old man, whose snow-white beard and hair covered his chest and shoulders, while his lower limbs were wrapt in Indian-web. Slowly and solemnly he approached, a staff in one hand, a string of beads in the other, the living likeness of some old Hebrew prophet, or anchorite of ancient legend. He bowed courteously to Amyas (who of course returned his salute), and was in act to speak, when his eye fell upon the Indians, who were laying down their burdens in a heap under the trees. His mild countenance assumed instantly an expression of the acutest sorrow and displeasure; and, striking his hands together, he spoke in Spanish—

"Alas! miserable me! Alas! unhappy Señors! Do my old eyes deceive me, and is it one of those evil visions of the past which haunt my dreams by night: or has the accursed thirst for gold, the ruin of my race, penetrated even into this my solitude? Oh, Señors, Señors, know you not that you bear with you your own poison, your own familiar fiend, the root of every evil? And is it not enough for you to load yourselves with the wedge of Achan, and partake his doom, but you must make these hapless heathens the victims of your greed and cruelty, and forestall for them on earth those torments which may await their unbaptized souls hereafter?"

"We have preserved, and not enslaved these Indians, ancient Señor," said Amyas proudly; "and to-morrow will see them as free as the birds over our heads."

"Free? Then you cannot be countrymen of mine! But pardon an old man, my son, if he has spoken too hastily in the bitterness of his own experience. But who and whence are you? And why are you bringing into this lonely wilderness that gold—for I know too well the shape of those accursed packets, which would God that I had never seen!"

"What we are, reverend sir, matters little, as long as we behave to you as the young should to the old. As for our gold, it will be a curse or blessing to us, I conceive, just as we use it well or ill; and so is a man's head, or his hand, or any other thing; but that is no reason for cutting off his limbs for fear of doing harm with them; neither is it for throwing away those packages, which, by your leave, we shall deposit in one of these caves. We must be your neighbors, I fear, for a day or two; but I can promise you that your garden shall be respected, on condition that you do not inform any human soul of our being here."

"God forbid, Señor, that I should try to increase the number of my visitors, much less to bring hither strife and blood, of which I have seen too much already. As you have come in peace, in peace depart. Leave me alone with God and my penitence, and may the Lord have mercy on you!"

And he was about to withdraw, when, recollecting himself, he turned suddenly to Amyas again:

"Pardon me, Señor, if, after forty years of utter solitude, I shrink at first from the conversation of human beings, and forget, in the habitual shyness of a recluse, the duties of a hospitable gentleman of Spain. My garden, and all which it produces, is at your service. Only let me entreat that these poor Indians shall have their share; for heathens though they be, Christ died for them; and I cannot but cherish in my soul some secret hope that He did not die in vain."

"God forbid!" said Brimblecombe. "They are no worse than we, for aught I see, whatsoever their fathers may have been; and they have fared no worse than we since they have been with us, nor will, I promise you."

The good fellow did not tell that he had been starving himself for the last three days to cram the children with his own rations; and that the sailors, and even Amyas, had been going out of their way every five minutes, to get fruit for their new pets.

A camp was soon formed; and that evening the old hermit asked Amyas, Cary, and Brimblecombe to come up into his cavern.

They went; and after the accustomed compliments had passed, sat down on mats upon the ground, while the old man stood, leaning against a slab of stone surmounted by a rude wooden cross, which served him as a place of prayer.

* * * * * * * * * * *

The talk lasted long into the night,[13] but Amyas was up long before daybreak, felling the trees; and as he and Cary walked back to breakfast, the first thing which they saw was the old man in his garden with four or five Indian children round him, talking smilingly to them.

"The old man's heart is sound still," said Will. "No man is lost who is still fond of little children."

13. The old hermit proves to be one of the survivors of Pizarro's company. He took part in the destruction of native civilization and was guilty of all the cruelties and barbarities that his race practiced. He is living now in the wilderness in an effort to atone for his terrible sins.

"Ah, Señors!" said the hermit as they came up, "you see that I have begun already to act upon your advice."

"And you have begun at the right end," quoth Amyas; "if you win the children, you win the mothers."

"And if you win the mothers," quoth Will, "the poor fathers must needs obey their wives, and follow in the wake."

The old man only sighed. "The prattle of these little ones softens my hard heart, Señors, with a new pleasure; but it saddens me, when I recollect that there may be children of mine now in the world —children who have never known a father's love— never known aught but a master's threats—"

"God has taken care of these little ones. Trust that He has taken care of yours."

That day Amyas assembled the Indians, and told them that they must obey the hermit as their king, and settle there as best they could: for if they broke up and wandered away, nothing was left for them but to fall one by one into the hands of the Spaniards. They heard him with their usual melancholy and stupid acquiescence, and went and came as they were bid, like animated machines; but the negroes were of a different temper; and four or five stout fellows gave Amyas to understand that they had been warriors in their own country, and that warriors they would be still; and nothing should keep them from Spaniard-hunting. Amyas saw that the presence of these desperadoes in the new colony would both endanger the authority of the hermit, and bring the Spaniards down upon it in a few weeks; so making a virtue of necessity, he asked them whether they would go Spaniard-hunting with him.

This was just what the bold Coromantees wished for; they grinned and shouted their delight at serving under so great a warrior, and then set to work most gallantly, getting through more in the day than any ten Indians, and indeed than any two Englishmen.

So went on several days, during which the trees were felled, and the process of digging them out began; while Ayacanora, silent and moody, wandered into the woods all day with her blow-gun, and brought home at evening a load of parrots, monkeys, and curassows; two or three old hands were sent out to hunt likewise; so that, what with the game and the fish of the river, which seemed inexhaustible, and the fruit of the neighboring palm-trees, there was no lack of food in the camp. But what to do with Ayacanora weighed heavily on the mind of Amyas. He opened his heart on the matter to the old hermit, and asked him whether he would take charge of her. The latter smiled, and shook his head at the notion. "If your report of her be true, I may as well take in hand to tame a jaguar." However, he promised to try; and one evening, as they were all standing together before the mouth of the cave, Ayacanora came up smiling with the fruit of her day's sport; and Amyas, thinking this a fit opportunity, began a carefully-prepared harangue to her, which he intended to be altogether soothing, and even pathetic,—to the effect that the maiden, having no parents, was to look upon this good old man as her father; that he would instruct her in the white man's religion and teach her how to be happy and good, and so forth; and that, in fine, she was to remain there with the hermit.

She heard him quietly, her great dark eyes opening wider and wider, her bosom swelling, her stature seeming to grow taller every moment, as she clenched her weapons firmly in both her hands. Beautiful as she always was, she had never looked so beautiful before; and as Amyas spoke of parting with her, it was like throwing away a lovely toy; but it must be done, for her sake, for his, perhaps for that of all the crew.

The last words had hardly passed his lips, when, with a shriek of mingled scorn, rage, and fear, she dashed through the astonished group.

"Stop her!" was Amyas' first word; but his next was, "Let her go!" for springing like a deer through the little garden, and over the flower-fence, she turned, menacing with her blow-gun the sailors, who had already started in her pursuit.

"Let her alone, for Heaven's sake!" shouted Amyas, who, he scarce knew why, shrank from the thought of seeing those graceful limbs struggling in the seamen's grasp.

She turned again, and in another minute her gaudy plumes had vanished among the dark forest stems, as swiftly as if she had been a passing bird.

All stood thunderstruck at this unexpected end to the conference.

At last Amyas spoke—

"There's no use in standing here idle, gentlemen. Staring after her won't bring her back. After all, I'm glad she's gone."

But Ayacanora did not return; and ten days

more went on in continual toil at the canoes without
any news of her from the hunters. Amyas, by the
bye, had strictly bidden these last not to follow the
girl, not even to speak to her, if they came across
her in their wanderings. He was shrewd enough
to guess that the only way to cure her sulkiness was
to out-sulk her; but there was no sign of her presence in any direction; and the canoes being finished
at last, the gold, and such provisions as they could
collect, were placed on board, and one evening the
party prepared for their fresh voyage.

They determined to travel as much as possible by
night, for fear of discovery, especially in the neighborhood of the few Spanish settlements which were
then scattered along the banks of the main stream.
These, however, the negroes knew, so that there was
no fear of coming on them unawares; and as for
falling asleep in their night journeys, "Nobody,"
the negroes said, "ever slept on the Magdalena; the
mosquitoes took too good care of that." Which fact
Amyas and his crew verified afterwards as thoroughly as wretched men could do.

The sun had sunk; the night had all but fallen;
the men were all on board; Amyas in command of
one canoe, Cary of the other. The Indians were
grouped on the bank, watching the party with their
listless stare, and with them the young guide, who
preferred remaining among the Indians, and was
made supremely happy by the present of a Spanish
sword and an English ax; while, in the midst, the
old hermit, with tears in his eyes, prayed God's
blessing on them.

"I owe to you, noble cavaliers, new peace, new
labor, I may say, new life. May God be with you,

and teach you to use your gold and your swords better than I used mine."

The adventurers waved their hands to him.

"Give way, men," cried Amyas; and as he spoke the paddles dashed into the water, to a right English hurrah! which sent the birds fluttering from their roosts, and was answered by the yell of a hundred monkeys, and the distant roar of the jaguar.

About twenty yards below, a wooded rock, some ten feet high, hung over the stream. The river was not there more than fifteen yards broad; deep near the rock, shallow on the farther side; and Amyas's canoe led the way, within ten feet of the stone.

As he passed, a dark figure leapt from the bushes on the edge, and plunged heavily into the water close to the boat. All started. A jaguar? No; he would not have missed so short a spring. What then? A human being? A head rose panting to the surface, and with a few strong strokes, the swimmer had clutched the gunwale. It was Ayacanora!

"Go back!" shouted Amyas. "Go back girl!"

She uttered the same wild cry with which she had fled into the forest.

"I will die, then!" and she threw up her arms. Another moment, and she had sunk.

To see her perish before his eyes! who could bear that? Her hands alone were above the surface. Amyas caught convulsively at her in the darkness, and seized her wrist.

A yell rose from the negroes: a roar from the crew as from a cage of lions. There was a rush and a swirl along the surface of the stream; and "Caiman![14] caiman!" shouted twenty voices.

14. A *caiman*, or *cayman*, is a species of alligator.

Now, or never, for the strong arm! "To larboard, men, or over we go!" cried Amyas, and with one huge heave, he lifted the slender body upon the gunwhale. Her lower limbs were still in the water, when, within arm's length, rose above the stream a huge muzzle. The lower jaw lay flat, the upper reached as high as Amyas's head. He could see the long fangs gleam white in the moonshine; he could see for one moment, full down the monstrous depths of that great gape, which would have crushed a buffalo. Three inches, and no more, from that soft side, the snout surged up—

There was the gleam of an ax from above, a sharp ringing blow, and the jaws came together with a clash which rang from bank to bank. He had missed her! Swerving beneath the blow, his snout had passed beneath her body, and smashed up against the side of the canoe, as the striker, over-balanced, fell headlong overboard upon the monster's back.

"Who is it?"

"Yeo!" shouted a dozen.

Man and beast went down together, and where they sank, the moonlight shone on a great swirling eddy, while all held their breaths, and Aya-canora cowered down into the bottom of the canoe, her proud spirit utterly broken, for the first time, by the terror of that great need, and by a bitter loss. For in the struggle, the holy trumpet, companion of all her wanderings, had fallen from her bosom; and her fond hope of bringing magic prosperity to her English friends had sunk with it to the bottom of the stream.

None heeded her; not even Amyas, round whose

knees she clung, fawning like a spaniel dog: for where was Yeo?

Another swirl; a shout from the canoe abreast of them, and Yeo rose, having dived clean under his own boat, and risen between the two.

"Safe as yet, lads! Heave me a line, or he'll have me after all."

But ere the brute reappeared, the old man was safe on board.

"The Lord has stood by me," panted he, as he shot the water from his ears. "We went down together: I knew the Indian trick, and being uppermost, had my thumbs in his eyes before he could turn: but he carried me down to the very mud. My breath was nigh gone, so I left go, and struck up: but my toes tingled as I rose again, I'll warrant. There the beggar is, looking for me, I declare!"

And true enough, there was the huge brute swimming slowly round and round, in search of his lost victim. It was too dark to put an arrow into his eye; so they paddled on, while Ayacanora crouched silently at Amyas's feet.

"Yeo!" asked he, in a low voice, "what shall we do with her?"

"Why ask me, sir?" said the old man, as he had a very good right to ask.

"Because, when one don't know oneself, one had best inquire of one's elders. Besides, you saved her life at the risk of your own, and have a right to a voice in the matter, if any one has, old friend."

"Then, my dear young captain, if the Lord puts a precious soul under your care, don't you refuse to bear the burden He lays on you."

Amyas was silent awhile; while Ayacanora, who

was evidently utterly exhausted by the night's adventure, and probably by long wanderings, watchings, and weepings which had gone before it, sank with her head against his knee, fell fast asleep, and breathed as gently as a child.

At last he rose in the canoe, and called Cary alongside.

"Listen to me, gentlemen, and sailors all. You know that we have a maiden on board here, by no choice of our own. Whether she will be a blessing to us, God alone can tell: but she may turn to the greatest curse which has befallen us ever since we came out over Bar three years ago. Promise me one thing, or I put her ashore the next beach; and that is, that you will treat her as if she were your own sister."

A BED OF NETTLES

By GRANT ALLEN

EACHING my hand into the hedge-row to pick a long, lithe, blossoming spray of black byrony—here it is, with its graceful climbing stem, its glossy, heart-shaped leaves and its pretty greenish lily flowers—I have stung myself rather badly against the nettles that grow rank and tall from the rich mud in the ditch below. Nothing soothes a nettle sting like philosophy and dock-leaf; so I shall rub a little of the leaf on my hand and then sit awhile on the Hole Farm gate here to philosophize about nettles and things generally, as is my humble wont. There is a great deal more in nettles, I believe, than most people are apt to imagine; indeed, the nettle-philosophy at present current with the larger part of the world seems to me lamentably one-sided. As a rule, the sting is the only point in the whole organization of the family over which we ever waste a single thought. This is our ordinary human narrowness; in each plant or animal we interest ourselves about that one part alone which has special reference to our own relations with it, for good or for evil. In a strawberry, we think only of the fruit; in a hawthorn, or the flowers; in a deadly nightshade, of the poisonous berry; and in a nettle, of the sting. Now, I frankly admit at the present

moment that the nettle sting has an obtrusive and unnecessarily pungent way of forcing itself upon the human attention; but it does not sum up the whole life-history of the plant in its own one peculiarity for all that. The nettle exists for its own sake, we may be sure, and not merely for the sake of occasionally inflicting a passing smart upon the meddlesome human fingers.

However, the sting itself, viewed philosophically, is not without decided interest of its own. It is one, and perhaps the most highly developed, among the devices by which plants guard themselves against the attacks of animals. Weeds and shrubs with juicy, tender leaves are very apt to be eaten down by rabbits, cows, donkeys and other herbivores. But if any individuals among such species happen to show any tendency to the development of any unpleasant habit, which prevents the herbivores from eating them, then those particular individuals will of course be spared when their neighbors are eaten, and will establish a new and specially protected variety in the course of successive generations. It does not matter what the peculiarity may be, provided only it in any way deters animals from eating the plant. In the arum, a violently acrid juice is secreted in the leaves, so as to burn the mouth of the aggressor. In the dandelion and wild lettuces, the juice is merely bitter. In houndstongue and catmint it has a nauseous taste. Then again, in the hawthorn and the blackthorn, some of the shorter branches have developed into stout, sharp spines, which tear the skin of would-be assailants. In the brambles, the hairs on the stem have thickened into pointed prickles, which answer the same purpose as the spines of their neighbors. In the thistles, the gorse and the holly, once more, it is the angles of the leaves themselves, which have grown into needle-like points so as to deter animals from browsing upon them. But the nettle probably carries the same tendency to the furthest possible limit. Not content with mere defense, it is to some extent actively aggressive. The hairs which clothe it have become filled with a poisonous, irritating juice, and when any herbivore thrusts his tender nose into the midst of a clump, the sharp points pierce his naked skin, the liquid gets into his veins in the very neighborhood of the most sensitive nerves, and the poor creature receives at once a lifelong warning against attacking nettles in future.

The way in which so curious a device has grown up is not, it seems to me, very difficult to guess. Many plants are armed with small sharp hairs which act as a protection to them against the incursions of ants and other destructive insects. These hairs are often enough more or less glandular in structure, and therefore liable to contain various waste products of the plant. Suppose one of these waste products in the ancestors of the nettle to be at first slightly pungent, by accident, as it were, then it would exercise a slightly deterrent effect upon nettle-eating animals. The more stinging it grew, the more effectual would the protection be; and as in each generation the least protected plants would get eaten down, while the more protected were spared, the tendency would be for the juice to grow more and more stinging till at last it reached the present high point of development. It is noticeable, too, that in our warrens and wild places, most of the plants are thus more or less protected in one way or another from the attacks of animals. These neglected spots are overgrown with gorse, brambles, nettles, blackthorn, and mullein, as well as with the bitter spurges, and the stringy inedible bracken. So, too, while in our meadows we purposely propagate tender fodder plants, like grasses and clovers, we find on the margins of our pastures and by our roadsides only protected species, such as thistles, houndstongue, cuckoo-pint, charlock, nettles (once more), and thorn bushes. The cattle or the rabbits eat down at once all juicy and succulent plants, leaving only these nauseous or prickly kinds, together with such stringy and innutritious weeds as chervil, plantain, and burdock. Here we see the mechanism of natural selection at work under our very eyes.

But the sting certainly does not exhaust the whole philosophy of the nettle. Look, for example, at the stem and leaves. The nettle has found its chance in life, its one fitting vacancy, among the ditches and waste-places by roadsides or near cottages; and it has laid itself out for the circumstances in which it lives. Its near relative, the hop, is a twisting climber; its southern cousins, the fig and the mulberry, are tall and spreading trees. But the nettle has made itself a niche in nature along the bare patches which diversify human cultivation; and it has adapted its stem and leaves to the station in life where it has pleased Providence to place it. Plants like the dock, the burdock, and the rhubarb, which lift their leaves straight above the ground, from large subterranean reservoirs of material, have usually big, broad, undivided leaves, that overshadow all beneath them, and push boldly out on every side to drink in the air and the sunlight. On the other hand, regular hedgerow plants, like cleavers, chervil, herb Robert, milfoil, and most ferns, which grow in the tangled shady undermath of the bank and thickets, have usually slender, bladelike, much-divided leaves, all split up into little long narrow pushing segments, because they cannot get sunlight and air enough to build up a single large respectable rounded leaf.

The nettle is just halfway between these two extremes. It does not grow out broad and solitary like the burdock, nor does it creep under the hedges like the little much-divided wayside weeds; but it springs up erect in tall, thick, luxuriant clumps, growing close together, each stem fringed with a considerable number of moderate-sized, heart-shaped, toothed and pointed leaves. Such leaves have just room enough to expand and to extract from the air all the carbon they need for their growth, without encroaching upon one another's food supply (for it must always be borne in mind that leaves grow out of the air, not, as most people fancy, out of the ground), and so without the consequent necessity for dividing up into little separate narrow segments. Accordingly, this type of leaf is very common among all those plants which spring up beside the hedgerows in the same erect shrubby manner as the nettles.

Then, again, there is the flower of the nettle, which in most plants is so much the most conspicuous part of all. Yet in this particular plant it is so unobtrusive that most people never notice its existence in any way. That is because the nettle is wind-fertilized, and so does not need bright and attractive petals. Here are the flowering branches, a lot of little forked antler-like spikes, sticking out at right angles from the stem, and half concealed by the leaves of the row above them. Like many other wind-fertilized flowers, the stamens and pistils are collected on different plants—a plan which absolutely insures cross-fertilization, without the aid of the insects. I pick one of the stamen-bearing clusters, and can see that it is made up of small separate green blossoms, each with four tiny leaf-like petals, and with four stamens doubled up in the center. I touch the flowers with the tip of my pocket knife, and in a second the four stamens jump out elastically as if alive, and dust the white pollen all over my fingers. Why should they act like this? Such tricks are not uncommon in bee-fertilized flowers, because they insure the pollen being shed only when a bee thrusts his head into the blossom; but what use can this device be to the wind-fertilized nettle? I think the object is somewhat after this fashion. If the pollen were shed during perfectly calm weather, it would simply fall upon the ground, without reaching the pistils of neighboring plants at all. But by having the stamens thus doubled up, with elastic stalks, it happens that even when ripe they do not open and shed the pollen unless upon the occurrence of some slight concussion. This concussion is given when the stems are waved about by the wind; and then the pollen is shaken out under circumstances which give it the best chance of reaching the pistil.

Finally, there is the question of fruit. In the fig and mulberry the fruit is succulent, and depends for its dispersion upon birds and animals. In the nettle it takes the form of a tiny, seed-like, flattened nut. Why is this, again? One might as well ask, why are we not all Lord Chancellors or Presidents of the Royal Academy. Each plant and each animal makes the best of such talents as it has got, and gets on by their aid; but all have not the same talents. One survives by dint of its prickles; another by dint of its attractive flowers; a third by its sweet fruit; a fourth by its hard nut-shell. As regards stings, the nettle is one of the best protected plants; as regards flower and fruit, it is merely one of the ruck. Every plant can only take advantage of any stray chances it happens to possess; and the same advantageous tendencies do not show themselves in all alike. It is said that once a certain American, hearing of the sums which Canova got for his handicraft, took his son to the great man's studio, and inquired how much he would ask to make the boy a sculptor. But there is no evidence to show that that aspiring youth ever produced an Aphrodite or a Discobolus.

WASHINGTON IRVING

URING the course of the revolution that changed the British colonies in America into the United States, there was born in the city of New York the first great writer of this new nation, Washington Irving. The parents of Irving had been in America but twenty years, the father being Scotch and the mother English, yet they sympathized so fully with the colonists that they spent much of their time and means in caring for the soldiers held as prisoners by the British.

The mother was unusually warm-hearted and charitable, but the father, though a kind and conscientious man, was very strict, especially in dealing with his children. He seemed to feel that nearly every kind of amusement that young people delighted in was sinful, and he held up before his children such sober ways of living that Washington at least came to think that everything pleasant was wicked. No amount of sternness, however, could keep the five boys of the family and their three sisters wholly out of mischief, nor hinder them from having many a harmless good time.

After spending two years in a primary school, Washington was sent when six years old to a school kept by a soldier who had fought in the Revolution, a man who dealt most harshly with disorderly pupils. Though Washington was always breaking

216

WASHINGTON IRVING
1783–1859

rules, he was so honest in admitting the wrong done that the teacher had a particular liking for him, and would call him by the envied title of "General." To bear this title, as well as the name of the foremost American of that time, and to have received a blessing from the great Washington himself, was honor enough for one boy.

Though it was not till several years later that he first went to the theater, yet when he was about ten he was fond of acting the part of some warrior knight of whom he had read, and would challenge one of his companions to a duel in the yard, where they would fight desperately with wooden swords. About this time, too, he came upon *Robinson Crusoe* and *Sindbad the Sailor,* and thus was awakened a great delight in books of travel and adventure. Most pleasing of all was *The World Displayed,* a series of volumes in which one could read of voyages to the most distant parts of the world. How exciting it was to read these books under cover of his desk at school, or in bed at night by the light of candles smuggled into his room! It is no wonder that he grew to wish with all his heart that he could go to sea, and that he haunted the wharves watching the out-going vessels.

When only fifteen years old, Washington finished his schooling. In later life he was always very sorry that he had not been sent to college at this time. Within a year he began the study of law, but he went at his work in such a half-hearted way that although he passed his examination in 1806, he was really very poorly fitted for his calling.

The last two years of this time had been passed in Europe, where he had been sent to recover his health; and it is safe to say that thoughts of his legal studies troubled young Irving but little during this interesting trip. If as a boy he had been thrilled merely in reading of voyages and travels, what was now his pleasure in journeying through one strange scene after another and meeting with such exciting adventures as that which befell him on the way from Genoa to Sicily, when the vessel on which he was sailing was boarded by pirates. On this occasion, as he could translate the questions of the attacking party and could answer these men in their own tongue, he was forced to go on the pirate ship, among an evil-looking crew, armed with stilettos, cutlasses and pistols, and act as interpreter before the captain. As it turned out that the booty was too small to be worth taking, Irving and his companions escaped without hurt. In the course of his further travels he found especial delight in the works of art at Rome, and in attending the theater and opera in Paris and London.

In January, 1807, several months after his return to America, Irving, with one of his brothers and a friend, began to publish *Salmagundi,* a magazine containing humorous articles on the social life of New York. This became so popular that twenty numbers were issued. Having found so much of interest in the life of his native city, Irving next wrote a comic *History of New York, by Diedrich Knickerbocker,* dealing with the early period when the city was ruled by the Dutch. The novel way in which this work was announced would do credit to the most clever advertiser. About six weeks before the book was published, appeared this notice in the *Evening Post*:

"Distressing.

"Left his lodgings some time since, and has not
since been heard of, a small elderly gentleman,
dressed in an old black coat and cocked hat, by the
name of Knickerbocker. As there are some reasons for believing he is not entirely in his right
mind, and as great anxiety is entertained about him,
any information concerning him left either at the
Columbian Hotel, Mulberry Street, or at the office
of this paper, will be *thankfully* received.

"P. S.— Printers of newspapers would be aiding
the cause of humanity by giving an insertion to the
above.—Oct. 25.*"*

Almost two weeks later a notice signed *A
Traveler,* told that the old man had been seen resting by the road over which the Albany stage coach
passed. Then in ten days followed this amusing
letter to the editor of the *Post*:

"Sir:—You have been good enough to publish
in your paper a paragraph about Mr. Diedrich
Knickerbocker, who was missing so strangely from
his lodgings some time since. Nothing satisfactory
has been heard of the old gentleman since; but a
very curious kind of a written book has been found
in his room in his own handwriting. Now I wish
you to notice him, if he is still alive, that if he does
not return and pay off his bill for board and lodg-
ing, I shall have to dispose of his Book, to satisfy
me for the same."

Needless to say, the book was issued in due time,
and it was warmly welcomed not only in the United
States but in England.

This year of great literary success was also one
of the saddest in Irving's life. He had become

deeply attached to Matilda Hoffman, daughter of one of the lawyers under whom he had studied, and was looking forward to the time when she should become his wife. The death of the young girl in 1809 caused a grief so deep that Irving almost never spoke of it. He remained true to the memory of this early love throughout his life, and never married.

By this time it had become plain that Irving could write with far more effect than he could ever hope to practice law. Yet the idea of using his pen in order to earn a living, not merely for his own amusement, was so distasteful to him that he put aside the thought of a literary career. Had he not had two kind and indulgent brothers, it might have gone hard with him at this time; but he was given a one-fifth share in their business, and being only a silent partner was allowed to spend his time in whatever ways he pleased.

In 1815, however, it became necessary for him to take his brother Peter's place for a time at the head of that part of the business which was carried on in Liverpool. Though he was a loyal American, he found England so much to his liking that there is no telling how long after his brother's recovery he would have kept on living in his half-idle way in his pleasant surroundings, had not the business in which he was interested failed in 1818. Thus roused to effort, he began publishing in 1819 the highly popular *Sketch Book,* by Geoffrey Crayon, a series of stories and essays in the first number of which appeared, with others, *Rip Van Winkle.* *The Legend of Sleepy Hollow* was contained in a later issue. *Bracebridge Hall* and *Tales of a*

Traveller, of the same nature as the *Sketch Book*, followed soon afterward, all three being sent to America and being published also in England.

A new and more serious kind of work opened before Irving in 1826 when he was invited to Madrid by the United States minister, to make a translation of Navarrete's *Voyages of Columbus*. Instead of translating, however, he wrote a valuable original work entitled the *Life and Voyages of Christopher Columbus*. Thus was awakened his deep interest in the romantic history and legends of Spain. He traveled about the country, staying for several weeks in the celebrated palace of the Alhambra, studied rare old books, and as a result produced several other works upon Spanish subjects. Of these *The Conquest of Granada* was written before he left Spain and *The Alhambra* was completed in England after his return in 1829 to fill the office of secretary of legation.

In 1824 Irving had written to a friend in America concerning New York: "There is a charm about that little spot of earth; that beautiful city and its environs, that has a perfect spell over my imagination. The bay, the rivers and their wild and woody shores, the haunts of my boyhood, both on land and water, absolutely have a witchery over my mind. I thank God for my having been born in so beautiful a place among such beautiful scenery; I am convinced I owe a vast deal of what is good and pleasant in my nature to the circumstance." It was not, however, until 1832 that he was able to return to his much-loved birthplace. Then, after seventeen years' absence, during which he had become a very famous writer, he was welcomed with the warmest greetings and the highest honors of his townspeople.

It was not long before he made a tour through the far West,—through the wilds of Missouri and Arkansas. From a point in the latter region he wrote of his party as "depending upon game, such as deer, elk, bear, for food, encamping on the borders of brooks, and sleeping in the open air under trees, with outposts stationed to guard us against any surprise by the Indians." The beautiful scenery and exciting events that marked this trip now part of the volume of *Crayon Miscellany.*

Having been a wanderer for a good many years, Irving now began to wish for a home. Accordingly he bought a little estate near Tarrytown on the Hudson River, and had the cottage on this land made over into "a little nookery somewhat in the Dutch style, quaint, but unpretending." In the first years spent in this pleasant home he contributed articles to the *Knickerbocker Magazine,* later collected and published under the title of *Wolfert's Roost,* and wrote *Abbotsford* and *Newstead Abbey,* now part of the volume of *Crayon Miscellany.*

So smoothly did the home life at Sunnyside flow along that Irving was none too well pleased to separate himself from it in 1842 when appointed minister of the United States to Spain. Nevertheless, he looked upon this event as the "crowning hour" of his life.

During the thirteen years that remained to him after returning to Sunnyside in 1846, he produced the *Life of Mahomet and his Successors,* a *Life of Goldsmith,* an author whom he especially admired and appreciated, and a biography of his celebrated namesake, which, though entitled a *Life of Washington,* is nothing less than a history of the Revolution. In the very year this last great work was completed, Irving died, surrounded by the household to whom he had become so much endeared (November 28, 1859).

In his writings Washington Irving has shown himself so gentle and unpretentious and so large-hearted, that his words concerning Oliver Goldsmith seem to apply with equal fitness to himself: "There are few writers for whom the reader feels such personal kindness." These same qualities were revealed also day by day in the smallest incidents of his life. Perhaps they were never more simply illustrated than on the occasion when he was traveling in a railway car behind a woman with two small children and a baby who was being constantly disturbed by the older children's efforts to climb to a seat by the window. Having taken in the situation, Irving began lifting first one and then the other of the little ones into his lap, allowing each just three minutes at the window, and this he continued until they had had enough, and the grateful mother had enjoyed a needed rest. Apparently he bore ill-will toward no one, and his ever-ready humor helped him to view the lives of others without harshness. Thus it is not only as a great literary artist, but as an American of the most worthy type, that he has won lasting honor.

THE KNICKERBOCKER HISTORY OF NEW YORK

By WASHINGTON IRVING

INTRODUCTORY NOTE

 *HISTORY of New York by Diedrich Knickerbocker* was published in 1809. Nearly forty years later Washington Irving, the real author, says it was his purpose in the history to embody the traditions of New York in an amusing form, to illustrate its local humors, customs and peculiarities in a whimsical narrative, which should help to bind the heart of the native inhabitant to his home. He adds:

"In this I have reason to believe I have in some measure succeeded. Before the appearance of my work the popular traditions of our city were unrecorded; the peculiar and racy customs and usages derived from our Dutch Progenitors were unnoticed, or regarded with indifference, or adverted to with a sneer. Now they form a convivial currency, and are brought forward on all occasions; they link our whole community together in good humor and good fellowship; they are the rallying-points of home feeling, the seasoning of our civic festivities, the staple of local tales and local pleasantries; and are so harped upon by our writers of popular fiction that I find myself almost crowded off the legendary ground which I was the first to explore by the host who have followed in my footsteps.

"I dwell on this head because, at the first appearance of my work, its aim and drift were misapprehended by some of the descendants of the Dutch worthies, and because I understand that now and then one may still be found to regard it with a captious eye. The far greater part, however, I have reason to flatter myself, receive my good-humored picturings in the same temper in which they were executed; and when I find, after a lapse of nearly forty years, this haphazard production of my youth still cherished among them; when I find its very name become a 'household word' and used to give the home stamp to everything recommended for popular acceptation, such as Knickerbocker societies; Knickerbocker insurance companies; Knickerbocker steamboats; Knickerbocker omnibuses; Knickerbocker bread; and Knickerbocker ice: and when I find New Yorkers of Dutch descent priding themselves upon being 'genuine Knickerbockers,' I please myself with the persuasion that I have struck the right chord; that my dealings with the good Dutch times, and the customs and usages derived from them, are in harmony with the feelings and humors of my townsmen; that I have opened a vein of pleasant associations and quaint characteristics peculiar to my native place, and which its inhabitants will not willingly suffer to pass away; and that, though other histories of New York may appear of higher claims to learned acceptation, and may take their dignified and appropriate rank in the family library, Knickerbocker's history will still be received with good-humored indulgence, and be thumbed and chuckled over by the family fire-side."

To give color to his fancy, Irving created the fanciful character of Diedrich Knickerbocker, whom he describes as follows:

"He was a small, brisk-looking old gentleman, dressed in a rusty black coat and a pair of olive velvet breeches and a small cocked hat. He had a few gray hairs plaited and clubbed behind. The only piece of finery which he bore about him was a bright pair of square silver shoe buckles, and all his baggage was contained in a pair of saddle bags which he carried under his arm."

He was "a very worthy good sort of an old gentleman, though a little queer in his ways. He would keep in his room for days together, and if any of the children cried or made a noise about his door he would bounce out in a great passion, with his hands full of papers and say something about 'deranging his ideas'."

According to the tale which Irving invented he resided for some time at the Independent Columbian Hotel, and from this place he disappeared, leaving his bills unpaid. However, in the saddle bag which he didn't take from his room the landlord found the manuscript of the *History of New York*, and published it in order to secure pay for the old gentleman's board.

The book met with marked success, and shortly after its publication a large part of New York was laughing at its humorous details, and Irving's estimate of its popularity as given above was modest indeed.

The history consists of eight books, the first of

which, in irony of some histories which had previously been published, gives a description of the world and a history of its creation, and in brief, the story of Noah and the discovery of America, and a dissertation on the origin of the American Indian.

The second book contains an account of Hudson's discovery of the river that bears his name and of the settlement of New Amsterdam.

A book is given to each of the first two Dutch governors, and three books to the rule of Peter Stuyvesant. The history then terminates with the surrender of New Amsterdam to the British.

The selections which appear here have been chosen for their rich humor rather than for their historical value, although, in his quaint way, Irving gives us a picture of the early Dutch settlers that is in many respects remarkably true to life. His exaggerations are usually so noticeable that it is not difficult to separate truth from fiction.

THE FOUNDING OF NEW AMSTERDAM

IT was some three or four years after the return of the immortal Hendrick that a crew of honest, Low Dutch colonists set sail from the city of Amsterdam for the shores of America. The ship in which these illustrious adventurers set sail was called the *Goede Vrouw,* or Good Woman, in compliment to the wife of the president of the West India Company, who was allowed by everybody (except her husband) to be a sweet-tempered lady. It was in truth a most gallant vessel, of the most approved Dutch construction, and made by the ablest ship carpenters of Amsterdam, who it is well known always model their ships after the fair forms of their countrywomen. Accordingly, it had one hundred feet in the beam, one hundred feet in the keel, and one hundred feet from the bottom of the stern-post to the tafferel.

The architect, who was somewhat of a religious man, far from decorating the ship with pagan idols, such as Jupiter, Neptune, or Hercules (which heathenish abominations I have no doubt occasion the misfortunes and shipwreck of many a noble vessel)—he, I say, on the contrary, did laudably erect for a head a goodly image of Saint Nicholas, equipped with a low, broad-brimmed hat, a huge pair of Flemish trunk hose, and a pipe that reached to the end of the bow-sprit. Thus gallantly furnished, the stanch ship floated sideways, like a majestic goose, out of the harbor of the great city of Amsterdam, and all the bells that were not otherwise engaged rang a triple bobmajor on the joyful occasion.

The voyage was uncommonly prosperous, for, being under the especial care of the ever-revered Saint Nicholas, the Goede Vrouw seemed to be endowed with qualities unknown to common vessels. Thus she made as much leeway as headway, could get along very nearly as fast with the wind ahead as when it was apoop, and was particularly great in a calm; in consequence of which singular advantages she made out to accomplish her voyage in a very few months, and came to anchor at the mouth of the Hudson a little to the east of Gibbet Island.

Here, lifting up their eyes, they beheld, on what

is at present called the Jersey shore, a small Indian village, pleasantly embowered in a grove of spreading elms, and the natives all collected on the beach gazing in stupid admiration at the Goede Vrouw. A boat was immediately dispatched to enter into a treaty with them, and, approaching the shore, hailed them through a trumpet in the most friendly terms; but so horribly confounded were these poor savages at the tremendous and uncouth sound of the Low Dutch language that they one and all took to their heels, and scampered over the Bergen hills; nor did they stop until they had buried themselves, head and ears, in the marshes on the other side, where they all miserably perished to a man, and their bones, being collected and decently covered by the Tammany Society of that day, formed that singular mound called Rattlesnake Hill which rises out of the center of the salt marshes a little to the east of the Newark causeway.

Animated by this unlooked-for victory, our valiant heroes sprang ashore in triumph, took•possession of the soil as conquerors in the name of their High Mightinesses the Lords States General, and, marching fearlessly forward, carried the village of Communipaw by storm, notwithstanding that it was vigorously defended by some half a score of old squaws and pappooses. On looking about them they were so transported with the excellencies of the place that they had very little doubt the blessed Saint Nicholas had guided them thither as the very spot whereon to settle their colony. The softness of the soil was wonderfully adapted to the driving of piles; the swamps and marshes around them afforded ample opportunities for the constructing of dykes and dams; the shallowness of the shore was peculiarly favorable to the building of docks —in a word this spot abounded with all the requisites for the foundation of a great Dutch city. On making a faithful report, therefore, to the crew of the Goede Vrouw, they one and all determined that this was the destined end of their voyage. Accordingly they descended from the Goede Vrouw, men, women, and children, in goodly groups, as did the animals of yore from the ark, and formed themselves into a thriving settlement, which they called by the Indian name Communipaw.

The crew of the Goede Vrouw being soon reinforced by fresh importations from Holland, the settlement went jollily on, increasing in magnitude and prosperity. The neighboring Indians in a short time became accustomed to the uncouth sound of the Dutch language, and an intercourse gradually took place between them and the newcomers.

A brisk trade for furs was soon opened: the Dutch traders were scrupulously honest in their dealings, and purchased by weight, establishing it as an invariable table of avoirdupois that the hand of a Dutchman weighed one pound and his foot two pounds.

It is true the simple Indians were often puzzled by the great disproportion between bulk and weight, for let them place a bundle of furs, never so large, in one scale, and a Dutchman put his hand or foot in the other, the bundle was sure to kick the beam—never was a package of furs known to weigh more than two pounds in the market of Communipaw!

The Dutch possessions in this part of the globe

began now to assume a very thriving appearance, and were comprehended under the general title of Nieuw Nederlandts, on account, as the sage Vander Douck observes, of their great resemblance to the Dutch Netherlands; which indeed was truly remarkable, excepting that the former were rugged and mountainous, and the latter level and marshy. About this time the tranquility of the Dutch colonists was doomed to suffer a temporary interruption. In 1614, Captain Sir Samuel Argal, sailing under a commission from Dale, governor of Virginia, visited the Dutch settlements on Hudson River and demanded their submission to the English crown and Virginian dominion. To this arrogant demand, as they were in no condition to resist it, they submitted for the time, like discreet and reasonable men.

Oloffe Van Kortlandt, a personage who was held in great reverence among the sages of Communipaw for the variety and darkness of his knowledge, had originally been one of a set of peripatetic philosophers who had passed much of their time sunning themselves on the side of the great canal of Amsterdam in Holland, enjoying, like Diogenes, a free and unencumbered estate in sunshine. His name Kortlandt (Shortland or Lackland) was supposed, like that of the illustrious Jean Sansterre, to indicate that he had *no land;* but he insisted, on the contrary, that he had great landed estates somewhere in Terra Incognita, and he had come out to the New World to look after them. He was the first great land speculator that we read of in these parts.

Like all land speculators, he was much given to

dreaming. Never did anything extraordinary happen to Communipaw but he declared that he had previously dreamt it, being one of those infallible prophets who predict events after they have come to pass.

As yet his dreams and speculations had turned to little personal profit, and he was as much a lackland as ever. Still, he carried a high head in the community; if his sugar-loaf hat was rather the worse for wear, he set it off with a taller cock's tail; if his shirt was none of the cleanest, he pulled it out the more at the bosom; and if the tail of it peeped out of a hole in his breeches, it at least proved that it really had a tail and was not mere ruffle.

The worthy Van Kortlandt urged the policy of emerging from the swamps of Communipaw and seeking some more eligible site for the seat of empire. Such, he said, was the advice of the good Saint Nicholas, who had appeared to him in a dream the night before, and whom he had known by his broad hat, his long pipe, and the resemblance which he bore to the figure on the bow of the Goede Vrouw.

This perilous enterprise was to be conducted by Oloffe himself, who chose as lieutenants or coadjutors Mynheers Jacobus Van Zandt, Abraham Hardenbroeck, and Winant Ten Broeck—three indubitably great men, but of whose history, although I have made diligent inquiry, I can learn but little previous to their leaving Holland.

Had I the benefit of mythology and classic fable, I should have furnished the first of the trio with a pedigree equal to that of the proudest hero of antiquity. His name, Van Zandt—that is to say, *from the sand,* or, in common parlance, from the dirt—gave reason to suppose that, like Triptolemus, the Cyclops, and the Titans, he had sprung from Dame Terra, or the earth! This supposition is strongly corroborated by his size, for it is well known that all the progeny of mother earth were of a gigantic stature; and Van Zandt, we are told, was a tall, raw-boned man, above six feet high, with an astonishingly hard head.

Of the second of the trio but faint accounts have reached to this time, which mention that he was a sturdy, obstinate, worrying, bustling little man, and, from being usually equipped in an old pair of buckskins, was familiarly dubbed Hardenbroeck; that is to say, Tough Breeches.

Ten Broeck completed this junto of adventurers. It is a singular but ludicrous fact—which, were I not scrupulous in recording the whole truth, I should almost be tempted to pass over in silence as incompatible with the gravity and dignity of history—that this worthy gentleman should likewise have been nicknamed from what in modern times is considered the most ignoble part of the dress; but in truth the small-clothes seem to have been a very dignified garment in the eyes of our venerated ancestors.

The name of Ten Broeck, or, as it was sometimes spelled, Tin Broeck, has been indifferently translated into Ten Breeches and Tin Breeches. Certain elegant and ingenious writers on the subject declare in favor of *Tin,* or rather *Thin,* Breeches; whence they infer that the original bearer of it was a poor but merry rogue, whose galligaskins were none of the soundest, and who, peradventure, may have been the author of that truly philosophical stanza:

"Then why should we quarrel for riches,
  Or any such glittering toys?
A light heart and *thin pair of breeches*
  Will go through the world, my brave boys!"

The more accurate commentators, however, declare in favor of the other reading, and affirm that the worthy in question was a burly, bulbous man, who, in sheer ostentation of his venerable progenitors, was the first to introduce into the settlement the ancient Dutch fashion of ten pair of breeches.

Such was the trio of coadjutors chosen by Oloffe the Dreamer, to accompany him in this voyage into unknown realms; as to the names of his crews, they have not been handed down by history.

And now the rosy blush of morn began to mantle in the east, and soon the rising sun, emerging from amid golden and purple clouds, shed his blithesome rays on the tin weathercocks of Communipaw. It was that delicious season of the year when Nature, breaking from the chilling thralldom of old winter, like a blooming damsel from the tyranny of a sordid old father, threw herself, blushing with ten thousand charms, into the arms of youthful spring. Every tufted copse and blooming grove resounded with the notes of hymeneal love. The very insects, as they sipped the dew that gemmed the tender grass of meadows, joined in the joyous epithalamium, the virgin bud timidly put forth its blushes, "the voice of the turtle was heard in the land," and the heart of man dissolved away in tenderness.

No sooner did the first rays of cheerful Phœbus

dart into the windows of Communipaw than the little settlement was all in motion. Forth issued from his castle the sage Van Kortlandt, and, seizing a conch-shell, blew a far-resounding blast, that soon summoned all his lusty followers. Then did they trudge resolutely down to the waterside, escorted by a multitude of relatives and friends, who all went down, as the common phrase expresses it, "to see them off."

The good Oloffe bestowed his forces in a squadron of three canoes, and hoisted his flag on board a little round Dutch boat, shaped not unlike a tub, which had formerly been the jolly-boat of the Goede Vrouw. And now, all being embarked, they bade farewell to the gazing throng upon the beach, who continued shouting after them even when out of hearing, wishing them a happy voyage, advising them to take good care of themselves, not to get drowned, with an abundance other of those sage and invaluable cautions generally given by landsmen to such as go down to the sea in ships and adventure upon the deep waters. In the meanwhile, the voyagers cheerily urged their course across the crystal bosom of the bay and soon left behind them the green shores of ancient Pavonia.

They coasted by Governor's Island, since terrible from its frowning fortress and grinning batteries. They would by no means, however, land upon this island, since they doubted much it might be the abode of demons and spirits, which in those days did greatly abound throughout this savage and pagan country.

Just at this time a shoal of jolly porpoises came rolling and tumbling by, turning up their sleek sides to the sun and spouting up the briny element in sparkling showers. No sooner did the sage Oloffe mark this than he was greatly rejoiced. "This," exclaimed he, "if I mistake not, augurs well; the porpoise is a fat, well-conditioned fish, a burgomaster among fishes; his looks betoken ease, plenty, and prosperity; I greatly admire this round fat fish, and doubt not but this is a happy omen of the success of our undertaking." So saying, he directed his squadron to steer in the track of these alderman fishes.

Turning, therefore, directly to the left, they swept up the strait vulgarly called the East River. And here the rapid tide which courses through this strait, seizing on the gallant tub in which Commodore Van Kortlandt had embarked, hurried it forward with a velocity unparalleled in a Dutch boat navigated by Dutchmen; insomuch that the good Commodore, who had all his life long been accustomed only to the drowsy navigation of canals, was more than ever convinced that they were in the hands of some supernatural power, and that the jolly porpoises were towing them to some fair haven that was to fulfill all their wishes and expectations.

Thus borne away by the resistless current, they doubled that boisterous point of land since called Corlear's Hook, and leaving to the right the rich winding cove of the Wallabout, they drifted into a magnificent expanse of water, surrounded by pleasant shores whose verdure was exceedingly refreshing to the eye. While the voyagers were looking around them on what they conceived to be a serene and sunny lake, they beheld at a distance a crew of painted savages busily employed in fishing, who seemed more like the genii of this romantic region, their slender canoe lightly balanced like a feather on the undulating surface of the bay.

At sight of these the hearts of the heroes of Communipaw were not a little troubled. But, as good fortune would have it, at the bow of the commodore's boat was stationed a very valiant man, named Hendrick Kip (which, being interpreted, means *chicken*, a name given him in token of his courage). No sooner did he behold these varlet heathens than he trembled with excessive valor, and although a good half mile distant he seized a musketoon that lay at hand, and, turning away his head, fired it most intrepidly in the face of the blessed sun. The blundering weapon recoiled and gave the valiant Kip an ignominious kick, which laid him prostrate with uplifted heels in the bottom of the boat. But such was the effect of this tremendous fire that the wild men of the woods, struck with consternation, seized hastily upon their paddles and shot away into one of the deep inlets of the Long Island shore.

This signal victory gave new spirits to the voyagers, and in honor of the achievement they gave the name of the valiant Kip to the surrounding bay, and it has continued to be called Kip's Bay from that time to the present. The heart of the good Van Kortlandt—who, having no land of his own, was a great admirer of other people's—expanded to the full size of a peppercorn at the sumptuous prospect of rich, unsettled country around him, and falling into a delicious reverie he straightway began to riot in the possession of vast meadows of salt marsh and interminable patches of cabbages.

From this delectable vision he was all at once awakened by the sudden turning of the tide, which would soon have hurried him from this land of promise, had not the discreet navigator given the signal to steer for shore, where they accordingly landed hard by the rocky heights of Bellevue—that

HERE THEY REFRESHED THEMSELVES

happy retreat where our jolly aldermen eat for the good of the city and fatten the turtle that are sacrificed on civic solemnities.

Here, seated on the green sward, by the side of a small stream that ran sparkling among the grass, they refreshed themselves after the toils of the seas by feasting lustily on the ample stores which they had provided for this perilous voyage.

By this time the jolly Phœbus, like some wan-

ton urchin sporting on the side of a green hill, began to roll down the declivity of the heavens; and
now, the tide having once more turned in their
favor, the Pavonians again committed themselves
to its discretion, and, coasting along the western
shores, were borne toward the straits of Blackwell's
Island.

And here the capricious wanderings of the current occasioned not a little marvel and perplexity
to these illustrious mariners. Now would they be
caught by the wanton eddies, and, sweeping around
a jutting point, would wind deep into some romantic little cave, that indented the fair island of Manna-hata; now were they hurried narrowly by the
very basis of impending rocks, mantled with the
flaunting grape-vine and crowned with groves
which threw a broad shade on the waves beneath;
and anon they were borne away into the mid-chan-
nel and wafted along with a rapidity that very much
discomposed the sage Van Kortlandt, who as he saw
the land swiftly receding on either side, began exceedingly to doubt that terra firma was giving them
the slip.

Wherever the voyagers turned their eyes a new
creation seemed to bloom around. No signs of human thrift appeared to check the delicious wildness
of Nature, who here reveled in all her luxuriant
variety. Those hills, now bristled, like the fretful
porcupine, with rows of poplars (vain upstart
plants! minions of wealth and fashion!), were then
adorned with the vigorous natives of the soil—the
hardy oak, the generous chestnut, the graceful elm
—while here and there the tulip tree reared its majestic head, the giant of the forest. Where now are

seen the gay retreats of luxury—villas half buried in twilight bowers, whence the amorous flute oft breathes the sighings of some city swain—there the fish-hawk built his solitary nest on some dry tree that overlooked his watery domain. The timid deer fed undisturbed along those shores now hallowed by the lover's moonlight walk and printed by the slender foot of beauty; and a savage solitude extended over those happy regions where now are reared the stately towers of the Joneses, the Schermerhornes, and the Rhinelanders.

Ah! witching scenes of foul delusion! Ah! hapless voyagers, gazing with simple wonder on these Circean shores! Such, alas! are they, poor easy souls who listen to the seductions of a wicked world —treacherous are its smiles, fatal its caresses. He who yields to its enticements launches upon a whelming tide, and trusts his feeble bark among the dimpling eddies of a whirlpool! And thus it fared with the worthies of Pavonia, who, little mistrusting the guileful scene before them, drifted quietly on until they were aroused by an uncommon tossing and agitation of their vessels. For now the late dimpling current began to brawl around them and the waves to boil and foam with horrific fury. Awakened as if from a dream, the astonished Oloffe bawled aloud to put about, but his words were lost amid the roaring of the waters. And now ensued a scene of direful consternation. At one time they were borne with dreadful velocity among tumultuous breakers; at another hurried down boisterous rapids. Now they were nearly dashed upon the Hen and Chickens (infamous rocks!—more voracious than Scylla and her whelps), and anon they

seemed sinking into yawning gulfs that threatened
to entomb them beneath the waves. All the elements combined to produce a hideous confusion.
The waters raged, the winds howled, and as they
were hurried along several of the astonished mariners beheld the rocks and trees of the neighboring
shores driving through the air!

At length the mighty tub of Commodore Van
Kortlandt was drawn into the vortex of that tremendous whirlpool called the Pot, where it was
whirled about in giddy mazes until the senses of
the good commander and his crew were overpowered by the horror of the scene and the strangeness of the revolution. How the gallant squadron
of Pavonia was snatched from the jaws of this
modern Charybdis has never been truly made
known, for so many survived to tell the tale, and,
what is still more wonderful, told it in so many different ways, that there has ever prevailed a great
variety of opinions on the subject.

As to the commodore and his crew, when they
came to their senses they found themselves stranded
on the Long Island shore. The worthy commodore,
indeed, used to relate many and wonderful stories
of his adventures in this time of peril—how that he
saw specters flying in the air and heard the yelling
of hobgoblins, and put his hand into the pot when
they were whirled round, and found the water scald-
ing hot, and beheld several uncouth-looking beings
seated on rocks and skimming it with huge ladles;
but particularly he declared, with great exultation,
that he saw the losel porpoises, which had betrayed
them into this peril, some broiling on the Gridiron
and others hissing on the Frying-pan!

These, however, were considered by many as mere fantasies of the commodore while he lay in a trance, especially as he was known to be given to dreaming, and the truth of them has never been clearly ascertained. It is certain, however, that to the accounts of Oloffe and his followers may be traced the various traditions handed down of this marvelous strait—as how the devil has been seen there sitting astride of the Hog's Back and playing on the fiddle, how he broils fish there before a storm, and many other stories in which we must be cautious of putting too much faith. In consequence of all these terrific circumstances the Pavonian commander gave this pass the name of *Hellegat,* or, as it has been interpreted, *Hell-Gate,*[1] which it continues to bear at the present day.

The darkness of the night had closed upon this disastrous day, and a doleful night was it to the shipwrecked Pavonians, whose ears were incessantly assailed with the raging of the elements and the howling of the hobgoblins that infested this perilous strait. But when the morning dawned the horrors of the preceding evening had passed away—rapids, breakers, whirlpools had disappeared, the stream again ran smooth and dimpling, and, having changed its tide, rolled gently back toward the quarter where lay their much-regretted home.

The woe-begone heroes of Communipaw eyed each other with rueful countenances; their squadron had been totally dispersed by the late disaster.

---

1. This is a narrow strait in East River, between Manhattan and Long Island. It is dangerous by reason of numerous rocks, shelves, and whirlpools. These have received sundry appellations, such as the Gridiron, Frying-pan, Hog's Back, Pot, etc.

I forbear to treat of the long consultation of Oloffe with his remaining followers, in which they determined that it would never do to found a city in so diabolical a neighborhood. Suffice it in simple brevity to say that they once more committed themselves, with fear and trembling, to the briny element, and steered their course back again through the scenes of their yesterday's voyage, determined no longer to roam in search of distant sites, but to settle themselves down in the marshy regions of Pavonia.

Scarce, however, had they gained a distant view of Communipaw when they were encountered by an obstinate eddy which opposed their homeward voyage. Weary and dispirited as they were, they yet tugged a feeble oar against the stream, until, as if to settle the strife, half a score of potent billows rolled the tub of Commodore Van Kortlandt high and dry on the long point of an island which divided the bosom of the bay.

Oloffe Van Kortlandt was a devout trencherman. Every repast was a kind of religious rite with him, and his first thought on finding himself once more on dry ground was how he should contrive to celebrate his wonderful escape from Hell-Gate and all its horrors by a solemn banquet. The stores which had been provided for the voyage by the good housewives of Communipaw were nearly exhausted, but in casting his eyes about the commodore beheld that the shore abounded with oysters. A great store of these was instantly collected; a fire was made at the foot of a tree; all hands fell to roasting and broiling and stewing and frying, and a sumptuous repast was soon set forth.

On the present occasion the worthy Van Kortlandt was observed to be particularly zealous in his
devotions to the trencher; for, having the cares of
the expedition especially committed to his care, he
deemed it incumbent on him to eat profoundly for
the public good. In proportion as he filled himself to the very brim with the dainty viands before
him, did the heart of this excellent burgher rise up
toward his throat, until he seemed crammed and almost choked with good eating and good nature.
And at such times it is, when a man's heart is in his
throat, that he may more truly be said to speak from
it and his speeches abound with kindness and good
fellowship. Thus, having swallowed the last possible morsel and washed it down with a fervent po-
tation, Oloffe felt his heart yearning and his whole
frame in a manner dilating with unbounded benev-
olence. Everything around him seemed excellent
and delightful, and, laying his hands on each side
of his capacious periphery, and rolling his half-
closed eyes around on the beautiful diversity of land
and water before him, he exclaimed, in a fat, half-
smothered voice, "What a charming prospect!" The
words died away in his throat, he seemed to ponder
on the fair scene for a moment, his eyelids heavily
closed over their orbits, his head drooped upon his
bosom, he slowly sank upon the green turf, and a
deep sleep stole gradually over him.

Van Kortlandt awoke from his sleep greatly instructed, and he aroused his companions and told
them that it was the will of Saint Nicholas that they
should settle down and build the city here. With
one voice all assented to this.

The great object of their perilous expedition,

therefore, being thus happily accomplished, the voyagers returned merrily to Communipaw, where they were received with great rejoicings.

It having been solemnly resolved that the seat of empire should be removed from the green shores of Pavonia to the pleasant island of Manna-hata, everybody was anxious to embark under the standard of Oloffe the Dreamer, and to be among the first sharers of the promised land. A day was appointed for the grand migration, and on that day little Communipaw was in a buzz and bustle like a hive in swarming-time. Houses were turned inside out and stripped of the venerable furniture which had come from Holland; all the community, great and small, black and white, man, woman and child, was in commotion, forming lines from the houses to the water-side, like lines of ants from an ant-hill; everybody laden with some article of household furniture, while busy housewives plied backward and forward along the lines, helping everything forward by the nimbleness of their tongues.

By degrees a fleet of boats and canoes were piled up with all kinds of household articles—ponderous tables; chests of drawers resplendent with brass ornaments; quaint corner cupboards; beds and bedsteads; with any quantity of pots, kettles, frying-pans and Dutch ovens. In each boat embarked a whole family, from the robustious burgher down to the cats and dogs and little negroes. In this way they set off across the mouth of the Hudson, under the guidance of Oloffe the Dreamer, who hoisted his standard on the leading boat.

As the little squadron from Communipaw drew near to the shores of Manna-hata, a sachem at the head of a band of warriors appeared to oppose their landing. Some of the most zealous of the pilgrims were for chastising this insolence with powder and ball, according to the approved mode of discoverers; but the sage Oloffe gave them the significant sign of Saint Nicholas, laying his finger beside his nose and winking hard with one eye, whereupon his followers perceived that there was something sagacious in the wink. He now addressed the Indians in the blandest terms, and made such tempting display of beads, hawks'-bells, and red blankets that he was soon permitted to land, and a great land speculation ensued. And here let me give the true story of the original purchase of the site of this renowned city about which so much has been said and written. Some affirm that the first cost was but sixty guilders. The learned Dominie Heckwelder records a tradition that the Dutch discoverers bargained for only so much land as the hide of a bullock would cover; but that they cut the hide in strips no thicker than a child's finger, so as to take in a large portion of land and to take in the Indians into the bargain. This, however, is an old fable which the worthy Dominie may have borrowed from antiquity. The true version is, that Oloffe Van Kortlandt bargained for just so much land as a man could cover with his nether garments. The terms being concluded, he produced his friend Mynheer Ten Broeck as the man whose breeches were to be used in measurement. The simple savages, whose ideas of a man's nether garments had never expanded beyond the dimensions of a breech-clout, stared with astonishment and dismay as they beheld this burgher peeled like an onion, and breeches after breeches spread forth over the land until they covered the actual site of this venerable city.

This is the true history of the adroit bargain by which the island of Manhattan was bought for sixty guilders; and in corroboration of it I will add that Mynheer Ten Breeches, for his services on this memorable occasion, was elevated to the office of land measurer, which he ever afterward exercised in the colony.

The land being thus fairly purchased of the Indians, a circumstance very unusual in the history of colonization, and strongly illustrative of the honesty of our Dutch progenitors, a stockade fort and a trading-house were forthwith erected on an eminence, the identical place at present known as the Bowling Green.

Around this fort a progeny of little Dutch-built houses, with tiled roofs and weathercocks, soon sprang up, nestling themselves under its walls for protection, as a brood of half-fledged chickens nestles under the wings of the mother hen. The whole was surrounded by an inclosure of strong palisadoes to guard against any sudden irruption of the savages. Outside of these extended the cornfields and cabbage-gardens of the community, with here and there an attempt at a tobacco-plantation; all covering those tracts of country at present called Broadway, Wall street, William street and Pearl street.

I must not omit to mention that in portioning out the land a goodly "bowerie" or farm was allotted to the sage Oloffe in consideration of the service he had rendered to the public by his talent at dreaming; and the site of his "bowerie" is known

by the name of Kortlandt (or Courtlandt) street
to the present day.

And now, the infant settlement having advanced in age and stature, it was thought high time
it should receive an honest Christian name. Hitherto it had gone by the original Indian name Manna-
hata, or, as some will have it, "The Manhattoes";
but this was now decried as savage and heathenish,
and as tending to keep up the memory of the pagan
brood that originally possessed it. Many were the
consultations held upon the subject without coming to a conclusion, for, though everybody condemned the old name, nobody could invent a new
one. At length, when the council was almost in
despair, a burgher, remarkable for the size and
squareness of his head, proposed that they should
call it New Amsterdam. The proposition took
everybody by surprise; it was so striking, so appo-
site, so ingenious. The name was adopted by acclamation, and New Amsterdam the metropolis
was thenceforth called. Still, however, the early
authors of the province continued to call it by the
general appellation of "The Manhattoes," and the
poets fondly clung to the euphonious name of
Manna-hata; but those are a kind of folk whose
tastes and notions should go for nothing in matters
of this kind.

Having thus provided the embryo city with a
name, the next was to give it an armorial bearing
or device. As some cities have a rampant lion,
others a soaring eagle, emblematical, no doubt, of
the valiant and high-flying qualities of the inhabitants, so after mature deliberation a sleek beaver
was emblazoned on the city standard as indicative

of the amphibious origin and patient and persevering habits of the New Amsterdammers.

WALTER THE DOUBTER

IT was in the year of our Lord 1629 that Mynheer Wouter Van Twiller was appointed governor of the province of Nieuw Nederlandts, under the commission and control of their High Mightinesses the Lords States General of the United Netherlands and the privileged West India Company.

The renowned Wouter (or Walter) Van Twiller was descended from a long line of Dutch burgo-masters, who had successively dozed away their lives and grown fat upon the bench of magistracy in Rotterdam, and who had comported themselves with such singular wisdom and propriety that they were never either heard or talked of; which, next to being universally applauded, should be the object of ambition of all magistrates and rulers. There are two opposite ways by which some men make a figure in the world—one by talking faster than they think, and the other by holding their tongues and not thinking at all. By the first many a smatterer acquires the reputation of a man of quick parts; by the other many a dunderpate, like the owl, the stupidest of birds, comes to be considered the very type of wisdom. This, by the way, is a casual remark, which I would not for the universe have it thought I apply to Governor Van Twiller. It is true he was a man shut up within himself, like an oyster, and rarely spoke except in monosyllables; but then it was allowed he seldom said a foolish thing. So invincible was his gravity that he was never known to laugh or even to smile through the whole course of a long and prosperous life. Nay, if a joke were uttered in his presence that set light-minded hearers in a roar, it was observed to throw him into a state of perplexity. Sometimes he would deign to inquire into the matter, and when, after much explanation, the joke was made as plain as a pike-staff, he would continue to smoke his pipe in silence, and at length, knocking out the ashes, would exclaim, "Well! I see nothing in all that to laugh about."

The person of this illustrious old gentleman was formed and proportioned, as though it had been molded by the hands of some cunning Dutch statuary, as a model of majesty and lordly grandeur. He was exactly five feet, six inches in height and six feet, five inches in circumference. His head was a perfect sphere, and of such stupendous dimensions that Dame Nature with all her sex's ingenuity would have been puzzled to construct a neck capable of supporting it; wherefore she wisely declined the attempt, and settled it firmly on the top of his backbone just between the shoulders. His body was oblong and particularly capacious at bottom; which was wisely ordered by Providence, seeing that he was a man of sedentary habits and very averse to the idle labor of walking. His legs were short, but sturdy in proportion to the weight they had to sustain, so that when erect he had not a little the appearance of a beer-barrel on skids. His face, that infallible index of the mind, presented a vast expanse, unfurrowed by any of those lines and angles which disfigure the human countenance with what is termed expression. Two small gray eyes twinkled feebly in the midst, like two stars of lesser magnitude in a hazy firmament, and his full-fed cheeks, which seemed to have taken toll of everything that went into his mouth, were curiously mottled and streaked with dusky red, like a spitzenberg apple.

In his council he presided with great state and solemnity. He sat in a huge chair of solid oak, hewn in the celebrated forest of The Hague, fabricated by an experienced timmerman of Amsterdam, and curiously carved about the arms and feet into exact imitations of gigantic eagle's claws. Instead of a scepter he swayed a long Turkish pipe, wrought with jasmine and amber, which had been presented to a stadtholder of Holland at the conclusion of a treaty with one of the petty Barbary powers. In this stately chair would he sit and this magnificent pipe would he smoke, shaking his right knee with a constant motion, and fixing his eye for hours upon a little print of Amsterdam which hung in a black frame against the opposite wall of the council-chamber. Nay, it has even been said that when any deliberation of extraordinary length and intricacy was on the carpet the renowned Wouter would shut his eyes for full two hours at a time, that he might not be disturbed by external objects; and at such times the internal commotion of his mind was evinced by certain regular guttural sounds, which his admirers declared were merely the noise of conflict made by his contending doubts and opinions.

The very outset of the career of this excellent magistrate was distinguished by an example of legal

acumen that gave flattering presage of a wise and
equitable administration. The morning after he
had been installed in office, and at the moment that
he was making his breakfast from a prodigious
earthen dish filled with milk and Indian pudding,
he was interrupted by the appearance of Wandle

HE WAS INTERRUPTED BY WANDLE SCHOONHOVEN

Schoonhoven, a very important old burgher of New
Amsterdam, who complained bitterly of one Barent
Bleecker, inasmuch as he refused to come to a settlement of accounts, seeing that there was a heavy
balance in favor of the said Wandle. Governor
Van Twiller, as I have already observed, was a man
of few words; he was likewise a mortal enemy to
multiplying writings or being disturbed at his
breakfast. Having listened attentively to the state-

ment of Wandle Schoonhoven, giving an occasional
grunt as he shoveled a spoonful of Indian pudding
into his mouth, either as a sign that he relished the
dish or comprehended the story, he called unto him
his constable, and, pulling out of his breeches pocket
a huge jack-knife, dispatched it after the defendant
as a summons, accompanied by his tobacco-box as
a warrant.

This summary process was as effectual in those
simple days as was the seal ring of the great Haroun
Alraschid among the true believers. The two parties
being confronted before him, each produced a book
of accounts written in a language and character that
would have puzzled any but a High Dutch com-
mentator or a learned decipherer of Egyptian
obelisks. The sage Wouter took them one after
the other, and, having poised them in his hands and
attentively counted over the number of leaves, fell
straightway into a very great doubt, and smoked
for half an hour without saying a word; at length,
laying his finger beside his nose and shutting his
eyes for a moment with the air of a man who had
just caught a subtle idea by the tail, he slowly took
his pipe from his mouth, puffed forth a column of
tobacco-smoke, and with marvelous gravity and
solemnity pronounced—that, having carefully
counted over the leaves and weighed the books, it
was found that one was just as thick and as heavy
as the other; therefore it was the final opinion of the
court that the accounts were equally balanced;
therefore Wandle should give Barent a receipt, and
Barent should give Wandle a receipt; and the constable should pay the costs.

This decision, being straightway made known,

diffused general joy throughout New Amsterdam, for the people immediately perceived that they had a very wise and equitable magistrate to rule over them. But its happiest effect was that not another lawsuit took place throughout the whole of his administration, and the office of constable fell into such decay that there was not one of those losel scouts known in the province for many years.

HOW THE COLONISTS LIVED IN THE DAYS OF WALTER THE DOUBTER

THE houses of the higher class were generally constructed of wood, excepting the gable end, which was of small black and yellow Dutch bricks, and always faced on the street, as our ancestors, like their descendants, were very much given to outward show, and were noted for putting the best leg foremost. The house was always furnished with abundance of large doors and small windows on every floor, the date of its erection was curiously designated by iron figures on the front, and on the top of the roof was perched a fierce little weathercock, to let the family into the important secret which way the wind blew. These, like the weathercocks on the tops of our steeples, pointed so many different ways that every man could have a wind to his mind; the most stanch and loyal citizens, however, always went according to the weathercock on the top of the governor's house, which was certainly the most correct, as he had a trusty servant employed every morning to climb up and set it to the right quarter.

In those good days of simplicity and sunshine

a passion for cleanliness was the leading principle in domestic economy and the universal test of an able housewife—a character which formed the utmost ambition of our unenlightened grandmothers. The front door was never opened except on marriages, funerals, New Year's days, the festival of Saint Nicholas, or some such great occasion. It was ornamented with a gorgeous brass knocker, curiously wrought, sometimes in the device of a dog, and sometimes of a lion's head, and was daily burnished with such religious zeal that it was ofttimes worn out by the very precautions taken for its preservation. The whole house was constantly in a state of inundation under the discipline of mops and brooms and scrubbing brushes; and the good housewives of those days were a kind of amphibious animal, delighting exceedingly to be dabbling in water, insomuch that an historian of the day gravely tells us that many of his townswomen grew to have webbed fingers like unto a duck; but this I look upon to be a mere sport of fancy, or, what is worse, a willful misrepresentation.

The grand parlor was the sanctum-sanctorum where the passion for cleaning was indulged without control. In this sacred apartment no one was permitted to enter excepting the mistress and her confidential maid, who visited it once a week for the purpose of giving it a thorough cleaning and putting things to rights, always taking the precaution of leaving their shoes at the door and entering devoutly in their stocking feet. After scrubbing the floor, sprinkling it with fine white sand, which was curiously stroked into angles, and curves, and rhomboids with a broom—after washing the windows, rubbing and polishing the furniture, and putting a new bunch of evergreen in the fireplace—the window shutters were again closed to keep out the flies, and the room carefully locked up until the revolution of time brought round the weekly cleaning day.

As to the family, they always entered in at the gate, and most generally lived in the kitchen. To have seen a numerous household assembled round the fire one would have imagined that he was transported back to those happy days of primeval simplicity which float before our imagination like golden visions. The fireplaces were of a truly patriarchal magnitude, where the whole family, old and young, master and servant, black and white— nay, even the very cat and dog—enjoyed a community of privilege and had each a right to a corner. Here the old burgher would sit in perfect silence, puffing his pipe, looking in the fire with half-shut eyes, and thinking of nothing for hours together; the goede vrouw on the opposite side would employ herself diligently in spinning yarn or knitting stockings. The young folks would crowd around the hearth, listening with breathless attention to some old crone of a negro who was the oracle of the family, and who, perched like a raven in a corner of the chimney, would croak forth for a long winter afternoon a string of incredible stories about New England witches, grisly ghosts, horses without heads, and hair-breadth escapes and bloody encounters among the Indians.

In those happy days a well-regulated family always rose with the dawn, dined at eleven, and went to bed at sunset. Dinner was invariably a private meal, and the fat old burghers showed incontestable signs of disapprobation and uneasiness at being surprised by a visit from a neighbor on such occasions. But, though our worthy ancestors were thus singularly adverse to giving dinners, yet they kept up the social bonds of intimacy by occasional banquetings called tea-parties.

These fashionable parties were generally confined to the higher classes—or noblesse—that is to say, such as kept their own cows and drove their own wagons. The company commonly assembled at three o'clock and went away about six, unless it was in winter time, when the fashionable hours were a little earlier, that the ladies might get home before dark. The tea-table was crowned with a huge earthen dish well stored with slices of fat pork fried brown, cut up into morsels, and swimming in gravy. The company, being seated round the genial board and each furnished with a fork, evinced their dexterity in launching at the fattest pieces in this mighty dish—in much the same manner as sailors harpoon porpoises at sea, or our Indians spear salmon in the lakes. Sometimes the table was graced with immense apple pies or saucers full of preserved peaches and pears; but it was always sure to boast an enormous dish of balls of sweetened dough, fried in hog's fat, and called doughnuts, or olykoeks—a delicious kind of cake at present scarce known in this city, except in genuine Dutch families.

The tea was served out of a majestic delft teapot ornamented with paintings of fat little Dutch shepherds and shepherdesses tending pigs, with boats sailing in the air, and houses built in the clouds, and sundry other ingenious Dutch fantasies. The beaux distinguished themselves by their adroitness in replenishing this pot from a huge copper tea-kettle which would have made the pigmy macaronies of these degenerate days sweat merely to look at it. To sweeten the beverage a lump of sugar was laid beside each cup, and the company alternately nibbled and sipped with great decorum, until an improvement was introduced by a shrewd and economic old lady, which was to suspend a large lump directly over the tea-table by a string from the ceiling, so that it could be swung from mouth to mouth—an ingenious expedient which is still kept up by some families in Albany, but which prevails without exception in Communipaw, Bergen, Flatbush, and all our uncontaminated Dutch villages.

At these primitive tea-parties the utmost propriety and dignity of deportment prevailed. No flirting nor coquetting; no gambling of old ladies nor hoyden chattering and romping of young ones; no self-satisfied struttings of wealthy gentlemen with their brains in their pockets; nor amusing conceits and monkey divertisements of smart young gentlemen with no brains at all. On the contrary, the young ladies seated themselves demurely in their rush-bottomed chairs and knit their own woollen stockings, nor ever opened their lips excepting to say *Yah, Mynheer,* or *Yah ya, Vrouw,* to any question that was asked them, behaving in all things like decent, well-educated damsels. As to the gentlemen, each of them tranquilly smoked his pipe and seemed lost in contemplation of the blue and white tiles with which the fireplaces were decorated,

whereon sundry passages of Scripture were pious-
ly portrayed: Tobit and his dog figured to great
advantage; Haman swung conspicuously on his
gibbet; and Jonah appeared most manfully bounc-
ing out of the whale, like Harlequin through a barrel of fire.

The parties broke up without noise and without
confusion. They were carried home by their own
carriages—that is to say, by the vehicles Nature had
provided them—excepting such of the wealthy as
could afford to keep a wagon. The gentlemen gallantly attended their fair ones to their respective
abodes, and took leave of them with a hearty smack
at the door, which as it was an established piece of
etiquette, done in perfect simplicity and honesty
of heart, occasioned no scandal at that time, nor
should it at the present: if our greatgrandfathers
approved of the custom, it would argue a great
want of reverence in their descendants to say a word
against it.

In this dulcet period of my history, when the
beauteous island of Manna-hata presented a scene
the very counterpart of those glowing pictures
drawn of the golden reign of Saturn, there was, as
I have before observed, a happy ignorance, an honest simplicity, prevalent among its inhabitants,
which, were I even able to depict, would be but
little understood by the degenerate age for which
I am doomed to write. Even the female sex, those
arch innovators upon the tranquillity, the honesty,
and gray-beard customs of society, seemed for a
while to conduct themselves with incredible sobriety
and comeliness.

Their hair, untortured by the abominations of

art, was scrupulously pomatumed back from their foreheads with a candle, and covered with a little cap of quilted calico which fitted exactly to their heads. Their petticoats of linsey-woolsey were striped with a variety of gorgeous dyes, though I must confess these gallant garments were rather short, scarce reaching below the knee; but then they made up in the number, which generally equalled that of the gentlemen's small-clothes; and, what is still more praiseworthy, they were all of their own manufacture, of which circumstance, as may well be supposed, they were not a little vain.

These were the honest days in which every woman stayed at home, read the Bible, and wore pockets —ay, and that too of a goodly size, fashioned with patchwork into many curious devices and ostentatiously worn on the outside. These, in fact, were convenient receptacles where all good housewives carefully stored away such things as they wished to have at hand, by which means they often came to be incredibly crammed; and I remember there was a story current when I was a boy that the lady of Wouter Van Twiller once had occasion to empty her right pocket in search of a wooden ladle, when the contents filled a couple of corn baskets, and the utensil was discovered lying among some rubbish in one corner. But we must not give too much faith to all these stories, the anecdotes of those remote periods being very subject to exaggeration.

Besides these notable pockets, they likewise wore scissors and pincushions suspended from their girdles by red ribbons, or among the more opulent and showy classes by brass, and even silver, chains—indubitable tokens of thrifty housewives and indus-

trious spinsters. I cannot say much in vindication
of the shortness of the petticoats: it doubtless was
introduced for the purpose of giving the stockings
a chance to be seen, which were generally of blue
worsted with magnificent red clocks, or perhaps
to display a well-turned ankle and a neat, though
serviceable foot, set off by a high-heeled leathern
shoe with a large and splendid silver buckle. Thus
we find that the gentle sex in all ages have shown
the same disposition to infringe a little upon the
laws of decorum in order to betray a lurking beauty
or gratify an innocent love of finery.

From the sketch here given it will be seen that
our good grandmothers differed considerably in
their ideas of a fine figure from their scantily
dressed descendants of the present day. A fine lady
in those times waddled under more clothes, even
on a fair summer's day, than would have clad the
whole bevy of a modern ball-room. Nor were they
the less admired by the gentlemen in consequence
thereof. On the contrary, the greatness of a lover's
passion seemed to increase in proportion to the magnitude of its object, and a voluminous damsel, ar-
rayed in a dozen of petticoats, was declared by a
Low Dutch sonneteer of the province to be radiant
as a sunflower and luxuriant as a full-blown cabbage. Certain it is that in those days the heart of
a lover could not contain more than one lady at a
time; whereas the heart of a modern gallant has
often room enough to accommodate half a dozen.
The reason of which I conclude to be, that either
the hearts of the gentlemen have grown larger or
the persons of the ladies smaller; this, however, is
a question for physiologists to determine.

But there was a secret charm in these petticoats which no doubt entered into the consideration of the prudent gallants. The wardrobe of a lady was in those days her only fortune, and she who had a good stock of petticoats and stockings was as absolutely an heiress as is a Kamschatka damsel with a store of bear skins or a Lapland belle with a plenty of reindeer. The ladies, therefore, were very anxious to display these powerful attractions to the greatest advantage; and the best rooms in the house, instead of being adorned with caricatures of Dame Nature in water colors and needlework, were always hung round with abundance of homespun garments, the manufacture and the property of the females—a piece of laudable ostentation that still prevails among the heiresses of our Dutch villages.

The gentlemen, in fact, who figured in the circles of the gay world in these ancient times corresponded, in most particulars, with the beauteous damsels whose smiles they were ambitious to deserve. True it is their merits would make but a very inconsiderable impression upon the heart of a modern fair; they neither drove their curricles nor sported their tandems, for as yet those gaudy vehicles were not even dreamt of, neither did they distinguish themselves by their brilliancy at the table, and their consequent renconters with watchmen, for our forefathers were of too pacific a disposition to need those guardians of the night, every soul throughout the town being sound asleep before nine o'clock. Neither did they establish their claims to gentility at the expense of their tailors, for as yet those offenders against the pockets of society and the tranquility of all aspiring young gentlemen were unknown in New Amsterdam; every good housewife made the clothes of her husband and family, and even the goede vrouw of Van Twiller himself thought it no disparagement to cut out her husband's linsey-woolsey galligaskins.

Not but what there were some two or three youngsters who manifested the first dawning of what is called fire and spirit, who held all labor in contempt, skulked about docks and market-places, loitered in the sunshine, squandered what little money they could procure at hustle-cap and chuck-farthing, swore, boxed, fought cocks, and raced their neighbors' horses; in short, who promised to be the wonder, the talk, and abomination of the town, had not their stylish career been unfortunately cut short by an affair of honor with a whipping-post.

Far other, however, was the truly fashionable gentleman of those days. His dress, which served for both morning and evening, street and drawing-room, was a linsey-woolsey coat, made, perhaps, by the fair hands of the mistress of his affections, and gallantly bedecked with abundance of large brass buttons; half a score of breeches heightened the proportions of his figure; his shoes were decorated by enormous copper buckles; a low-crowned, broad-brimmed hat overshadowed his burly visage; and his hair dangled down his back in a queue of eel-skin.

Thus equipped, he would manfully sally forth with pipe in mouth to besiege some fair damsel's obdurate heart—not such a pipe, good reader, as that which Acis did sweetly tune in praise of his

Galatea, but one of true Delft manufacture and furnished with a charge of fragrant tobacco. With this would he resolutely set himself down before the fortress, and rarely failed, in the process of time, to smoke the fair enemy into a surrender upon honorable terms.

Happy would it have been for New Amsterdam could it always have existed in this state of lowly simplicity; but alas! the days of childhood are too sweet to last! Cities, like men, grow out of them in time, and are doomed alike to grow into the bustle, the cares, and miseries of the world.

WILLIAM THE TESTY

ILHELMUS KIEFT, who in 1634 ascended the gubernatorial chair (to borrow a favorite though clumsy appellation of modern phraseologists), was of a lofty descent, his father being inspector of windmills in the ancient town of Saardam; and our hero, we are told, when a boy made very curious investigations into the nature and operation of these machines, which was one reason why he afterward came to be so ingenious a governor. His name according to the most authentic etymologists, was a corruption of Kyver—that is to say, a *wrangler* or *scolder*—and expressed the characteristic of his family, which for nearly two centuries had kept the windy town of Saardam in hot water, and produced more tartars and brimstones than any ten families in the place; and so truly did he inherit this family peculiarity that he had not been a year in the government of the province before he was uni-

versally denominated William the Testy. His appearance answered to his name. He was a brisk, wiry, waspish little old gentleman; such a one as may now and then be seen stumping about our city

WILLIAM THE TESTY

in a broad-skirted coat with huge buttons, a cocked hat stuck on the back of his head, and a cane as high as his chin. His face was broad but his features were sharp, his cheeks were scorched into a dusky red by two fiery little gray eyes; his nose turned up, and the corners of his mouth turned down, pretty much like the muzzle of an irritable pug-dog.

I have heard it observed by a profound adept in human physiology that if a woman waxes fat with the progress of years, her tenure of life is somewhat precarious, but if haply she withers as she grows old she lives forever. Such promised to be the case with William the Testy, who grew tough in proportion as he dried. He had withered, in fact, not through the process of years, but through the tropical fervor of his soul, which burnt like a vehement rushlight in his bosom, inciting him to incessant broils and bickerings.

Wilhelmus Kieft was a great legislator on a small scale, and had a microscopic eye in public affairs. He had been greatly annoyed by the factious meetings of the good people of New Amsterdam, but, observing that on these occasions the pipe was ever in their mouth, he began to think that the pipe was at the bottom of the affair, and that there was some mysterious affinity between politics and tobacco smoke. Determined to strike at the root of the evil, he began, forthwith, to rail at tobacco as a noxious, nauseous weed, filthy in all its uses; and as to smoking, he denounced it as a heavy tax upon the public pocket, a vast consumer of time, a great encourager of idleness, and a deadly bane to the prosperity and morals of the people. Finally, he issued an edict prohibiting the smoking of tobacco throughout the New Netherlands. Ill-fated Kieft! Had he lived in the present age and attempted to check the unbounded license of the press, he could not have struck more sorely upon the sensibilities

of the million. The pipe, in fact, was the great
organ of reflection and deliberation of the New
Netherlander. It was his constant companion and
solace: was he gay, he smoked; was he sad, he
smoked; his pipe was never out of his mouth; it
was a part of his physiognomy; without it his best
friends would not know him. Take away his pipe?
You might as well take away his nose!

THE TESTY WILLIAM ISSUED FORTH LIKE A WRATHFUL SPIDER

The immediate effect of the edict of William the
Testy was a popular commotion. A vast multitude,
armed with pipes and tobacco boxes and an immense supply of ammunition, sat themselves down
before the governor's house and fell to smoking with
tremendous violence. The Testy William issued
forth like a wrathful spider, demanding the reason
of this lawless fumigation. The sturdy rioters replied by lolling back in their seats and puffing away
with redoubled fury, raising such a murky cloud
that the governor was fain to take refuge in the interior of his castle.

A long negotiation ensued through the medium of Antony the Trumpeter. The governor was at first wrathful and unyielding, but was gradually smoked into terms. He concluded by permitting the smoking of tobacco, but he abolished the fair long pipes used in the days of Wouter Van Twiller, denoting ease, tranquillity and sobriety of deportment; these he condemned as incompatible with the dispatch of business; in place whereof he substituted little captious short pipes, two inches in length, which he observed could be stuck in one corner of the mouth or twisted in the hat-band, and would never be in the way. Thus ended this alarming insurrection, which was long known by the name of The Pipe Plot, and which, it has been somewhat quaintly observed, did end, like most plots and seditions, in mere smoke.

But mark, O reader! the deplorable evils which did afterward result. The smoke of these villainous little pipes, continually ascending in a cloud about the nose, penetrated into and befogged the cerebellum, dried up all the kindly moisture of the brain, and rendered the people who used them as vaporish and testy as the governor himself. Nay, what is worse, from being goodly, burly, sleek-conditioned men, they became, like our Dutch yeomanry who smoke short pipes, a lantern-jawed, smoke-dried, leathern-hided race.

Nor was this all. From this fatal schism we may date the rise of parties in Nieuw Nederlandts. The rich burghers, who could afford to be lazy, adhered to the ancient fashion and were known as *Long Pipes;* while the lower order were branded with the plebeian name of *Short Pipes.*

PETER THE HEADSTRONG

ETER STUYVESANT was the last, and, like the renowned Wouter Van Twiller, the best, of our ancient Dutch governors, Wouter having surpassed all who preceded him, and Pieter or Piet, as he was sociably called by the old Dutch burghers, who were ever prone to familiarize names, having never been equalled by any successor. He was, in fact, the very man fitted by Nature to retrieve the desperate fortunes of her beloved province, had not the fates, those most potent and unrelenting of all ancient spinsters, destined them to inextricable confusion.

To say merely that he was a hero would be doing him great injustice: he was in truth a combination of heroes; for he was of a sturdy, raw-boned make like Ajax Telamon, with a pair of round shoulders that Hercules would have given his hide for (meaning his lion's hide) when he undertook to ease old Atlas of his load. He was, moreover, as Plutarch describes Coriolanus, not only terrible for the force of his arm, but likewise of his voice, which sounded as though it came out of a barrel; and, like the self-same warrior, he possessed a sovereign contempt for the sovereign people, and an iron aspect which was enough of itself to make the very bowels of his adversaries quake with terror and dismay. All this martial excellency of appearance was inexpressibly heightened by an accidental advantage with which I am surprised that neither Homer nor Virgil have graced any of their heroes. This was nothing less than a wooden leg, which was the only prize he had gained in bravely fighting the battles of his country, but of which he was so proud that he was often heard to declare he valued it more than all his other limbs put together; indeed, so highly did he esteem it that he had it gallantly enchased and relieved with silver devices, which caused it to be related in divers histories and legends that he wore a silver leg.

Like that choleric warrior Achilles, he was somewhat subject to extempore bursts of passion, which were rather unpleasant to his favorites and attendants, whose perceptions he was apt to quicken, after the manner of his illustrious imitator, Peter the Great, by anointing their shoulders with his walking-staff.

He was, in fact, the very reverse of his predecessors, being neither tranquil and inert like Walter the Doubter, nor restless and fidgeting like William the Testy, but a man of such uncommon activity and decision of mind that he never sought nor accepted the advice of others, depending bravely upon his single head, as would a hero of yore upon his single arm, to carry him through all difficulties. To tell the simple truth, he wanted nothing more to complete him as a statesman than to think always right, for nc one can say but that he always acted as he thought. He was never a man to flinch when he found himself in a scrape, but to dash forward through thick and thin, trusting by hook or by crook to make all things straight in the end. In a word, he possessed in an eminent degree that great quality in a statesman called perseverance by the polite, but nicknamed obstinacy by the vulgar. A wonderful salve for official blunders, since he who perseveres in error without flinching gets the credit of boldness and consistency, while he who wavers in seeking to do what is right gets stigmatized as a trimmer. This much is certain—and it is a maxim well worthy the attention of all legislators great and small who stand shaking in the wind, irresolute which way to steer—that a ruler who follows his own will pleases himself, while he who seeks to satisfy the wishes and whims of others runs great risk of pleasing nobody. There is nothing, too, like putting down one's foot resolutely when in doubt, and letting things take their course. The clock that stands still points right twice in the four and twenty hours, while others may keep going continually and be continually going wrong.

Nor did this magnanimous quality escape the discernment of the good people of Nieuw Nederlandts; on the contrary, so much were they struck with the independent will and vigorous resolution displayed on all occasions by their new governor that they universally called him Hard-Koppig Piet, or Peter the Headstrong—a great compliment to the strength of his understanding.

THE BATTLE WITH THE SWEDES

OW had the Dutchmen snatched a huge repast, and, finding themselves wonderfully encouraged and animated thereby, prepared to take the field. Expectation, says the writer of the Stuyvesant manuscript—expectation now stood on stilts. The world forgot to turn round, or rather stood still, that it might witness the affray, like a round-bellied alderman watch-

ing the combat of two chivalrous flies upon his jerkin. The eyes of all mankind, as usual in such cases,
were turned upon Fort Christina. The sun, like a
little man in a crowd at a puppet-show, scampered
about the heavens, popping his head here and there,
and endeavoring to get a peep between the unman-
nerly clouds that obtruded themselves in his way.
The historians filled their inkhorns; the poets went
without their dinners, either that they might buy
paper and goose-quills or because they could not
get anything to eat; Antiquity scowled sulkily out
of its grave to see itself outdone, while even Posterity stood mute, gazing in gaping ecstasy of retro-
spection on the eventful field.

The immortal deities, who whilom had seen service at the "affair" of Troy, now mounted their
feather-bed clouds and sailed over the plain, or
mingled among the combatants in different dis-
guises, all itching to have a finger in the pie. Jupiter sent off his thunderbolt to a noted coppersmith
to have it furbished up for the direful occasion.
The noted bully Mars stuck two horse-pistols into
his belt, shouldered a rusty firelock, and gallantly
swaggered at the elbow of the Swedes as a drunken
corporal; while Apollo trudged in their rear as a
bandy-legged fifer, playing most villainously out of
tune.

On the other hand, the ox-eyed Juno, who had
gained a pair of black eyes overnight in one of her
curtain lectures with old Jupiter, displayed her
haughty beauties on a baggage wagon; while Vul-
can halted as a club-footed blacksmith lately promoted to be a captain of militia. All was silent awe
or bustling preparation: War reared his horrid

front, gnashed loud his iron fangs, and shook his direful crest of bristling bayonets.

And now the mighty chieftains marshalled out their hosts. Here stood stout Risingh, firm as a thousand rocks, incrusted with stockades, and intrenched to the chin in mud batteries. He was a gigantic Swede, who, had he not been rather knock-kneed and splay-footed, might have served for the model of Samson or a Hercules. He was no less rapacious than mighty, and withal as crafty as he was rapacious, so that there is very little doubt that had he lived some four or five centuries since he would have figured as one of those wicked giants who took a cruel pleasure in pocketing beautiful princesses and distressed damsels when gadding about the world, and locking them up in enchanted castles without a toilet, a change of linen, or any other convenience; in consequence of which enormities they fell under the high displeasure of chivalry, and all true, loyal, and gallant knights were instructed to attack and slay outright any miscreant they might happen to find above six feet high; which is doubtless one reason why the race of large men is nearly extinct, and the generations of latter ages are so exceedingly small. His valiant soldiery lined the breastworks in grim array, each having his mustachios fiercely greased and his hair pomatumed back, and queued so stiffly that he grinned above the ramparts like a grisly death's head.

There came on the intrepid Peter, his brows knit, his teeth set, his fists clinched, almost breathing forth volumes of smoke, so fierce was the fire that raged within his bosom. His faithful squire Van Corlear trudged valiantly at his heels, with his trumpet gorgeously bedecked with red and yellow ribbons, the remembrances of his fair mistress at the Manhattoes. Then came waddling on the sturdy chivalry of the Hudson. There were the Van Wycks, and the Van Dycks, and the Ten Eycks; the Van Nesses, the Van Tassels, the Van Grools, the Van Hoesens, the Van Giesons, and the Van Blarcoms; the Van Warts, the Van Winkles, the Van Dams; the Van Pelts, the Van Rippers and the Van Brunts. There were the Van Hornes, the Van Hooks, the Van Bunschotens; the Van Gelders, the Van Arsdales, and the Van Bummels; the Vander Belts, the Vander Hoofs and the Vander Voorts, the Vander Lyns, the Vander Pools and the Vander Spiegles. There came the Hoffmans, the Hooghlands, the Hoppers, the Cloppers, the Ryckmans, the Dyckmans, the Hogebooms, the Rosebooms, the Oothouts, the Quakenbosses, the Roerbacks, the Garrebrantzes, the Bensons, the Brouwers, the Waldrons, the Onderdonks, the Varra Vangers, the Schermerhorns, the Stoutenburghs, the Brinkerhoffs, the Bontecous, the Knickerbockers, the Hockstrassers, the Ten Breecheses, and the Tough Breecheses, with a host more of worthies whose names are too crabbed to be written, or if they could be written it would be impossible for man to utter—all fortified with a mighty dinner, and, to use the words of a great Dutch poet:

"Brimful of wrath and cabbage."

For an instant the mighty Peter paused in the midst of his career, and, mounting on a stump, addressed his troops in eloquent Low Dutch, exhorting them to fight like *duyvels,* and assuring them that if they conquered they should get plenty of

THERE CAME ON THE INTREPID
PETER

booty; if they fell they should be allowed the satisfaction, while dying, of reflecting that it was in the service of their country, and after they were dead of seeing their names inscribed in the temple of renown, and handed down, in company with all the other great men of the year, for the admiration of posterity. Finally, he swore to them, on the word of a governor (and they knew him too well to doubt it for a moment), that if he caught any mother's son of them looking pale or playing craven, he would curry his hide till he made him run out of it like a snake in spring-time. Then, lugging out his trusty saber, he branished it three times over his head, ordered Van Corlear to sound the charge, and, shouting the words, "Saint Nicholas and the Manhattoes!" courageously dashed forward. His warlike followers, who had employed the interval in lighting their pipes, instantly stuck them into their mouths, gave a furious puff, and charged gallantly under cover of the smoke.

The Swedish garrison, ordered by the cunning Risingh not to fire until they could distinguish the whites of their assailants' eyes, stood in horrid silence on the covert-way until the eager Dutchmen had ascended the glacis. Then did they pour into them such a tremendous volley that the very hills quaked around, and certain springs burst forth from their sides which continue to run unto the present day. Not a Dutchman but would have bitten the dust beneath that dreadful fire had not the protecting Minerva kindly taken care that the Swedes should, one and all, observe their usual custom of shutting their eyes and turning away their heads at the moment of discharge.

The Swedes followed up their fire by leaping the counterscarp and falling tooth and nail upon the foe with furious outcries. And now might be seen prodigies of valor unmatched in history or song. Here was the sturdy Stuffel Brinkerhoff brandishing his quarter-staff, like the giant Blanderon his oak tree (for he scorned to carry any other weapon), and drumming a horrific tune upon the hard heads of the Swedish soldiery. There were the Van Kortlandts, posted at a distance, like the Locrian archers of yore, and plying it most potently with the long-bow, for which they were so justly renowned. On a rising knoll were gathered the valiant men of Sing-Sing, assisting marvelously in the fight by chanting the great song of Saint Nicholas; but as to the Gardeniers of Hudson, they were absent on a marauding-party, laying waste the neighboring watermelon-patches.

In a different part of the field were the Van Grolls of Antony's nose, struggling to get to the thickest of the fight, but horribly perplexed in a defile between two hills by reason of the length of their noses. So also the Van Bunschotens of Nyack and Kakiat, so renowned for kicking with the left foot, were brought to a stand for want of wind in consequence of the hearty dinner they had eaten and would have been put to utter rout, but for the arrival of a gallant corps of voltigeurs, composed of the Hoppers, who advanced nimbly to their assistance on one foot. Nor must I omit to mention the valiant achievements of Antony Van Corlear, who for a good quarter of an hour waged stubborn fight with a little pursy Swedish drummer, whose hide he drummed most magnificently, and whom he would infallibly have annihilated on the spot but that he had come into the battle with no other weapon but his trumpet.

But now the combat thickened. On came the mighty Jacobus Varra Vanger and the fighting men of the Wallabout; after them thundered the Van Pelts of Esopus, together with the Van Rippers and the Van Brunts, bearing down all before them; then the Suy Dams and the Van Dams, pressing forward with many a blustering oath at the head of the warriors of Hell-Gate, clad in their thunder-and-lightning gaberdines; and lastly the standard-bearers and body-guards of Peter Stuyvesant, bearing the great beaver of the Manhattoes.

And now commenced the horrid din, the desperate struggle, the maddening ferocity, the frantic desperation, the confusion and self-abandonment of war. Dutchman and Swede, commingled, tugged, panted, and blowed. The heavens were darkened with a tempest of missiles. Bang! went the guns—whack! went the broadswords—thump! went the cudgels—crash! went the musket-stocks—blows, kicks, cuffs, scratches, black eyes, and bloody noses swelling the horrors of the scene! Thick thwack, cut and hack, helter-skelter, higgledy-piggledy, hurly-burly, head over heels, rough and tumble! Dunder and blixum! swore the Dutchmen; splitter and splutter! cried the Swedes; storm the works! shouted Hardkoppig Pieter; fire the mine! roared stout Risingh; tanta-ra-ra-ra! twanged the trumpet of Antony Van Corlear—until all voice and sound became unintelligible, grunts of pain, yells of fury, and shouts of triumph mingling in one hideous clamor. The earth shook as if struck with a paralytic stroke—trees shrunk aghast and withered at the sight—rocks burrowed in the ground like rabbits—and even Christina Creek turned from its course and ran up a hill in breathless terror!

Long hung the contest doubtful, for though a heavy shower of rain, sent by the "cloud-compelling Jove," in some measure cooled their ardor, as doth a bucket of water thrown on a group of fighting mastiffs, yet did they but pause for a moment, to return with tenfold fury to the charge. Just at this juncture a vast and dense column of smoke was seen slowly rolling toward the scene of battle. The combatants paused for a moment, gazing in mute astonishment, until the wind, dispelling the murky cloud, revealed the flaunting banner of Michael Paw, the patroon of Communipaw. That valiant chieftain came fearlessly on at the head of a phalanx of oyster-fed Pavonians and a corps de reserve of the Van Arsdales and Van Bummels, who had remained behind to digest the enormous dinner they had eaten. These now trudged manfully forward, smoking their pipes with outrageous vigor, so as to raise the awful cloud that has been mentioned; but marching exceedingly slow, being short of leg and of great rotundity in the belt.

And now the deities who watched over the fortunes of the Nederlandters having unthinkingly left the field and stepped into a neighboring tavern to refresh themselves with a pot of beer, a direful catastrophe had well-nigh ensued. Scarce had the myrmidons of Michael Paw attained the front of battle, when the Swedes instructed by the cunning Risingh, levelled a shower of blows full at their tobacco-pipes. Astounded at this assault and dismayed at the havoc of their pipes, these ponderous warriors gave way and like a drove of frightened elephants broke through the ranks of their own army. The little Hoppers were borne down in the surge; the sacred banner emblazoned with the gigantic oyster of Communipaw was trampled in the dirt; on blundered and thundered the heavy-sterned fugitives, the Swedes pressing on their rear and applying their feet *a parte poste* of the Van Arsdales and the Van Bummels with a vigor that prodigiously accelerated their movements, nor did the renowned Michael Paw himself fail to receive divers grievous and dishonorable visitations of shoe-leather.

But what, O Muse! was the rage of Peter Stuyvesant when from afar he saw his army giving way! In the transports of his wrath he sent forth a roar enough to shake the very hills. The men of the Manhattoes plucked up new courage at the sound, or, rather, they rallied at the voice of their leader, of whom they stood more in awe than of all the Swedes in Christendom. Without waiting for their aid the daring Peter dashed, sword in hand, into the thickest of the foe. Then might be seen achievements worthy of the days of the giants. Wherever he went the enemy shrank before him; the Swedes fled to right and left or were driven, like dogs, into their own ditch; but as he pushed forward singly with headlong courage the foe closed behind and hung upon his rear. One aimed a blow full at his heart; but the protecting power which watches over the great and good turned aside the hostile blade and directed it to a side-pocket, where reposed an

enormous iron tobacco-box endowed, like the shield
of Achilles, with supernatural powers, doubtless
from bearing the portrait of the blessed Saint
Nicholas. Peter Stuyvesant turned like an angry
bear upon the foe, and seizing him as he fled by an
immeasurable queue, "Ah, caterpillar!" roared he,
"here's what shall make worm's meat of thee!" So
saying, he whirled his sword and dealt a blow that
would have decapitated the varlet, but that the pity-
ing steel struck short and shaved the queue forever
from his crown. At this moment an arquebusier
levelled his piece from a neighboring mound with
deadly aim; but the watchful Minerva, who had
just stopped to tie up her garter, seeing the peril
of her favorite hero, sent old Boreas with his bel-
lows, who as the match descended to the pan gave a
blast that blew the priming from the touch-hole.

Thus waged the fight, when the stout Risingh,
surveying the field from the top of a little ravelin,
perceived his troops banged, beaten, and kicked by
the invincible Peter. Drawing his falchion and ut-
tering a thousand anathemas, he strode down to the
scene of combat with some such thundering strides
as Jupiter is said by Hesiod to have taken when he
strode down the spheres to hurl his thunderbolts at
the Titans.

When the rival heroes came face to face each
made a prodigious start in the style of a veteran
stage champion. Then did they regard each other
for a moment with the bitter aspect of two furious
tom-cats on the point of a clapper-clawing. Then
did they throw themselves into one attitude, then
into another striking their swords on the ground
first on the right side, then on the left; at last at it

they went with incredible ferocity. Words cannot tell the prodigies of strength and valor displayed in this direful encounter—an encounter compared to which the far-famed battles of Ajax with Hector, of Æneas with Turnus, Orlando with Rodomont, Guy of Warwick with Colbrand the Dane, or of that renowned Welsh knight Sir Owen of the mountains with the giant Guylon, were all gentle sports and holiday recreations. At length the valiant Peter, watching his opportunity, aimed a blow, enough to cleave his adversary to the very chine; but Risingh nimbly raising his sword, warded it off so narrowly that glancing on one side, it shaved away a huge canteen in which he carried his liquor; thence, pursuing its trenchant course, it severed off a deep coat-pocket stored with bread and cheese; which provant, rolling among the armies, occasioned a fearful scrambling between the Swedes and Dutchmen, and made the general battle to wax ten times more furious than ever.

Enraged to see his military stores laid waste, the stout Risingh, collecting all his forces, aimed a mighty blow full at the hero's crest. In vain did his fierce little cocked hat oppose its course. The biting steel clove through the stubborn ram-beaver, and would have cracked the crown of any one not endowed with supernatural hardness of head; but the brittle weapon shivered in pieces on the skull of Hardkoppig Piet, shedding a thousand sparks like beams of glory round his grizzly visage.

The good Peter reeled with the blow, and, turning up his eyes, beheld a thousand suns, beside moons and stars, dancing about the firmament. At length, missing his footing by reason of his wooden leg, down he came on his seat of honor with a crash which shook the surrounding hills, and might have wrecked his frame had he not been received into a cushion softer than velvet which Providence had benevolently prepared for his reception.

The furious Risingh, in despite of the maxim, cherished by all true knights, that "fair play is a jewel," hastened to take advantage of the hero's fall; but as he stooped to give a fatal blow, Peter Stuyvesant dealt him a thwack over the sconce with his wooden leg, which set a chime of bells ringing triple bobmajors in his cerebellum. The bewildered Swede staggered with the blow, and the wary Peter seizing a pocket-pistol which lay hard by, discharged it full at the head of the reeling Risingh. Let not my reader mistake: it was not a murderous weapon loaded with powder and ball, but a little sturdy stone pottle charged to the muzzle with a double dram of true Dutch courage, which the knowing Antony Van Corlear carried about him by way of replenishing his valor and which had dropped from his wallet during his furious encounter with the drummer. The hideous weapon sang through the air, and true to its course as was the fragment of a rock discharged at Hector by bully Ajax, encountered the head of the gigantic Swede with matchless violence.

This heaven-directed blow decided the battle. The ponderous pericranium of General Jan Risingh sank upon his breast, his knees tottered under him, a death-like torpor seized upon his frame, and he tumbled to the earth with such violence that old Pluto started with affright, lest he should have broken through the roof of his infernal palace.

His fall was the signal of defeat and victory: the Swedes gave way, the Dutch pressed forward; the former took to their heels, the latter hotly pursued. Some entered with them, pell-mell, through the sally-port; others stormed the bastion, and others scrambled over the curtain. Thus in a little while the fortress of Fort Christina, which, like another Troy, had stood a siege of full ten hours, was carried by assault without the loss of a single man on either side. Victory, in the likeness of a gigantic ox-fly, sat perched upon the cocked hat of the gallant Stuyvesant, and it was declared by all the writers whom he hired to write the history of his expedition that on this memorable day he gained a sufficient quantity of glory to immortalize a dozen of the greatest heroes in Christendom!

THE BATTLE OF TRAFALGAR

By ROBERT SOUTHEY

NOTE.—The great naval hero of England is Horatio, Viscount Nelson, who was born in September, 1758, in a country village of Norfolk. Under the guardianship of his uncle, Captain Suckling, he entered the navy as a midshipman when he was but twelve years old, and he was promoted rapidly. By the time war broke out with France in 1793 he had risen so high that he was made commander of the sixty-four gun ship *Agamemnon*. In 1797 he was made rear-admiral, and he received other honors for conspicuous gallantry in action. In an unsuccessful attack on Santa Cruz, in the island of Teneriffe, Nelson lost his right arm. The first of his very great achievements was the destruction of the French fleet in the Battle of Aboukir Bay, in 1798; the last was the famous Battle of Trafalgar, the account of which we quote from Southey's *Life of Nelson*. He had been made, in 1803, Commander in Chief of the Mediterranean fleet, and on his flagship *Victory* had spent two years watching the French and hampering their movements. He prevented Napoleon from invading England.

T Portsmouth, Nelson, at length, found news of the combined fleet. Sir Robert Calder, who had been sent out to intercept their return, had fallen in with them on the 22nd of July, sixty leagues west of Cape Finisterre. Their force consisted of twenty sail of the line, three fifty-gun ships, five frigates, and two brigs: his, of fifteen line of battle ships, two frigates,

284

a cutter, and a lugger. After an action of four
hours he had captured an 84 and a 74, and then
thought it necessary to bring-to the squadron, for
the purpose of securing their prizes. The hostile
fleets remained in sight of each other till the 26th,
when the enemy bore away.

The capture of two ships from so superior a
force, would have been considered as no inconsiderable victory a few years earlier; but Nelson had
introduced a new era in our naval history, and the
nation felt, respecting this action, as he had felt on
a somewhat similar occasion. They regretted that
Nelson, with his eleven ships, had not been in Sir
Robert Calder's place; and their disappointment
was generally and loudly expressed.

Frustrated as his own hopes had been, Nelson
had yet the high satisfaction of knowing that his
judgment had never been more conspicuously approved, and that he had rendered essential service
to his country by driving the enemy from those islands, where they expected there could be no force
capable of opposing them. The West India mer-
chants in London, as men whose interests were more
immediately benefited, appointed a deputation to
express their thanks for his great and judicious exertions. It was now his intention to rest awhile
from his labours, and recruit himself, after all his
fatigues and cares, in the society of those whom
he loved. All his stores were brought up from the
Victory; and he found in his house at Merton the
enjoyment which he had anticipated.

Many days had not elapsed before Captain
Blackwood, on his way to London with despatches,
called on him at five in the morning. Nelson, who

was already dressed, exclaimed, the moment he saw him: "I am sure you bring me news of the French and Spanish fleets! I think I shall yet have to beat them!"

They had refitted at Vigo, after the indecisive action with Sir Robert Calder; then proceeded to

I SHALL YET HAVE TO BEAT THEM!

Ferrol, brought out the squadron from thence, and with it entered Cadiz in safety.

"Depend on it, Blackwood," he said, "I shall give M. Villeneuve a drubbing."

But, when Blackwood had left him, he wanted resolution to declare his wishes to Lady Hamilton and his sisters, and endeavored to drive away the thought. "I have done enough," he said; "let the man trudge it who has lost his budget."

His countenance belied his lips; and as he was pacing one of the walks in the garden, which he used to call the quarter-deck, Lady Hamilton came up to him, and told him she saw he was uneasy.

He smiled and said:

"No, I am as happy as possible; I am surrounded by my family; my health is better since I have been on shore, and I would not give sixpence to call the king my uncle?"

She replied, that she did not believe him,—that she knew he was longing to get at the combined fleets,—that he considered them as his own property—that he would be miserable if any man but himself did the business, and that he ought to have them, as the price and reward of his two years' long watching, and his hard chase.

"Nelson," said she, "however we may lament your absence, offer your services; they will be accepted, and you will gain a quiet heart by it: you will have a glorious victory, and then you may return here and be happy." He looked at her with tears in his eyes—"Brave Emma! Good Emma!— If there were more Emmas there would be more Nelsons."

His services were as willingly accepted as they were offered; and Lord Barham, giving him the list of the navy, desired him to choose his own officers.

"Choose yourself, my lord," was his reply: "the same spirit actuates the whole profession: you cannot choose wrong."

Lord Barham then desired him to say what ships, and how many, he would wish, in addition to the fleet which he was going to command, and said they should follow him as soon as each was ready.

No appointment was ever more in unison with the feelings and judgment of the whole nation. They, like Lady Hamilton, thought that the destruction of the combined fleets ought properly be Nelson's work: that he, who had been

"Half around the sea-girt ball,
The hunter of the recreant Gaul,"

ought to reap the spoils of the chase, which he had watched so long, and so perseveringly pursued.

Unremitting exertions were made to equip the ships which he had chosen, and especially to refit the *Victory,* which was once more to bear his flag.

Before he left London he called at his upholsterer's, where the coffin, which Captain Hallowell had given him, was deposited; and desired that its history might be engraven upon the lid, saying, it was highly probable that he might want it on his return. He seemed, indeed, to have been impressed with an expectation that he should fall in the battle. In a letter to his brother, written immediately after his return, he had said: "We must not talk of Sir Robert Calder's battle—I might not have done so much with my small force. If I had fallen in with them, you might probably have been a lord before I wished; for I know they meant to make a dead set at the *Victory.*"

Nelson had once regarded the prospect of death with gloomy satisfaction: it was when he anticipated the upbraidings of his wife, and the displeasure of his venerable father. The state of his feelings now was expressed, in his private journal, in these words:

"Friday night (Sept. 13), at half-past ten, I drove from dear, dear Merton, where I left all which I hold dear in this world, to go to serve my king and country. May the great God, whom I adore, enable me to fulfil the expectations of my country! and, if it is His good pleasure that I should return, my thanks will never cease being offered up to the throne of His mercy. If it is His good providence to cut short my days upon earth, I bow with the greatest submission; relying that He will protect those so dear to me, whom I may leave behind! His will be done! Amen! Amen! Amen!"

Early on the following morning he reached Portsmouth; and, having despatched his business on shore, endeavoured to elude the populace by taking a by-way to the beach; but a crowd collected in his train, pressing forward to obtain a sight of his face;—many were in tears, and many knelt down before him, and blessed him as he passed. England has had many heroes, but never one who so entirely possessed the love of his fellow-countrymen as Nelson. All men knew that his heart was as humane as it was fearless; that there was not in his nature the slightest alloy of selfishness or cupidity; but that, with perfect and entire devotion, he served his country with all his heart, and with all his soul, and with all his strength; and, therefore, they loved him as truly and as fervently as he loved England. They pressed upon the parapet to gaze after him when his barge pushed off, and he was returning their cheers by waving his hat. The sentinels, who endeavoured to prevent them from trespassing upon this ground, were wedged among the crowd; and an officer, who, not very prudently

upon such an occasion, ordered them to drive the
people down with their bayonets, was compelled
speedily to retreat; for the people would not be de-
barred from gazing, till the last moment, upon the
hero, the darling hero of England.

He arrived off Cadiz on the 29th of September,
—his birthday. Fearing that, if the enemy knew
his force, they might be deterred from venturing to
sea, he kept out of sight of land, desired Collingwood to fire no salute and hoist no colours, and
wrote to Gibraltar, to request that the force of the
fleet might not be inserted there in the *Gazette*.
His reception in the Mediterranean fleet was as
gratifying as the farewell of his countrymen at
Portsmouth: the officers, who came on board to
welcome him, forgot his rank as commander, in
their joy at seeing him again.

On the day of his arrival, Villeneuve received
orders to put to sea the first opportunity. Villeneuve, however, hesitated when he heard that Nelson had resumed the command. He called a council
of war; and their determination was, that it would
not be expedient to leave Cadiz, unless they had
reason to believe themselves stronger by one-third
than the British force.

In the public measures of this country secrecy
is seldom practicable, and seldom attempted: here,
however, by the precautions of Nelson and the wise
measures of the Admiralty, the enemy were for
once kept in ignorance: for, as the ships appointed
to reinforce the Mediterranean fleet were despatched singly—each as soon as it was ready—their
collected number was not stated in the newspapers,
and their arrival was not known to the enemy. But

the enemy knew that Admiral Louis, with six sail, had been detached for stores and water to Gibraltar. Accident also contributed to make the French admiral doubt whether Nelson himself had actually taken the command. An American, lately arrived from England, maintained that it was impossible, for he had seen him only a few days before in London, and, at that time, there was no rumour of his going again to sea.

The station which Nelson had chosen was some fifty or sixty miles to the west of Cadiz, near Cape Saint Mary's. At this distance he hoped to decoy the enemy out, while he guarded against the danger of being caught with a westerly wind near Cadiz, and driven within the Straits. The blockade of the port was rigorously enforced; in hopes that the combined fleet might be forced to sea by want.

There was now every indication that the enemy would speedily venture out: officers and men were in the highest spirits at the prospect of giving them a decisive blow, such, indeed, as would put an end to all further contest upon the seas. Theatrical amusements were performed every evening in most of the ships, and *God Save the King* was the hymn with which the sports concluded.

"I verily believe," said Nelson (writing on the 6th of October), "that the country will soon be put to some expense on my account; either a monument, or a new pension and honours; for I have not the smallest doubt but that a very few days, almost hours, will put us in battle. The success no man can ensure; but for the fighting them, if they can be got at, I pledge myself.—The sooner the better; I don't like to have these things upon my mind."

At this time he was not without some cause of anxiety: he was in want of frigates—the eyes of the fleet—as he always called them—to the want of which, the enemy before were indebted for their escape, and Bonaparte for his arrival in Egypt. He had only twenty-three ships—others were on the way—but they might come too late; and, though Nelson never doubted of victory, mere victory was not what he looked to—he wanted to annihilate the enemy's fleet. The Carthagena squadron might effect a junction with this fleet on the one side; and, on the other, it was to be expected that a similar attempt would be made by the French from Brest; —in either case, a formidable contingency to be apprehended by the blockading force. The Rochefort squadron did push out, and had nearly caught the *Agamemnon* and *l'Aimable,* in their way to reinforce the British admiral. Yet Nelson at this time weakened his own fleet. He had the unpleasant task to perform of sending home Sir Robert Calder, whose conduct was to be made the subject of a court-martial, in consequence of the general dissatisfaction which had been felt and expressed at his imperfect victory.

On the 9th Nelson sent Collingwood what he called, in his dairy, the Nelson-touch. "I send you," said he, "my plan of attack, as far as a man dare venture to guess at the very uncertain position the enemy may be found in: but it is to place you perfectly at ease respecting my intentions, and to give full scope to your judgment for carrying them into effect. We can, my dear Coll, have no little jealousies. We have only one great object in view, that of annihilating our enemies, and getting a

glorious peace for our country. No man has more
confidence in another than I have in you; and no
man will render your services more justice than
your very old friend Nelson and Bronté."

The order of sailing was to be the order of battle;
the fleet in two lines, with an advanced squadron
of eight of the fastest sailing two-deckers. The
second in command, having the entire direction of
his line, was to break through the enemy, about the
twelfth ship from their rear: he would lead through
the centre, and the advanced squadron was to cut
off three or four ahead of the centre. This plan
was to be adapted to the strength of the enemy,
so that they should always be one-fourth superior
to those whom they cut off.

Nelson said, "My admirals and captains, knowing my precise object to be that of a close and
decisive action, will supply any deficiency of signals,
and act accordingly. In case signals cannot be
seen or clearly understood, no captain can do wrong
if he places his ship alongside that of an enemy."

One of the last orders of this admirable man
was, that the name and family of every officer, seaman, and marine, who might be killed or wounded
in action, should be, as soon as possible, returned
to him, in order to be transmitted to the chairman
of the Patriotic Fund, that the case might be taken
into consideration, for the benefit of the sufferer
or his family.

About half-past nine in the morning of the 19th,
the *Mars,* being the nearest to the fleet of the ships
which formed the line of communication with the
frigates in shore, repeated the signal that the enemy
were coming out of port. The wind was at this

time very light, with partial breezes, mostly from the S.S.W. Nelson ordered the signal to be made for a chase in the southeast quarter. About two, the repeating ships announced that the enemy were at sea.

All night the British fleet continued under all sail, steering to the southeast. At daybreak they were in the entrance of the Straits, but the enemy was not in sight. About seven, one of the frigates made signal that the enemy were bearing north. Upon this the *Victory* hove to; and shortly afterwards Nelson made sail again to the northward. In the afternoon the wind blew fresh from the southwest, and the English began to fear that the foe might be forced to return to port. A little before sunset, however, Blackwood, in the *Euryalus,* telegraphed that they appeared determined to go to the westward,—"And that," said the admiral in his diary, "they shall not do, if it is in the power of Nelson and Bronté to prevent them."

Nelson had signified to Blackwood, that he depended upon him to keep sight of the enemy. They were observed so well, that all their motions were made known to him; and, as they wore twice, he inferred that they were aiming to keep the port of Cadiz open, and would retreat there as soon as they saw the British fleet: for this reason he was very careful not to approach near enough to be seen by them during the night.

At daybreak the combined fleets were distinctly seen from the *Victory's* deck, formed in a close line of battle ahead, on the starboard tack, about twelve miles to leeward, and standing to the south. Our fleet consisted of twenty-seven sail of the line and

four frigates; theirs of thirty-three, and seven large
frigates. Their superiority was greater in size, and
weight of metal, than in numbers. They had four
thousand troops on board; and the best riflemen
who could be procured, many of them Tyrolese,
were dispersed through the ships. Little did the
Tyrolese, and little did the Spaniards, at that day,
imagine what horrors the wicked tyrant whom they
served was preparing for their country!

Soon after daylight Nelson came upon deck.
The 21st of October was a festival in his family;
because on that day his uncle, Captain Suckling,
in the *Dreadnought,* with two other line of battle
ships, had beaten off a French squadron of four
sail of the line and three frigates. Nelson, with
that sort of superstition from which few persons
are entirely exempt, had more than once expressed
his persuasion that this was to be the day of his
battle also; and he was well pleased at seeing his
prediction about to be verified.

The wind was now from the west,—light breezes,
with a long heavy swell. Signal was made to bear
down upon the enemy in two lines; and the fleet
set all sail. Collingwood, in the *Royal Sovereign,*
led the lee-line of thirteen ships; the *Victory* led
the weather-line of fourteen.

Having seen that all was as it should be, Nelson
retired to his cabin, and wrote this prayer:—

"May the Great God, whom I worship, grant
to my country, and for the benefit of Europe in
general, a great and glorious victory; and may no
misconduct in any one tarnish it; and may humanity after victory be the predominant feature in the

British fleet! For myself individually, I commit my life to Him that made me, and may His blessing alight on my endeavours for serving my country faithfully! To Him I resign myself, and the just cause which is intrusted to me to defend. Amen, Amen, Amen."

Blackwood went on board the *Victory* about six. He found Nelson in good spirits, but very calm; not in that exhilaration which he had felt upon entering into battle at Aboukir and Copenhagen; he knew that his own life would be particularly aimed at, and seems to have looked for death with almost as sure an expectation as for victory. His whole attention was fixed upon the enemy. They tacked to the northward, and formed their line on the larboard tack; thus bringing the shoals of Trafalgar and St. Pedro under the lee of the British, and keeping the port of Cadiz open for themselves. This was judiciously done: and Nelson, aware of all the advantages which it gave them, made signal to prepare to anchor.

Villeneuve was a skilful seaman; worthy of serving a better master and a better cause. His plan of defence was as well conceived, and as original, as the plan of attack. He formed the fleet in a double line, every alternate ship being about a cable's length to windward of her second ahead and astern.

Nelson, certain of a triumphant issue to the day, asked Blackwood what he should consider as a victory. That officer answered, that, considering the handsome way in which battle was offered by the enemy, their apparent determination for a fair trial

of strength, and the situation of the land, he
thought it would be a glorious result if fourteen
were captured. He replied: "I shall not be satisfied with less than twenty."

Soon afterwards he asked him if he did not think
there was a signal wanting. Captain Blackwood
made answer that he thought the whole fleet seemed
very clearly to understand what they were about.
These words were scarcely spoken before that signal was made, which will be remembered as long
as the language, or even the memory, of England
shall endure—Nelson's last signal:—

"England expects every man to do his duty!"

It was received throughout the fleet with a shout
of answering acclamation, made sublime by the
spirit which it breathed and the feeling which it
expressed. "Now," said Lord Nelson, "I can do
no more. We must trust to the Great Disposer of
all events, and the justice of our cause. I thank
God for this great opportunity of doing my duty."

He wore that day, as usual, his admiral's frock
coat, bearing on the left breast four stars of the
different orders with which he was invested. Ornaments which rendered him so conspicuous a mark
for the enemy, were beheld with ominous appre-
hensions by his officers. It was known that there
were riflemen on board the French ships, and it
could not be doubted but that his life would be particularly aimed at. They communicated their fears
to each other; and the surgeon, Mr. Beatty, spoke
to the chaplain, Dr. Scott, and to Mr. Scott, the
public secretary, desiring that some person would

entreat him to change his dress, or cover the stars: but they knew that such a request would highly displease him. "In honour I gained them," he had said when such a thing had been hinted to him formerly, "and in honour I will die with them." Mr. Beatty, however, would not have been deterred by any fear of exciting his displeasure, from speaking to him himself upon a subject in which the weal of England as well as the life of Nelson was concerned, but he was ordered from the deck before he could find an opportunity.

This was a point upon which Nelson's officers knew that it was hopeless to remonstrate or reason with him; but both Blackwood, and his own captain, Hardy, represented to him how advantageous to the fleet it would be for him to keep out of action as long as possible; and he consented at last to let the *Leviathan* and the *Temeraire,* which were sailing abreast of the *Victory,* be ordered to pass ahead. Yet even here the last infirmity of this noble mind was indulged; for these ships could not pass ahead if the *Victory* continued to carry all her sail; and so far was Nelson from shortening sail, that it was evident he took pleasure in pressing on, and rendering it impossible for them to obey his own orders.

A long swell was setting into the Bay of Cadiz: our ships, crowding all sail, moved majestically before it, with light winds from the southwest. The sun shone on the sails of the enemy; and their well-formed line, with their numerous three-deckers, made an appearance which any other assailants would have thought formidable; but the British sailors only admired the beauty and the splendour of the spectacle; and, in full confidence of winning what they saw, remarked to each other, what a fine sight yonder ships would make at Spithead!

The French admiral, from the *Bucentaure,* beheld the new manner in which his enemy was advancing, Nelson and Collingwood each leading his line; and, pointing them out to his officers, he is said to have exclaimed, that such conduct could not fail to be successful. Yet Villeneuve had made his own dispositions with the utmost skill, and the fleets under his command waited for the attack with perfect coolness.

Ten minutes before twelve they opened their fire. Eight or nine of the ships immediately ahead of the *Victory,* and across her bows, fired single guns at her, to ascertain whether she was yet within their range. As soon as Nelson perceived that their shot passed over him, he desired Blackwood, and Captain Prowse, of the *Sirius,* to repair to their respective frigates; and, on their way, to tell all the captains of the line of battle ships that he depended on their exertions; and that, if by the prescribed mode of attack they found it impracticable to get into action immediately, they might adopt whatever they thought best, provided it led them quickly and closely alongside an enemy.

As they were standing on the front of the poop, Blackwood took him by the hand, saying, he hoped soon to return and find him in possession of twenty prizes. He replied: "God bless you, Blackwood! I shall never see you again."

Nelson's column was steered about two points more to the north than Collingwood's, in order to cut off the enemy's escape into Cadiz: the lee-line, therefore, was first engaged.

"See," cried Nelson, pointing to the *Royal Sovereign,* as she steered right for the centre of the enemy's line, cut through it astern of the *Santa Anna,* three-decker, and engaged her at the muzzle of her guns on the starboard side: "see how that noble fellow, Collingwood, carries his ship into action!"

Collingwood, delighted at being first in the heat of the fire, and knowing the feelings of his commander and old friend, turned to his captain, and exclaimed, "Rotherham, what would Nelson give to be here!"

Both these brave officers, perhaps, at this moment thought of Nelson with gratitude, for a circumstance which had occurred on the preceding day. Admiral Collingwood, with some of the captains, having gone on board the *Victory* to receive instructions, Nelson inquired of him where his captain was and was told, in reply, that they were not upon good terms with each other. "Terms!" said Nelson;—"good terms with each other!" Immediately he sent a boat for Captain Rotherham; led him, as soon as he arrived, to Collingwood, and said, "Look, yonder are the enemy! Shake hands like Englishmen."

The enemy continued to fire a gun at a time at the *Victory,* till they saw that a shot had passed through her main-topgallant-sail; then they opened their broadsiders, aiming chiefly at her rigging, in the hope of disabling her before she could close with them.

Nelson, as usual, had hoisted several flags, lest one should be shot away. The enemy showed no colors till late in the action, when they began to feel the necessity of having them to strike. For this reason, the *Santissima Trinidad,* Nelson's old acquaintance, as he used to call her, was distinguishable only by her four decks; and to the bow of this opponent he ordered the *Victory* to be steered. Meantime an incessant raking fire was kept up upon the *Victory.* The admiral's secretary was one of the first who fell: he was killed by a cannon-shot, while conversing with Hardy. Captain Adair, of the marines, with the help of a sailor, endeavoured to remove the body from Nelson's sight, who had a great regard for Mr. Scott; but he anxiously asked, "Is that poor Scott that's gone?" and being informed that it was indeed so, exclaimed, "Poor fellow!"

Presently a double-headed shot struck a party of marines, who were drawn up on the poop, and killed eight of them: upon which Nelson immediately desired Captain Adair to disperse his men round the ship, that they might not suffer so much from being together.

A few minutes afterwards a shot struck the fore brace bits on the quarter-deck, and passed between Nelson and Hardy, a splinter from the bit tearing off Hardy's buckle and bruising his foot. Both stopped, and looked anxiously at each other, each supposing the other to be wounded. Nelson then smiled, and said, "This is too warm work, Hardy, to last long."

The *Victory* had not yet returned a single gun: fifty of her men had been by this time killed or wounded, and her main-topmast, with all her studding sails and their booms, shot away. Nelson declared that, in all his battles, he had seen nothing which surpassed the cool courage of his crew on this occasion.

At four minutes after twelve she opened her fire from both sides of her deck. It was not possible to break the enemy's line without running on board one of their ships: Hardy informed him of this, and asked which he would prefer.

Nelson replied: "Take your choice, Hardy, it does not signify much."

The master was then ordered to put the helm to port, and the *Victory* ran on board the *Redoubtable,* just as her tiller ropes were shot away. The French ship received her with a broadside; then instantly let down her lower-deck ports, for fear of being boarded through them, and never afterwards fired a great gun during the action. Her tops, like those of all the enemy's ships, were filled with riflemen. Nelson never placed musketry in his tops; he had a strong dislike to the practice, not merely because it endangers setting fire to the sails, but also because it is a murderous sort of warfare, by which individuals may suffer, and a commander, now and then, be picked off, but which never can decide the fate of a general engagement.

Captain Harvey, in the *Temeraire,* fell on board the *Redoubtable* on the other side. Another enemy was in like manner on board the *Temeraire;* so that these four ships formed as compact a tier as if they had been moored together, their heads lying all the same way. The lieutenants of the *Victory,* seeing this, depressed their guns of the middle and lower decks, and fired with a diminished charge, lest the shot should pass through, and injure the *Temeraire.* And because there was danger that

the *Redoubtable* might take fire from the lower-
deck guns, the muzzles of which touched her side
when they were run out, the fireman of each gun
stood ready with a bucket of water, which, as soon
as the gun was discharged, he dashed into the hole
made by the shot. An incessant fire was kept up
from the *Victory* from both sides; her larboard
guns playing upon the *Bucentaure* and the huge
Santissima Trinidad.

AN INCESSANT FIRE WAS KEPT UP BY THE "VICTORY"

It had been part of Nelson's prayer that the
British fleet might be distinguished by humanity in
the victory which he expected. Setting an example
himself, he twice gave orders to cease firing upon
the *Redoubtable,* supposing that she had struck,
because her great guns were silent; for, as she carried no flag, there was no means of instantly ascertaining the fact.

From this ship, which he had thus twice spared,
he received his death. A ball fired from her mizzen-top, which, in the then situation of the two
vessels, was not more than fifteen yards from that
part of the deck where he was standing, struck the
epaulette on his left shoulder,—about a quarter
after one, just in the heat of the action. He fell

upon his face, on the spot which was covered with his poor secretary's blood. Hardy, who was a few steps from him, turning round, saw three men raising him up.

"They have done for me at last, Hardy," said he.

"I hope not!" cried Hardy.

"Yes," he replied; "my backbone is shot through."

Yet even now, not for a moment losing his presence of mind, he observed, as they were carrying him down the ladder, that the tiller ropes, which had been shot away, were not yet replaced, and ordered that new ones should be rove immediately: —then, that he might not be seen by the crew, he took out his handkerchief, and covered his face and his stars.—Had he but concealed these badges of honour from the enemy, England, perhaps, would not have had cause to receive with sorrow the news of the battle of Trafalgar.

The cockpit was crowded with wounded and dying men, over whose bodies he was with some difficulty conveyed, and laid upon a pallet in the midshipmen's berth. It was soon perceived, upon examination, that the wound was mortal. This, however, was concealed from all, except Captain Hardy, the chaplain, and the medical attendants. He himself being certain, from the sensation in his back, and the gush of blood which he felt momently within his breast, that no human care could avail him, insisted that the surgeon should leave him, and attend to those to whom he might be useful: "For," said he, "you can do nothing for me."

All that could be done was to fan him with paper,

and frequently to give him lemonade, to alleviate
his intense thirst. He was in great pain, and expressed much anxiety for the event of the action,
which now began to declare itself. As often as a

HE FELL UPON HIS FACE

ship struck, the crew of the *Victory* hurrahed, and
at every hurrah a visible expression of joy gleamed
in the eyes, and marked the countenance of the
dying hero. But he became impatient to see Captain Hardy; and as that officer, though often sent

for, could not leave the deck, Nelson feared that some fatal cause prevented him, and repeatedly cried: "Will no one bring Hardy to me? He must be killed! He surely is dead!"

An hour and ten minutes elapsed, from the time when Nelson received his wound, before Hardy could come to him. They shook hands in silence: Hardy in vain struggling to suppress the feelings of that most painful, and yet sublimest moment.

"Well, Hardy," said Nelson, "how goes the day with us?"

"Very well," replied Hardy. "Ten ships have struck, but five of their van have tacked, and show an intention of bearing down upon the *Victory.* I have called two or three of our fresh ships round, and have no doubt of giving them a drubbing."

"I hope," said Nelson, "none of our ships struck."

Hardy answered, "There was no fear of that."

Then and not till then, Nelson spoke of himself. "I am a dead man, Hardy," he said; "I am going fast; it will be all over with me soon. Come nearer to me. My back is shot through. Beatty will tell you so."

Captain Hardy then once more shook hands with him; and, with a heart almost bursting, hastened upon deck. By this time all feeling below the breast was gone, and Nelson, having made the surgeon ascertain this, said: "You know I am gone. I know it. I feel something rising in my breast" —putting his hand to his left side—"which tells me so." And upon Beatty's inquiring whether his pain was very great, he replied, "So great that I wish I was dead. Yet," said he, in a lower voice, "one would like to live a little longer, too!"

Captain Hardy, some fifty minutes after he had left the cockpit, returned; and, again taking the hand of his dying friend and commander, congratulated him upon having gained a complete victory. How many of the enemy were taken he did not know, as it was impossible to perceive them distinctly—but fourteen or fifteen of them at least.

"That's well," cried Nelson; "but I bargained for twenty." And then, in a stronger voice, he said, "Anchor, Hardy; anchor."

Hardy upon this, hinted that Admiral Collingwood would take upon himself the direction of affairs.

"Not while I live, Hardy!" said the dying Nelson, ineffectually endeavouring to raise himself from the bed; "do you anchor."

His previous order for preparing to anchor had shown how clearly he foresaw the necessity of this. Presently, calling Hardy back, he said to him in a low voice, "Don't throw me overboard"; and he desired that he might be buried by his parents, unless it should please the king to order otherwise.

Then, reverting to his private feelings: "Kiss me, Hardy," said he. Hardy knelt down and kissed his cheek: and Nelson said, "Now I am satisfied. Thank God, I have done my duty."

Hardy stood over him in silence for a minute or two; then knelt again, and kissed his forehead.

"Who is that?" said Nelson; and being informed, he replied, "God bless you, Hardy." And Hardy then left him forever.

Nelson now desired to be turned on his right side, and said: "I wish I had not left the deck; for I shall soon be gone."

Death was, indeed, rapidly approaching. He said to his chaplain: "Doctor, I have not been a great sinner." His articulation now became difficult; but he was distinctly heard to say, "Thank God, I have done my duty!" These words he had repeatedly pronounced; and they were the last words he uttered. He expired at thirty minutes after four,— three hours and a quarter after he had received his wound.

Within a quarter of an hour after Nelson was wounded, above fifty of the *Victory's* men fell by the enemy's musketry. They, however, on their part, were not idle; and it was not long before there were only two Frenchmen left alive in the mizzen-top of the *Redoubtable*. One of them was the man who had given the fatal wound: he did not live to boast of what he had done. An old quartermaster had seen him fire; and easily recognized him, because he wore a glazed cocked hat and a white frock. This quartermaster, and two midshipmen, Mr. Collingwood and Mr. Pollard, were the only persons left on the *Victory's* poop; the two midshipmen kept firing at the top, and he supplied them with cartridges. One of the Frenchmen, attempting to make his escape down the rigging, was shot by Mr. Pollard, and fell on the poop. But the old quartermaster, as he cried out, "That's he, that's he," and pointed at the other, who was coming forward to fire again, received a shot in his mouth, and fell dead. Both the midshipmen then fired, at the same time, and the fellow dropped in the top. When they took possession of the prize, they went into the mizzen-top, and found him dead; with one ball through his head, and another through his breast.

The *Redoubtable* struck within twenty minutes after the fatal shot had been fired from her. During that time she had been twice on fire,—in her fore-chains and in her forecastle. The French, as they had done in other battles, made use, in this, of fireballs and other combustibles—implements of destruction which other nations, from a sense of

AN OLD QUARTERMASTER HAD SEEN HIM FIRE

honour and humanity, have laid aside—which add to the sufferings of the wounded, without determining the issue of the combat—which none but the cruel would employ, and which never can be successful against the brave.

Once they succeeded in setting fire, from the *Redoubtable,* to some ropes and canvas on the *Victory's* booms. The cry ran through the ship, and reached the cockpit; but even this dreadful

cry produced no confusion: the men displayed that
perfect self-possession in danger by which English
seamen are characterized; they extinguished the
flames on board their own ship, and then hastened
to extinguish them in the enemy, by throwing
buckets of water from the gangway. When the
Redoubtable had struck, it was not practicable to
board her from the *Victory;* for, though the two
ships touched, the upper works of both fell in so
much, that there was a great space between their
gangways; and she could not be boarded from the
lower or middle decks, because her ports were
down. Some of our men went to Lieutenant Quil-
liam, and offered to swim under her bows and get
up there; but it was thought unfit to hazard brave
lives in this manner.

What our men would have done from gallantry, some of the crew of the *Santissima Trinidad*
did to save themselves. Unable to stand the tremendous fire of the *Victory,* whose larboard guns
played against this great four-decker, and not
knowing how else to escape them, nor where else
to betake themselves for protection, many of them
leapt overboard, and swam to the *Victory;* and were
actually helped up her sides by the English during
the action.

The Spaniards began the battle with less vivac-
ity than their unworthy allies, but they continued
it with greater firmness. The *Argonauta* and *Ba-
hama* were defended till they had each lost about
four hundred men; the *San Juan Nepomuceno*
lost three hundred and fifty. Often as the superiority of British courage has been proved against
France upon the sea, it was never more conspicuous

than in this decisive conflict. Five of our ships were engaged muzzle to muzzle with five of the French. In all five Frenchmen lowered their lower-deck ports, and deserted their guns; while our men continued deliberately to load and fire, till they had made the victory secure.

Once, amid his sufferings, Nelson had expressed a wish that he were dead; but immediately the spirit subdued the pains of death, and he wished to live a little longer; doubtless that he might hear the completion of the victory which he had seen so gloriously begun. That consolation—that joy—that triumph was afforded him. He lived to know that the victory was decisive; and the last guns which were fired at the flying enemy were heard a minute or two before he expired.

The total British loss in the battle of Trafalgar amounted to 1,587. Twenty of the enemy struck, —unhappily the fleet did not anchor, as Nelson, almost with his dying breath, had enjoined,—a gale came on from the southwest; some of the prizes went down, some went on shore; one effected its escape into Cadiz; others were destroyed; four only were saved, and those by the greatest exertions. The wounded Spaniards were sent ashore, an assurance being given that they should not serve till regularly exchanged; and the Spaniards, with a generous feeling, which would not, perhaps, have been found in any other people, offered the use of their hospitals for our wounded, pledging the honour of Spain that they should be carefully attended there. When the storm after the action drove some of the prizes upon the coast, they declared that the English, who were thus thrown into their hands,

should not be considered as prisoners of war; and
the Spanish soldiers gave up their own beds to their
shipwrecked enemies.

It is almost superfluous to add that all the honors
which a grateful country could bestow were heaped
upon the memory of Nelson. A public funeral
was decreed, and a public monument. Statues and
monuments also were voted by most of our principal cities. The leaden coffin, in which he was
brought home, was cut in pieces, which were distributed as relics of Saint Nelson,—so the gunner
of the *Victory* called them,—and when, at his in-
terment, his flag was about to be lowered into the
grave, the sailors who had assisted at the ceremony,
with one accord rent it in pieces, that each might
preserve a fragment while he lived.

The death of Nelson was felt in England as
something more than a public calamity: men started
at the intelligence, and turned pale, as if they had
heard of the loss of a dear friend. An object of
our admiration and affection, of our pride and of
our hopes, was suddenly taken from us; and it
seemed as if we had never, till then, known how
deeply we loved and reverenced him. What the
country had lost in its great naval hero—the greatest of our own, and of all former times—was
scarcely taken into the account of grief. So perfectly, indeed, had he performed his part, that the
maritime war, after the Battle of Trafalgar, was
considered at an end; the fleets of the enemy were
not merely defeated, but destroyed; new navies
must be built, and a new race of seamen reared for
them, before the possibility of their invading our
shores could again be contemplated.

CASABIANCA

By FELICIA HEMANS

NOTE.—Young Casabianca, a boy about thirteen years old, son of the Admiral of the *Orient*, remained at his post (in the Battle of the Nile) after the ship had taken fire and all the guns had been abandoned, and perished in the explosion of the vessel, when the flames had reached the powder.

THE boy stood on the burning deck,
Whence all but him had fled;
The flame that lit the battle's wreck
Shone round him o'er the dead.

Yet beautiful and bright he stood,
As born to rule the storm;
A creature of heroic blood,
A proud though childlike form.

The flames rolled on; he would not go
Without his father's word;
That father, faint in death below,
His voice no longer heard.

He called aloud, "Say, father, say,
If yet my task be done?"
He knew not that the chieftain lay
Unconscious of his son.

"Speak, father!" once again he cried,
"If I may yet be gone!"
And but the booming shots replied,
And fast the flames rolled on.

Upon his brow he felt their breath,
   And in his waving hair,
And looked from that lone post of death
   In still yet brave despair;

And shouted but once more aloud,
   "My father! must I stay?"
While o'er him fast, through sail and **shroud**
   The wreathing fires made way.

They wrapt the ship in splendor wild,
   They caught the flag on high,
And streamed above the gallant child,
   Like banners in the sky.

There came a burst of thunder sound;
   The boy,—Oh! where was *he?*
Ask of the winds, that far around
   With fragments strewed the sea,—

With shroud and mast and pennon fair,
   That well had borne their part,—
But the noblest thing that perished there
   Was that young, faithful heart.

THE ROMANCE OF THE SWAN'S NEST

By ELIZABETH BARRETT BROWNING

LITTLE Ellie sits alone
　'Mid the beeches of a meadow,
　　By a stream-side on the grass,
And the trees are showering down
　Doubles of their leaves in shadow,
　　On her shining hair and face.

She has thrown her bonnet by,
　And her feet she has been dipping
　　In the shallow water's flow;
Now she holds them nakedly
　In her hands, all sleek and dripping,
　　While she rocketh to and fro.

Little Ellie sits alone,
　And the smile she softly uses
　　Fills the silence like a speech,
While she thinks what shall be done,
　And the sweetest pleasure chooses
　　For her future within reach.

Little Ellie in her smile
　Chooses, "I will have a lover,
　　Riding on a steed of steeds:
He shall love me without guile,
　And to *him* I will discover
　　The swan's nest among the reeds.

"And the steed shall be red roan,
　And the lover shall be noble,

With an eye that takes the breath.
And the lute[1] he plays upon
  Shall strike ladies into trouble,
    As his sword strikes men to death.

"And the steed it shall be shod
  All in silver, housed in azure;[2]
    And the mane shall swim the wind;
And the hoofs along the sod
  Shall flash onward, and keep measure,
    Till the shepherds look behind.

"But my lover will not prize
  All the glory that he rides in,
    When he gazes in my face.
He will say, 'O Love, thine eyes
  Build the shrine my soul abides in,
    And I kneel here for thy grace!'

"Then, aye, then shall he kneel low,
  With the red-roan steed anear him,
    Which shall seem to understand,
Till I answer, 'Rise and go!
  For the world must love and fear him
    Whom I gift with heart and hand.'

"Then he will arise so pale,
  I shall feel my own lips tremble
    With a *yes* I must not say:

1. It would seem strange to us now if a soldier rode about playing upon a lute; but in the old days of chivalry about which little Ellie had been reading, it was looked upon as almost necessary for a knight to be able to play and sing sweet songs to his lady.

2. The saddle-cloth or housing of the medieval knights was sometimes very large and gorgeous.

LITTLE ELLIE SITS ALONE

Nathless[3] maiden-brave, 'Farewell,'
  I will utter, and dissemble—
    'Light to-morrow with to-day!'

"Then he'll ride among the hills
  To the wide world past the river,
    There to put away all wrong,
To make straight distorted wills,
  And to empty the broad quiver
    Which the wicked bear along.

"Three times shall a young foot page
  Swim the stream, and climb the mountain,
    And kneel down beside my feet:
'Lo! my master sends this gage,[4]
  Lady, for thy pity's counting.
    What wilt thou exchange for it?'

"And the first time I will send
  A white rosebud for a guerdon—[5]
    And the second time, a glove;
But the third time—I may bend
  From my pride, and answer—'Pardon,
    If he comes to take my love.'

"Then the young foot page will run—
  Then my lover will ride faster,
    Till he kneeleth at my knee:
'I am a duke's eldest son!
  Thousand serfs do call me master,—
    But, O Love, I love but *thee!*'" . . .

3. *Nathless* is an old word meaning *nevertheless*. Mrs. Browning
uses an occasional old word, in order to give the atmosphere of the
tales of chivalry.

4. The *gage* was a cap or glove, or some other symbol to show that
he had performed the deeds which Ellie had demanded of him.

5. *Guerdon* means *reward*.

Little Ellie, with her smile
  Not yet ended, rose up gayly,
    Tied the bonnet, donned the shoe,
And went homeward, round a mile,
  Just to see, as she did daily,
    What more eggs were with the two.

Pushing through the elm-tree copse,
  Winding up the stream, light-hearted,
    Where the osier pathway leads,
Past the boughs she stoops, and stops.
  Lo! the wild swan had deserted,
    And a rat had gnawed the reeds!

Ellie went home sad and slow.
  If she found the lover ever,
    With his red-roan steed of steeds,
Sooth I know not; but I know
  She could never show him—never,
    That swan's nest among the reeds.

Mrs. Browning tells us very little of Ellie directly, yet she leaves us with a charming picture of an innocent, imaginative, romantic child. Ellie has been reading or listening to tales of knight-errantry, and her mind is full of them, so that the "sweetest pleasure . . . for her future" is a lover riding straight out of one of the romances. That she is only a child, with a child's ideas, we may see from the fact that she can think, in her simplicity, of no greater reward for her noble lover than a sight of the swan's nest among the reeds, of which she alone knows.

Mrs. Browning's purpose in writing this little story in verse was to show us how suddenly and how rudely unpleasant facts can break in upon our dreams. Ellie could never show her lover the swan's nest, as she had planned; and we are left with the feeling that she never found the lover of whom she dreamed—that all of her dream proved as false as the beautiful thought about the swan's nest.

THE COTTER'S SATURDAY NIGHT

By ROBERT BURNS

NOTE.—There are many homes we like to visit in imagination, even if we cannot really go into them. It does not matter so much if they are not the homes of people in our own country who live as we do. For instance, Robert Burns described so well for us once the simple little home of a poor Scotch farmer that we read his words again and again with pleasure. It is such a poor little place, low-walled, thatched-roofed, part stable, that it would be unpleasant to us if we did not see it full of the spirit that makes true homes everywhere. The hard-working old farmer, his faithful wife, their industrious children, the oldest girl Jenny and her lover, all seem to us like very real people, whose joys and griefs are ours as much as theirs. We should like to sit with them at their humble table, to join in the good old hymns, and finally to kneel among them while the gentle old man said the evening prayer. We would not notice their homely clothes, coarse hands and simple, unscholarly language, for their real manliness and womanliness would win our esteem and love.

On the pages that follow we have printed the poem as Burns wrote it, except for some few stanzas it has seemed best to omit. The first nine stanzas contain many Scottish words and expressions, but after the ninth stanza, Burns uses plain English. It was a habit he had of writing sometimes in Scotch dialect and sometimes in fine English. People who have studied his work say that when he speaks right from his heart and because he really cannot help writing, he uses the dialect, but when he tries to teach a lesson, to advise any one, or to moralize, he always uses the English phraseology.

I

NOVEMBER chill blaws loud wi' angry sugh;[1]
　　The short'ning winter day is near a close;
The miry beasts retreating frae[2] the pleugh;[3]
　　The black'ning trains o' craws to their re-
　　　pose:
The toil-worn cotter frae his labor goes,
　　This night his weekly moil[4] is at an end,
Collects his spades, his mattocks,[5] and his hoes,
　　Hoping the morn in ease and rest to spend,
And weary, o'er the moor, his course does hame-
　　ward bend.

II

At length his lonely cot appears in view,
　　Beneath the shelter of an agèd tree:
Th' expectant wee-things, toddlin' stacher[6] thro'
　　To meet their dad, wi' flichterin'[7] noise an'
　　　glee.
His wee bit ingle, blinkin' bonnily,
　　His clean hearth-stane, his thriftie wifie's
　　　smile,
The lisping infant prattling on his knee,
　　Does a' his weary carking[8] cares beguile,
An' makes him quite forget his labour and his toil.

1. *Sugh* means a hollow, roaring sound. It is our word *sough*.
2. *Frae* is the Scotch word meaning from.
3. *Pleugh* means *plow*.
4. *Moil* is a Scotch word meaning *drudgery*.
5. A mattock is a two-bladed instrument for digging.
6. *Stacher* is the Scotch form of *stagger*.
7. *Flichtering* means *fluttering*.
8. *Carking* is *trying*.

III

Belyve,[9] the elder bairns come drappin' in,
  At service out, amang the farmers roun';
Some ca'[10] the pleugh, some herd, some tentie[11]
  rin
A cannie[12] errand to a neebor town:

TH' EXPECTANT WEE-THINGS

Their eldest hope, their Jenny, woman grown,
  In youthfu' bloom, love sparklin in her e'e,
Comes hame, perhaps, to show a braw[13] new
  gown,

9. *Belyve* means *soon.*
10. *Ca'* means *drive.*
11. *Tentie* means *carefully.*
12. *Cannie* means here *prudent*, or *trusty.*
13. *Braw* is *fine, gay.*

Or deposit her sair-won[14] penny fee,
To help her parents dear, if they in hardship be.

IV

Wi' joy unfeign'd, brothers and sisters meet,
    And each for other's weelfare kindly spiers:[15]
The social hours, swift-wing'd, unnoticed fleet:
    Each tells the uncos[16] that he sees or hears;
The parents, partial, eye their hopeful years;
    Anticipation forward points the view;
The mother, wi' her needle an' her shears,
    Gars auld claes look amaist as weel's the new;[17]
The father mixes a' wi' admonition due.

V

Their master's an' their mistress's command,
    The younkers[18] a' are warned to obey:
"An' mind their labours wi' an eydent[19] hand,
    An' ne'er, tho' out o' sight, to jauk[20] or play:
An' O! be sure to fear the Lord alway!
    An' mind your duty, duly, morn an' night!
Lest in temptation's path ye gang astray,
    Implore his counsel and assisting might:
They never sought in vain, that sought the Lord
        aright!"

VI

But hark! a rap comes gently to the door;
    Jenny, wha kens the meaning o' the same,

14. *Sair-won* is *hard-earned.*
15. *Spiers* means enquires.
16. The *uncos* is the *news.*
17. This line means *Makes old clothes look almost as well as new ones.*
18. The *younkers* are the *youngsters.*
19. *Eydent* is *diligent.*
20. To *jauk* is to *trifle.*

Tells how a neebor lad cam' o'er the moor,
To do some errands and convoy her hame.[21]
The wily mother sees the conscious flame
    Sparkle in Jenny's e'e,[22] and flush her cheek;
With heart-struck, anxious care, inquires his
        name,
    While Jenny hafflins[23] is afraid to speak;
Weel pleas'd the mother hears, it's nae[24] wild,
    worthless rake.

VII

Wi' kindly welcome, Jenny brings him ben:[25]
    A strappin' youth; he takes the mother's eye;
Blythe Jenny sees the visit's no ill ta'en;[26]
    The father cracks[27] of horses, pleughs, and
        kye.[28]
The youngster's artless heart o'erflows wi' joy,
    But blate[29] and laithfu',[30] scarce can weel be-
        have;
The mother, wi' a woman's wiles, can spy
    What makes the youth sae[31] bashfu' an' sae
        grave;
Weel pleas'd to think her bairn's respected like
    the lave.[32]

21. *Hame* is the Scotch form of our word *home*.
22. *E'e* is a contraction for *eye*.
23. *Hafflins* means *partly*.
24. *Nae* means *no*.
25. *Ben* means *into the room*.
26. That is, *the visit is not unwelcome*.
27. *Cracks* is a Scotch word meaning *chats*.
28. *Kye* are *cattle*.
29. *Blate* means *modest*.
30. *Laithfu'* is *bashful*.
31. *Sae* is the Scotch form of *so*.
32. *The lave* is *the others;* that is, the neighbors' girls.

VIII

But now the supper crowns their simple board,
   The halesome parritch,[33] chief o' Scotia's
      food:
The sowpe[34] their only Hawkie[35] does afford,
   That 'yont the hallan[36] snugly chows her
      cood;[37]
The dame brings forth in complimental mood
   To grace the lad, her weel-hain'd[38] kebbuck[39]
      fell—
An' aft he's prest, an' aft he ca's it guid;[40]
The frugal wifie, garrulous, will tell,
How 'twas a towmond[41] auld, sin' lint was i' the
      bell;[42]

IX

The cheerfu' supper done, wi' serious face,
   They, round the ingle, form a circle wide;
The sire turns o'er, wi' patriarchal grace,
   The big ha'-Bible,[43] ance[44] his father's pride;
His bonnet[45] rev'rently is laid aside,
   His lyart[46] haffets[47] wearing thin an' bare;

33. The *halesome parritch* is the *wholesome porridge* of oatmeal.
34. *Sowpe* here means a little quantity of milk.
35. *Hawkie* is a *white-faced cow.*
36. That is, *beyond the partition.*
37. *Chows her cood* means *chews her cud.*
38. *Weel-hain'd* means *carefully preserved.*
39. *Kebbuck* is *cheese.*
40. This line, in English, would read *And often he is urged* (to take more*) and often he calls it good.*
41. A *towmond* is a *twelvemonth,* a *year.*
42. *Since flax was in blossom.*
43. The *ha'-Bible* is the family Bible, which is kept in the *hall,* or the best room.
44. *Ance* is the Scotch form of *once.*
45. That is, his hat.
46. *Lyart* means *gray.*
47. *Haffets* means *temples.*

Those strains that once did sweet in Zion glide,
He wales[48] a portion with judicious care;
And "Let us worship God!" he says, with solemn
   air.

ROUND THE INGLE

X

They chant their artless notes in simple guise;
   They tune their hearts, by far the noblest aim:

48. *Wales* means *chooses.*

Perhaps Dundee's wild warbling measures rise
  Or plaintive Martyrs, worthy of the name,
Or noble Elgin beats the heav'nward flame,
  The sweetest far of Scotia's holy lays.
Compared with these, Italian trills are tame;
  The tickl'd ears no heart-felt raptures raise;
Nae unison hae they with our Creator's praise.

XI

The priest-like father reads the sacred page,
  How Abram was the friend of God on high;
Or, Moses bade eternal warfare wage
  With Amalek's ungracious progeny;
Or how the royal bard did groaning lie
  Beneath the stroke of Heav'n's avenging ire;
Or Job's pathetic plaint, and wailing cry;
  Or rapt Isaiah's wild, seraphic fire;
Or other holy seers that tune the sacred lyre.

XII

Perhaps the Christian volume is the theme,
  How guiltless blood for guilty man was shed;
How He, who bore in heaven the second name,
  Had not on earth whereon to lay his head;
How his first followers and servants sped;
  The precepts sage they wrote to many a land:
How *he,* who lone in Patmos banished,
  Saw in the sun a mighty angel stand,
And heard great Bab'lon's doom pronounc'd by
      Heaven's command.

XIII

Then kneeling down, to Heaven's Eternal King,
  The saint, the father, and the husband prays.

Hope "springs exultant on triumphant wing:"
  That thus they all shall meet in future days
There ever bask in uncreated rays,
  No more to sigh, or shed the bitter tear,
Together hymning their Creator's praise,
  In such society, yet still more dear;
While circling time moves round in an eternal
    sphere.

XIV

Compar'd with this, how poor Religion's pride,
  In all the pomp of method and of art,
When men display to congregations wide,
  Devotion's ev'ry grace, except the heart!
The Pow'r, incensed, the pageant will desert,
  The pompous strain, the sacerdotal stole;
But, haply, in some cottage far apart,
  May hear, well pleased, the language of the soul;
And in the book of life the inmates poor enroll.

XV

Then homeward all take off their sev'ral way;
  The youngling cottagers retire to rest:
The parent-pair their secret homage pay,
  And proffer up to Heaven the warm request,
That He, who stills the raven's clam'rous nest,
  And decks the lily fair in flow'ry pride,
Would, in the way his wisdom sees the best,
  For them and for their little ones provide;
But, chiefly, in their hearts with grace divine pre-
    side.

CHARLES AND MARY LAMB

 NE of the most tragic, and at the same time one of the most heroic, of true stories is that of Charles and Mary Lamb, the brother and sister who are known to millions of young people as the writers of *Tales from Shakespeare*.

Charles Lamb was rather a short man, with a spare body and legs so small and thin that Thomas Hood once spoke of them as "immaterial legs." His head, however, was large, and his brow fine; his nose, large and hooked, was in a face which early showed lines of care and trouble; his eyes were large and expressive, twinkling with humor but full of piercing inquiry, and searching with keen interest everything about him; his mouth was large and firm, but around it there flitted a smile that showed the genial, humorous soul of the big-hearted boy.

Lamb's habits were peculiar, there is no denying that, and his habits of dress made him even more noticeable. Almost always he wore a black coat, knickerbockers and black gaiters. The old-fashioned cut of his clothes and their worn appearance showed the narrowness of his means, which, however, never caused him to neglect either clothing or person, for he was remarkably neat in his ways.

Although a poor boy, he was educated in the

CHARLES LAMB
1775–1834

famous old Christ's Hospital School in London, but when he was ready for college he found himself barred by his stammering, stuttering tongue. Giving up his hope of further schooling, he was glad to take a small clerkship in a government office, where he remained for thirty-three years, a long period with little or no advancement.

It was in 1792, when Charles was about seventeen years of age, that he was given his clerkship, and for nearly four years he lived happily, supporting his parents and his sister in their humble home. Mary was eleven years older than Charles, a quiet gentle creature whom everybody loved, though in some respects she was peculiar. There were things, too, that troubled the family and made them reserved and inclined to be oversensitive. Not only were they very poor, but there had been insanity on the mother's side, and Charles, himself, had at one time been in brief confinement for irrational actions. Mary, too, had occasionally shown signs of madness, but no one anticipated the dreadful event which took place in 1796.

It came upon them like a stroke of lightning out of a clear sky. All were gathered together for their noon meal when Mary leaped to her feet and ran wildly about the room, shrieking in the terrifying tones of the insane. She caught the forks and spoons from the table, threw them about the room, and then, seizing a case knife, plunged it into the heart of her mother. Although one of the flying forks had struck her aged father in the head and wounded him severely, Mary sprang upon him and would certainly have killed the feeble old man then and there had not Charles caught her and in a terrible struggle overpowered her and wrested the knife from her grasp. Friends and neighbors came in, and the poor woman was taken to an asylum, where in a short time she recovered her reason and learned of the awful consequences of her madness. In those days hospitals for the insane were much more poorly managed than they are at present, and Charles could not be contented to think of his sister confined within their walls. Accordingly he went to the authorities, and after much persuasion they released her, under the condition that she should be constantly under care.

Then began the long career of brotherly devotion which can scarcely be matched, and which never fails to excite our sympathy and admiration. We may well think it a terrible penance, for Mary's attacks recurred again and again, and more than once Charles had to take her back to the hospital for a brief time while her violence remained too great for him to control. There were long lucid intervals, however, and after a while both learned to recognize the symptoms which preceded an attack, and the two would wend their way to the asylum, where she could take refuge. They carried a straight-jacket with them for use in case she should suddenly become violent, for never could either escape from the nightmare of that first awful catastrophe.

For forty years this companionship, this sublime devotion continued, even to the time of Charles Lamb's death in 1834. Both made many friends, and when the brother was laid away these friends came forward and took up the burden of Mary's care until she, too, died, nearly thirteen years later.

The last years of Lamb's life were full of further trouble, that, combined with his crushing anxiety for Mary, broke his genial spirit and left him sad and melancholy.

One of the greatest blows he suffered in his later life was the death of his life-long friend, Samuel Taylor Coleridge. See how fondly he wrote of this friend:

"Since I feel how great a part he was of me his great and dear spirit haunts me. I cannot think a thought, I cannot make a criticism on men or books without an ineffectual turning and reference to him. . . . He was my fifty-years-old friend without a dissension. I seem to love the house he died at more passionately than when he lived. . . . What was his mansion is consecrated to me a chapel."

It is said that when his sister was first stricken Lamb was engaged to be married to Ann Simmons, a sweet woman, whom he loved passionately. So awful was the blow and so heavy the responsibility he assumed that the match was broken off, and the gentle man resigned his hope of home and family. We shall see, however, that he never quite forgot his love.

Sad as their life certainly was, there were many pleasant days for both brother and sister. Between her spells of violence Mary was a charming companion, a helpful adviser and a writer of great ability, as loyal to her brother as he was to her. When Lamb was engaged to write the *Tales from Shakespeare,* she took up the pen with him and wrote the stories of the great poet's comedies while Charles wrote the tragedies.

How strong his affection and respect for her really were we may see from his own words: "I am a fool bereft of her co-operation. I am used to look up at her in the worst and biggest perplexities. To say all that I find her would be more than I think anybody could possibly understand. She is older, wiser, and better than I am, and all my wretched imperfections I cover to myself by resolutely thinking on her goodness. She would share life and death with me."

A more lovable character than Lamb's is hard to find. Full of fun he was when with his friends, punning, quibbling and joking in quaint and original ways that made him welcome wherever he went. "The best acid is assiduity" was one of his favorite puns, and "*No* work is worse than *over-work*" is one of his wise and witty remarks.

The stuttering which in some persons might have seemed an annoyance only served to add a certain spiciness to his good-natured quips. It is said that a certain gushing lady once went into a long description of her children and her own passionate love for them. Suddenly interrupting herself she said to Lamb, "And how do you like babies, Mr. Lamb?" With a sober face, but unable to conceal the humorous twinkle in his sharp eyes, Charles replied, "Bub-bub-boiled, Madam!"

Lamb's friendship for Coleridge was fully returned, as we may see from many things the latter wrote. At one time he said: "Lamb's character is a sacred one with me. No associations that he may form can hurt the purity of his mind. . . . . Nothing ever left a stain on that gentle creature's mind."

In 1825 Lamb's health became so poor that he was compelled to give up his clerkship, and thereafter he lived most of his time at Edmonton. The British government gave him an annual pension of £441, which sufficed for the simple wants of himself and his sister.

The immediate cause of his death was a slight accident that befell him a few months after the burial of Coleridge. Unconsciousness came before he had been long ill and before any of his intimate friends could reach him, yet it was their names that were last on his lips. They buried him in the churchyard at Edmonton, as he wished, where on his tombstone may be read:

"Farewell, dear friend?—that smile, that harmless mirth,
No more shall gladden our domestic hearth;
That rising tear, with pain forbid to flow—
Better than words—no more assuage our woe.
That hand outstretch'd from small but well-earned store
Yield succor to the destitute no more.
Yet art thou not all lost. Through many an age,
With sterling sense and humour, shall thy page
Win many an English bosom, pleased to see
That old and happier vein revived in thee.
This for our earth; and if with friends we share
Our joys in heaven we hope to meet thee there."

Besides the *Tales from Shakespeare,* Charles Lamb wrote many beautiful sketches which are known as the *Essays of Elia. Elia* was the name of one of the clerks in the South Sea House, where Lamb worked at one time.

A reader can easily form some idea of a writer's character from his work, but Lamb was always so wholly himself, and he threw himself so freely into his essays, that you can tell just what manner of

man he was as you read. A large part of the
pleasure of reading him comes from this trait. We
seem to be sitting with a charming friend whenever
we hold one of his books, and to feel that the friend
is pouring out his whole heart for our delight and
inspiration. Naturally a person must keep alert
when he is reading from Charles Lamb, for no
one can predict what course the brilliant mind will
take. When once a reader has learned to understand his oddities, delicate sentiment, bright wit and
loving faithfulness, every word becomes a living
thing, and every reading a new delight, a higher
inspiration. In none of his essays is he seen to
greater advantage than in *Dream Children,* which
follows this brief sketch. The only people young
or old who do not love this beautiful essay are those
who have not read it or who have read it without
really understanding it. You may need to read it
once just to see what it is about; again with the aid
of the notes and comments we make upon it; a third
time to let it cast its spell upon you. If you do
that you will not forget it, but will return to it
often as years go on and the hard world buffets
you with those stern experiences which make you
men and women. Every time you read it you will
find new graces, more touching sentiment.

Will you read it now for the first time, paying
only so much attention to the footnotes as may be
necessary for you to understand the language?

DREAM CHILDREN: A REVERY

By Charles Lamb

CHILDREN love to listen to stories about their elders when *they* were children; to stretch their imagination to the conception of a traditionary great-uncle, or grandame, whom they never saw.

It was in this spirit that my little ones crept about me the other evening to hear about their great-grandmother Field,[1] who lived in a great house in Norfolk (a hundred times bigger than that in which they and papa lived) which had been the scene—so at least it was generally believed in that part of the country—of the tragic incidents which they had lately become familiar with from the ballad of the Children in the Wood.[2]

Certain it is that the whole story of the children and their cruel uncle was to be seen fairly carved out in wood upon the chimney-piece of the great hall,[3] the whole story down to the Robin Redbreast; till a foolish person pulled it down to set up a marble one of modern invention in its stead, with no story upon it.

1. Lamb's grandmother, Mary Field, was for a long time house-keeper in one of the great English country houses, but not in the county alluded to in the text.

2. This means that the incidents had but lately become familiar to the children. The story is the old one of the *Babes in the Wood*, as it is sometimes called.

3. One of Lamb's fancies; the chimney-carving in the real house represented stag and boar hunts.

Here Alice put out one of her dear mother's looks, too tender to be called upbraiding.

Then I went on to say, how religious and how good their great-grandmother Field was, how beloved and respected by everybody, though she was not indeed the mistress of this great house, but had only the charge of it (and yet in some respects she might be said to be the mistress of it too) committed to her by the owner, who preferred living in a newer and more fashionable mansion which he had purchased somewhere in the adjoining county; but still she lived in it in a manner as if it had been her own, and kept up the dignity of the great house in a sort while she lived. Afterwards it came to decay, and was nearly pulled down, and all its old ornaments stripped and carried away to the owner's other house, where they were set up, and looked as awkward as if some one were to carry away the old tombs they had lately seen at the Abbey,[4] and stick them up in Lady C.'s[5] tawdry gilt drawing-room. Here John smiled, as much as to say, "that would be foolish indeed."

And then I told how, when she came to die, her funeral was attended by a concourse of all the poor, and some of the gentry, too, of the neighborhood for many miles around, to show their respect for her memory, because she had been such a good and religious woman; so good indeed that she knew all the Psaltery[7] by heart, ay, and a great part of the Testament[8] besides.

4. Westminster Abbey.
5. An imaginary person with a cheap, showy drawing-room.
7. The Book of Psalms, or such a portion of it as is used in the services of the English Church.
8. New Testament.

Here little Alice spread her hands.

Then I told what a tall, upright, gracious person their great-grandmother Field once was; and how in her youth she was esteemed the best dancer, —here Alice's little right foot played an involuntary movement, till, upon my looking grave, it desisted,—the best dancer, I was saying, in the country, till a cruel disease, called a cancer, came, and bowed her down with pain, but it could never bend her good spirits, or make them stoop, but they were still upright, because she was so good and religious.

Then I told how she used to sleep by herself in a lone chamber of the great lone house; and how she believed that an apparition of two infants was to be seen at midnight gliding up and down the great staircase near where she slept, but she said "those innocents would do her no harm;" and how frightened I used to be, though in those days I had my maid to sleep with me, because I was never half so good or religious as she,—and yet I never saw the infants.

Here John expanded all his eyebrows and tried to look courageous.

Then I told how good she was to all her grandchildren, having us to the great house in the holidays, where I in particular used to spend many hours by myself, in gazing upon the old busts of the twelve Caesars, that had been Emperors of Rome, till the old marble heads would seem to live again, or I to be turned into marble with them; how I never could be tired with roaming about that huge mansion, with its vast empty rooms, with their worn-out hangings, fluttering tapestry, and carved

oaken panels, with the gilding almost rubbed out,—
sometimes in the spacious old-fashioned gardens,
which I had almost to myself, unless when now and
then a solitary gardening man would cross me,—
and how the nectarines and peaches hung upon the
walls,[9] without my ever offering to pluck them,
because they were forbidden fruit, unless now and
then,—and because I had more pleasure in strolling
about among the old melancholy-looking yew-
trees,[10] or the firs, and picking up the red berries,
and the fir apples, which were good for nothing but
to look at,—or in lying about upon the fresh grass
with all the fine garden smells around me,—or
basking in the orangery,[11] till I could almost fancy
myself ripening too along with the oranges and the
limes in that grateful warmth,—or in watching the
dace[12] that darted to and fro in the fish-pond, at
the bottom of the garden, with here and there a
great sulky pike hanging midway down the water
in silent state, as if it mocked at their impertinent
friskings,—I had more pleasure in these busy-idle
diversions than in all the sweet flavors of peaches,
nectarines, oranges, and such-like common baits of
children.

Here John slyly deposited back upon the plate a
bunch of grapes, which, not unobserved by Alice

9. The trees were planted on the south side of the walls, which
protected them from the north wind and ripened them by reflected
warmth.

10. The foliage of the yews is very dark, and because these trees
are so often planted about cemeteries they give a hint of sadness to
every one.

11. The glass house which protected the trees in the winter and
hastened the ripening of the fruit in summer.

12. A small fish resembling our chub—usually seen in schools in
still waters.

ROAMING ABOUT THAT HUGE MANSION

he had meditated dividing with her, and both
seemed willing to relinquish them for the present
as irrelevant.

Then, in somewhat a more heightened tone, I
told how, though their great-grandmother Field
loved all her grandchildren, yet in an especial manner she might be said to love their uncle, John
L——,[13] because he was so handsome and spirited
a youth, and a king to the rest of us; and, instead
of moping about in solitary corners, like some of
us, he would mount the most mettlesome horse he
could get, when but an imp no bigger than themselves, and make it carry him half over the county
in a morning, and join the hunters when there were
any out,—and yet he loved the old great house
and gardens too, but had too much spirit to be
always pent up within their boundaries;—and how
their uncle grew up to man's estate as brave as he
was handsome, to the admiration of everybody,
but of their great-grandmother Field most especially; and how he used to carry me upon his
back when I was a lame-footed[14] boy—for he was
a good bit older than I—many a mile when I could
not walk for pain; and how in after life he became
lame-footed too, and I did not always (I fear)
make allowances enough for him when he was impatient and in pain, nor remember sufficiently how
considerate he had been to me when I was lame-
footed;—and how when he died,[15] though he had
not been dead an hour, it seemed as if he had died
a great while ago, such a distance there is betwixt

13. Lamb's brother John—twelve years his senior. John was
rather a lazy, selfish fellow—at least he never gave up his own
pleasures and comforts to assist his family, even in their greatest
need.

life and death; and how I bore his death as I
thought pretty well at first, but afterwards it
haunted and haunted me; and though I did not
cry or take it to heart as some do, and as I think
he would have done if I had died, yet I missed
him all day long, and knew not till then how much

HE WOULD MOUNT A METTLESOME HORSE

I had loved him. I missed his kindness, and I
missed his crossness, and wished him to be alive
again, to be quarreling with him (for we quarreled
sometimes), rather than not to have him again,
and was as uneasy without him, as he their poor
uncle must have been when the doctor took off his
limb.

14. This probably alludes to some temporary affliction, for Charles
Lamb was not lame.
15. John Lamb died just before this essay was written.

Here the children fell a-crying, and asked if their little mourning which they had on was not for Uncle John, and they looked up, and prayed me not to go on about their uncle, but to tell them some stories about their pretty dead mother.

Then I told how, for seven long years, in hope sometimes, sometimes in despair, yet persisting ever, I courted the fair Alice W———n;[16] and, as much as children could understand, I explained to them what coyness, and difficulty, and denial meant in maidens.

When suddenly turning to Alice, the soul of the first Alice looked out at her eyes with such a reality of representment, that I became in doubt which of them stood before me, or whose that bright hair was; and while I stood gazing, both the children gradually grew fainter to my view, receding, and still receding, till nothing at last but two mournful features were seen in the uttermost distance, which, without speech, strangely impressed upon me the effects of speech:

"We are not of Alice, nor of thee, nor are we children at all. The children of Alice call Bartram father. We are nothing; less than nothing, and dreams. We are only what might have been, and must wait upon the tedious shores of Lethe[17] millions of ages before we have existence, and a name."

And immediately awaking, I found myself quietly seated in my bachelor armchair, where I had fallen asleep, with the faithful Bridget[18] unchanged

16. It is not known positively whether Alice Warren was a real or an imaginary character.

17. *Lethe* was among the ancient Greeks the name given to the river of oblivion, of whose waters spirits drank to gain forgetfulness.

18. Bridget Elia is his sister, Mary Lamb.

by my side,—but John L. (or James Elia) was
gone forever.

You know Lamb's pathetic history, and you can see how
Dream Children came right out of his own sad heart, and
how it teems with affectionate recollection.   The children,
too,—do they not seem like living beings?   Can you believe that Alice and John never lived?   Let us go back to
the essay and see how little it is that he really says about
them.   Here it is:

ALICE

1.   *Here Alice put out
one of her dear mother's
looks, too tender to be upbraiding.*

She thought it very sad
that any one should pull
down the beautiful mantel-
piece in the great hall, but
she would not find fault with
him—she was too gentle, too
tender for that!

2.   *Here little A l i c e
spread her hands.*

Don't you think she knew
her Psaltery by heart, and
a great part of the Testament besides?   "Of course it
is very w o n d e r f u l that
grandma knew so much—
but then, I know it too."

3.   *Here Alice's little
right foot played an involuntary movement, till, upon
my looking grave, it de-
sisted.*

The mere suggestion of a

JOHN

1.   *Here John smiled as
much as to say, "that would
be foolish indeed."*

John is quite the boy—
wise enough to see how ridiculous it was to put a fine,
rich old carved chimney
among a lot of gilt gim-
cracks—and rather anxious
to show his wisdom.

2.   *Here John expanded
all his eyebrows and tried to
look courageous.*

The tale of the ghostly
infants has frightened John
a little, but he does not like
to admit any timidity there
with his father and sister,
so he straightens up, ex-
pands his eyebrows and
looks very brave and manly.

3.   *Here John slyly de-
posited back upon the plate
a bunch of grapes which, not
unobserved by Alice, he had
meditated dividing with her;
and both seemed willing to*

dance sets the little foot in motion, and you and I know that Alice is a lively girl who would be as proud of being the best dancer in the country as she was of knowing as much Scripture as her grandmother knew. But how quickly she stops when her father looks grave! We do not think that he objects to Alice dancing, but he knows that he is going to tell her the sad part of the story, and that the dancing accompaniment of Alice's little right foot would be very much out of place.

Later, Alice joined with John in wishing for the grapes, but she was equally willing to give them up when it seemed childish to take them.

relinquish them for the present as irrelevant.

While the father has been telling of his glorious childhood among the rich fruit on the great estate, John has quietly picked up a bunch of grapes, and his quick-witted father, seeing the act, sneers a little at *such-like common baits of children.* John, wishing to be manly, puts the grapes back without a word, though evidently he will be glad enough to return to them at the proper time.

Not a selfish child at all was John, for he meditated dividing the grapes with Alice, and they would have been so sweet and cooling while the children stood there listening to the story.

4. *Here the children fell a-crying and asked if their little mourning which they had on was not for Uncle John, and they looked up and prayed me not to go on about their uncle, but to tell them some stories about their pretty dead mother.*

How tender-hearted they both are, and yet until now they had hardly realized that it was for Uncle John that they were wearing their fresh mourning. This was a new grief too sad to them, but it turned their gentle sympathies to their pretty dead mother, of whom they were always glad to hear. The father has scarcely begun to speak when he sees in Alice so much resemblance to his dead wife that he almost thinks it is the mother who stands beside him. So violent is his emotion that he gradually comes out of his reverie, and as he does so the children fade away and recede into the distance, saying, *"We are nothing; less than nothing, and dreams."*

Is it not a wonderful thing that with so few words a writer can put his heart so much into yours that you believe almost as much as he does in the reality of the vision?

In the sketch of Lamb we said that his character was very strongly reflected in his writings, and this essay shows the fact wonderfully well. Imagine the man, lonely, heartbroken, weary from the awful task he had set himself, sitting in his bachelor armchair by the fire, dreaming his evening away. Who are the people that come to him in his dreams and what are the incidents? First his grandmother Field, with whom he had spent a great deal of his childhood; then his sweetheart Alice, now married to another, with children of her own; then his brother, by no means a pleasing character, but a lazy and selfish man who, however, in the rich, loving heart of his brother stands out as handsome, affectionate, noble and brave. How keenly he feels the bitter loss which comes to him with tenfold severity when he awakens, and which he makes the closing thought in the essay! Lastly, the faithful Mary, unchanged, appears at his side,—his waking companion, his greatest burden and his greatest joy.

Besides these evidences of his devoted and affectionate disposition, we find proof of his vivid imagination when as a child he gazes *upon the old busts of the twelve Cæsars that had been emperors of Rome, till the old marble heads would seem to live again, or I to be turned into marble with them.* In his *busy-idle* amusements at the great house he shows the innocence and simplicity of his pleasures, and in the delicate way in which he reproves Alice and John, his genial, sympathetic disposition as well as his abundant good humor. How much finer it was to say, *"and suchlike common baits of children"* than to have said, "John, put the grapes back on the plate."

READING SHAKESPEARE

HE greatest author the world has known is William Shakespeare, and his writings will afford more pleasure, instruction and information than those of any other author. They may be read again and again, for so charged are they with living knowledge and so full of literary charm, that no one can exhaust them in a single reading. Not every reader of Shakespeare loves him, but that is because not every reader appreciates him. He wrote in the English of his times, and used many words and expressions that have since dropped out of the language, changed their meaning, or become unfamiliar in common speech. Then again, his knowledge of life is so profound and his insight into human nature so keen and penetrating, that the casual reader is liable not to follow his thought. In other words, Shakespeare must be studied to be appreciated; but if he is studied and appreciated, he gives a pleasure and exerts an influence that cannot be equaled.

Young people are liable to think that study is laborious and uninteresting, a nuisance and a bore. Nothing of that sort is true of the study of Shakespeare, because for every effort there is a present reward, there is no waiting to see results. Of course there are right ways and wrong ways to study, just as there are right ways and wrong ways

WILLIAM SHAKESPEARE
1564–1616

of doing anything. Sometimes teachers fail entirely to interest their classes in Shakespeare, and parents say they cannot make their children like Shakespeare. None of this is the fault of the poet or of the children; the fault lies in the methods used to create an interest. If a person begins properly and proceeds as he should, there will never be a lack of interest. Teachers are not needed, and parents may leave their children to learn to be happy in reading by themselves, if the books are prepared properly for them.

In the first place, one of the wonders of Shakespeare is the great variety of his plays. In fact, they cover the whole range of human activities, and introduce characters from almost every walk in life. The stories they tell run from the light and gay to those of more somber hue, from comedy to deepest tragedy. Wit and humor, pathos and sublimity may sometimes be found in the same play, and smiles and tears may be drawn from the same page. What play to select for a beginner becomes then a question of some moment. *The Tempest* is one of the best, for it is not difficult to read, is an interesting story, has amusing characters, and carries good food for thought.

Will you then, our young readers, go hand in hand with us into the reading of Shakespeare? Do as we say this one time, and read as we ask you to, even if it does take some time from your play. If, while you are doing it, you do not enjoy yourselves, or if at the end you do not feel repaid, then take your own course in your reading thereafter. It will be a better course for having studied one great play carefully.

However, before we begin the play, let us read the charming tale written by Charles and Mary Lamb. It will give us briefly the story of *The Tempest,* though a wealth of incidents is omitted.

THE TEMPEST

A TALE FROM SHAKESPEARE BY CHARLES AND MARY LAMB

HERE was a certain island in the sea, the only inhabitants of which were an old man, whose name was Prospero, and his daughter Miranda, a very beautiful young lady. She came to this island so young, that she had no memory of having seen any other human face than her father's. They lived in a cave or cell, made out of a rock; it was divided into several apartments, one of which Prospero called his study; there he kept his books, which chiefly treated of magic, a study at that time much affected by all learned men; and the knowledge of this art he found very useful to him; for being thrown by a strange chance upon this island, which had been enchanted by a witch called Sycorax, who died there a short time before his arrival, Prospero, by virtue of his art, released many good spirits that Sycorax had imprisoned in the bodies of large trees, because they had refused to execute her wicked commands. These gentle spirits were ever after obedient to the will of Prospero. Of these, Ariel was the chief.

The lively little sprite Ariel had nothing mischievous in his nature, except that he took rather too much pleasure in tormenting an ugly monster called Caliban, for he owed him a grudge because he was the son of his old enemy Sycorax. This Caliban, Prospero found in the woods, a strange misshapen thing, far less human in form than an ape: he took him home to his cell, and taught him to speak; and Prospero would have been very kind to him, but the bad nature which Caliban inherited from his mother Sycorax, would not let him learn anything good or useful: therefore he was employed like a slave, to fetch wood, and do the most laborious offices; and Ariel had the charge of compelling him to these services.

When Caliban was lazy and neglected his work, Ariel (who was invisible to all eyes but Prospero's) would come slily and pinch him, and sometimes tumble him down in the mire; and then Ariel, in the likeness of an ape, would make mouths at him. Then swiftly changing his shape, in the likeness of a hedgehog, he would lie tumbling in Caliban's way, who feared the hedgehog's sharp quills would prick his bare feet. With a variety of suchlike vexatious tricks Ariel would often torment him whenever Caliban neglected the work which Prospero commanded him to do.

Having these powerful spirits obedient to his will, Prospero could by their means command the winds, and the waves of the sea. By his orders they raised a violent storm, in the midst of which, and struggling with the wild sea-waves that every moment threatened to swallow it up, he showed his daughter a fine large ship, which he told her was full of living beings like themselves. "O my dear father," said she, "if by your art you have raised this dreadful storm, have pity on their sad distress. See! the vessel will be dashed to pieces. Poor souls! they will all perish. If I had power, I would sink the sea beneath the earth, rather than the good ship should be destroyed, with all the precious souls within her."

"Be not so amazed, daughter Miranda," said Prospero; "there is no harm done. I have so ordered it, that no person in the ship shall receive any hurt. What I have done has been in care of you, my dear child. You are ignorant who you are, or where you came from, and you know no more of me, but that I am your father, and live in this poor cave. Can you remember a time before you came to this cell? I think you cannot, for you were not then three years of age."

"Certainly I can, sir," replied Miranda.

"By what?" asked Prospero; "by any other house or person? Tell me what you can remember, my child."

Miranda said, "It seems to me like the recollection of a dream. But had I not once four or five women who attended upon me?"

Prospero answered, "You had, and more. How is it that this still lives in your mind? Do you remember how you came here?"

"No, sir," said Miranda, "I remember nothing more."

"Twelve years ago, Miranda," continued Prospero, "I was duke of Milan, and you were a princess, and my only heir. I had a younger brother, whose name was Antonio, to whom I trusted everything; and as I was fond of retirement and deep study, I commonly left the management of my state affairs to your uncle, my false brother (for so indeed he proved). I, neglecting all worldly ends, buried among my books, did dedicate my whole time to the bettering of my mind. My brother Antonio, being thus in possession of my power, began to think himself the duke indeed. The opportunity I gave him of making himself popular among my subjects awakened in his bad nature a proud ambition to deprive me of my dukedom; this he soon effected with the aid of the king of Naples, a powerful prince, who was my enemy."

"Wherefore," said Miranda, "did they not that hour destroy us?"

"My child," answered her father, "they durst not, so dear was the love that my people bore me. Antonio carried us on board a ship, and when we were some leagues out at sea, he forced us into a small boat, without either tackle, sail, or mast: there he left us, as he thought, to perish. But a kind lord of my court, one Gonzalo, who loved me, had privately placed in the boat water, provisions, apparel, and some books which I prize above my dukedom."

"O my father," said Miranda, "what a trouble must I have been to you then!"

"No, my love," said Prospero, "you were a little cherub that did preserve me. Your innocent smiles made me to bear up against my misfortunes. Our food lasted till we landed on this island, since when my chief delight has been in teaching you, and well have you profited by my instructions."

"Heaven thank you, my dear father," said Miranda. "Now pray tell me, sir, your reason for raising this sea-storm?"

"Know then," said her father, "that by means of this storm, my enemies, the king of Naples, and my cruel brother, are cast ashore upon this island."

Having so said, Prospero gently touched his daughter with his magic wand, and she fell fast asleep; for the spirit Ariel just then presented himself before his master, to give an account of the tempest, and how he had disposed of the ship's company, and though the spirits were always invisible to Miranda, Prospero did not choose she should hear him holding converse (as would seem to her) with the empty air.

"Well, my brave spirit," said Prospero to Ariel, "how have you performed your task?"

Ariel gave a lively description of the storm, and of the terrors of the mariners; and how the king's son, Ferdinand, was the first who leaped into the sea; and his father thought he saw his dear son swallowed up by the waves and lost. "But he is safe," said Ariel, "in a corner of the isle, sitting with his arms folded, sadly lamenting the loss of the king, his father, whom he concludes drowned. Not a hair of his head is injured, and his princely garments, though drenched in the sea-waves, look fresher than before."

"That's my delicate Ariel," said Prospero. "Bring him hither: my daughter must see this prince. Where is the king, and my brother?"

"I left them," answered Ariel, "searching for Ferdinand, whom they have little hopes of finding, thinking they saw him perish. Of the ship's crew not one is missing; though each one thinks himself the only one saved: and the ship, though invisible to them, is safe in the harbor."

FERDINAND LEAPED

"Ariel," said Prospero, "thy charge is faithfully performed; but there is more work yet."

"Is there more work?" said Ariel. "Let me remind you, master, you have promised me my liberty. I pray, remember, I have done you worthy service, told you no lies, made no mistakes, served you without grudge or grumbling."

"How now!" said Prospero. "You do not recollect what a torment I freed you from. Have you forgot the wicked witch Sycorax, who with age and envy was almost bent double? Where was she born? Speak; tell me."

"Sir, in Algiers," said Ariel.

"O was she so?" said Prospero. "I must recount what you have been, which I find you do not remember. This bad witch, Sycorax, for her witchcrafts, too terrible to enter human hearing, was banished from Algiers, and here left by the sailors; and because you were a spirit too delicate to execute her wicked commands, she shut you up in a tree, where I found you howling. This torment, remember, I did free you from."

"Pardon me, dear master," said Ariel, ashamed to seem ungrateful; "I will obey your commands."

"Do so," said Prospero, "and I will set you free." He then gave orders what further he would have him do; and away went Ariel, first to where he had left Ferdinand, and found him still sitting on the grass in the same melancholy posture.

"O my young gentleman," said Ariel, when he saw him, "I will soon move you. You must be brought, I find, for the Lady Miranda to have a sight of your pretty person. Come, sir, follow me." He then began singing,

"Full fathom five thy father lies:
  Of his bones are coral made;
Those are pearls that were his eyes:
  Nothing of him that doth fade,
But doth suffer a sea-change
Into something rich and strange.
Sea-nymphs hourly ring his knell:
Hark! now I hear them,—Ding-dong, bell."

This strange news of his lost father soon roused
the prince from the stupid fit into which he had
fallen. He followed in amazement the sound of
Ariel's voice, till it led him to Prospero and Miranda, who were sitting under the shade of a large
tree. Now Miranda had never seen a man before,
except her own father.

"Miranda," said Prospero, "tell me what you are
looking at yonder."

"O father," said Miranda, in a strange surprise,
"surely that is a spirit. Lord! how it looks about!
Believe me, sir, it is a beautiful creature. Is it not
a spirit?"

"No, girl," answered her father: "it eats and
sleeps, and has senses such as we have. This young
man you see was in the ship. He is somewhat altered by grief, or you might call him a handsome
person. He has lost his companions, and is wandering about to find them."

Miranda, who thought all men had grave faces
and gray beards like her father, was delighted with
the appearance of this beautiful young prince; and
Ferdinand, seeing such a lovely maiden in this
desert place, and from the strange sounds he had
heard, expecting nothing but wonders, thought he
was upon an enchanted island, and that Miranda

was the goddess of the place, and as such he began to address her.

She timidly answered, she was no goddess, but a simple maid, and was going to give him an account of herself, when Prospero interrupted her. He was well pleased to find they admired each other, for he plainly perceived they had (as we say) fallen in love at first sight: but to try Ferdinand's constancy, he resolved to throw some difficulties in their way: therefore advancing forward, he addressed the prince with a stern air, telling him, he came to the island as a spy, to take it from him who was the lord of it. "Follow me," said he, "I will tie you neck and feet together. You shall drink sea-water; shell-fish, withered roots, and husks of acorns shall be your food." "No," said Ferdinand, "I will resist such entertainment, till I see a more powerful enemy," and drew his sword; but Prospero, waving his magic wand, fixed him to the spot where he stood so that he had no power to move.

Miranda hung upon her father, saying, "Why are you so ungentle? Have pity, sir; I will be his surety. This is the second man I ever saw, and to me he seems a true one."

"Silence," said the father; "one word more will make me chide you, girl! What! an advocate for an impostor! You think there are no more such fine men, having seen only him and Caliban. I tell you, foolish girl, most men as far excel this, as he does Caliban." This he said to prove his daughter's constancy; and she replied, "My affections are most humble. I have no wish to see a goodlier man."

"Come on, young man," said Prospero to the prince; "you have no power to disobey me."

"I have not indeed," answered Ferdinand; and not knowing that it was by magic he was deprived of all power of resistance, he was astonished to find himself so strangely compelled to follow Prospero: looking back on Miranda as long as he could see her, he said, as he went after Prospero into the cave, "My spirits are all bound up, as if I were in a dream; but this man's threats, and the weakness which I feel, would seem light to me if from my prison I might once a day behold this fair maid."

Prospero kept Ferdinand not long confined within the cell: he soon brought out his prisoner, and set him a severe task to perform, taking care to let his daughter know the hard labor he had imposed on him, and then pretending to go into his study, he secretly watched them both.

Prospero had commanded Ferdinand to pile up some heavy logs of wood. King's sons not being much used to laborious work, Miranda soon after found her lover almost dying with fatigue. "Alas!" said she, "do not work so hard; my father is at his studies, he is safe for these three hours; pray rest yourself."

"O my dear lady," said Ferdinand, "I dare not. I must finish my task before I take my rest."

"If you will sit down," said Miranda, "I will carry your logs the while." But this Ferdinand would by no means agree to. Instead of a help Miranda became a hindrance, for they began a long conversation, so that the business of log-carrying went on very slowly.

Prospero, who had enjoined Ferdinand this task merely as a trial of his love, was not at his books, as his daughter supposed, but was standing by them invisible, to overhear what they said.

Ferdinand inquired her name, which she told, saying it was against her father's express command she did so. Prospero only smiled at this first instance of his daughter's disobedience, for having by his magic art caused his daughter to fall in love so suddenly, he was not angry that she showed her love by forgetting to obey his commands. And he listened well pleased to a long speech of Ferdinand's, in which he professed to love her above all the ladies he ever saw.

In answer to his praises of her beauty, which he said exceeded all the women in the world, she replied, "I do not remember the face of any woman, nor have I seen any more men than you, my good friend, and my dear father. How features are abroad, I know not; but, believe me, sir, I would not wish any companion in the world but you, nor can my imagination form any shape but yours that I could like. But, sir, I fear I talk to you too freely, and my father's precepts I forget."

At this Prospero smiled, and nodded his head, as much as to say, "This goes on exactly as I could wish; my girl will be queen of Naples."

And then Ferdinand, in another fine long speech (for young princes speak in courtly phrases), told the innocent Miranda he was heir to the crown of Naples, and that she should be his queen.

"Ah! sir," said she, "I am a fool to weep at what I am glad of. I will answer you in plain and holy innocence. I am your wife if you will marry me."

Prospero prevented Ferdinand's thanks by appearing visible before them.

"Fear nothing, my child," said he; "I have overheard and approve of all you have said. And, Ferdinand, if I have too severely used you, I will make you rich amends, by giving you my daughter. All your vexations were but trials of your love, and you have nobly stood the test. Then as my gift, which your true love has worthily purchased, take my daughter, and do not smile that I boast she is above all praise." He then, telling them that he had business which required his presence, desired they would sit down and talk together till he returned; and this command Miranda seemed not at all disposed to disobey.

When Prospero left them, he called his spirit Ariel, who quickly appeared before him, eager to relate what he had done with Prospero's brother and the king of Naples. Ariel said he had left them almost out of their senses with fear, at the strange things he had caused them to see and hear. When fatigued with wandering about, and famished for want of food, he had suddenly set before them a delicious banquet, and then, just as they were going to eat, he appeared visible before them in the shape of a harpy, a voracious monster with wings, and the feast vanished away. Then, to their utter amazement, this seeming harpy spoke to them, reminding them of their cruelty in driving Prospero from his dukedom, and leaving him and his infant daughter to perish in the sea; saying, that for this cause these terrors were suffered to afflict them.

The king of Naples, and Antonio, the false brother, repented the injustice they had done to

Prospero; and Ariel told his master he was certain their penitence was sincere, and that he, though a spirit, could not but pity them.

"Then bring them hither, Ariel," said Prospero: "if you, who are but a spirit, feel for their distress, shall not I, who am a human being like themselves, have compassion on them? Bring them quickly, my dainty Ariel."

Ariel soon returned with the king, Antonio, and old Gonzalo in their train, who had followed him wondering at the wild music he played in the air to draw them on to his master's presence. This Gonzalo was the same who had so kindly provided Prospero formerly with books and provisions, when his wicked brother left him, as he thought, to perish in an open boat in the sea.

Grief and terror had so stupefied their senses, that they did not know Prospero. He first discovered himself to the good old Gonzalo, calling him the preserver of his life; and then his brother and the king knew that he was the injured Prospero.

Antonio with tears, and sad words of sorrow and true repentance, implored his brother's forgiveness, and the king expressed his sincere remorse for having assisted Antonio to depose his brother: and Prospero forgave them; and, upon their engaging to restore his dukedom, he said to the king of Naples, "I have a gift in store for you too;" and opening a door, showed him his son Ferdinand playing at chess with Miranda.

Nothing could exceed the joy of the father and the son at this unexpected meeting, for they each thought the other drowned in the storm.

"O wonder!" said Miranda, "what noble creatures these are! It must surely be a brave world that has such people in it."

The king of Naples was almost as much astonished at the beauty and excellent graces of the young Miranda as his son had been.

"Who is this maid?" said he; "she seems the goddess that has parted us, and brought us thus together."

"No, sir," answered Ferdinand, smiling to find his father had fallen into the same mistake that he had done when he first saw Miranda, "she is a mortal, but by immortal Providence she is mine; I chose her when I could not ask you, my father, for your consent, not thinking you were alive. She is the daughter to this Prospero, who is the famous duke of Milan, of whose renown I have heard so much, but never saw him till now: of him I have received a new life: he has made himself to me a second father, giving me this dear lady."

"Then I must be her father," said the king; "but oh! how oddly will it sound, that I must ask my child forgiveness."

"No more of that," said Prospero: "let us not remember our troubles past, since they so happily have ended."

And then Prospero embraced his brother, and again assured him of his forgiveness; and said that a wise overruling Providence had permitted that he should be driven from his poor dukedom of Milan, that his daughter might inherit the crown of Naples, for that by their meeting in this desert island, it had happened that the king's son had loved Miranda.

These kind words which Prospero spoke, meaning to comfort his brother, so filled Antonio with shame and remorse, that he wept and was unable to speak; and the kind old Gonzalo wept to see this joyful reconciliation, and prayed for blessings on the young couple.

Prospero now told them that their ship was safe in the harbor, and the sailors on board her, and that he and his daughter would accompany them home the next morning. "In the meantime," said he, "partake of such refreshments as my poor cave affords; and for your evening's entertainment I will relate the history of my life from my first landing in this desert island." He then called for Caliban to prepare some food, and set the cave in order; and the company were astonished at the uncouth form and savage appearance of this ugly monster, who (Prospero said) was the only attendant he had to wait upon him.

Before Prospero left the island, he dismissed Ariel from his service, to the great joy of that lively little spirit; who, though he had been a faithful servant to his master, was always longing to enjoy his free liberty, to wander uncontrolled in the air, like a wild bird, under green trees, among pleasant fruits, and sweet-smelling flowers. "My quaint Ariel," said Prospero to the little sprite when he made him free, "I shall miss you; yet you shall have your freedom." "Thank you, my dear master," said Ariel; "but give me leave to attend your ship home with prosperous gales, before you bid farewell to the assistance of your faithful spirit; and then, master, when I am free, how merrily I shall live!" Here Ariel sang this pretty song:

"Where the bee sucks there suck I;
In a cowslip's bell I lie:
There I couch when owls do cry.
On the bat's back I do fly
After summer merrily.
Merrily, merrily shall I live now
Under the blossom that hangs on the bough."

Prospero then buried deep in the earth his magical books and wand, for he was resolved never more to make use of the magic art. And having thus overcome his enemies, and being reconciled to his brother and the king of Naples, nothing now remained to complete his happiness, but to revisit his native land, to take possession of his dukedom, and to witness the happy nuptials of his daughter and Prince Ferdinand, which the king said should be instantly celebrated with great splendor on their return to Naples. At which place, under the safe convoy of the spirit Ariel, they, after a pleasant voyage, soon arrived.

THE TEMPEST

By WILLIAM SHAKESPEARE

INTRODUCTORY NOTE

HAVING read Lamb's version of the story, we are ready for the play as Shakespeare wrote it. To begin with, we will read it through from beginning to end with as little hesitation and delay as possible. We shall not expect to understand it all, and will pass over the more difficult passages without attempting to master them. If at times we are unable to go on intelligently, we will look at the notes at the bottom of the pages and get the help we need. This reading, however, is intended merely to give us a general idea of the play. We are spying out the land as a general might do it, trying to see what kind of a country we are invading, and to locate the places where we are liable to meet with resistance. We will stop a moment now and then to shudder at Caliban, to admire Prospero, to love the sweet Miranda or to laugh at the nonsense of the jester and the drunken butler, but we will hasten on to the end nevertheless, knowing that we will become better acquainted with the people at another time.

Having finished the play, we will return to the beginning for a second, a slower, more careful reading. Now many things that at first seemed obscure will have cleared themselves by our greater knowledge of the play. This time, however, we must read every sentence carefully and try to understand the meaning of all. The footnotes should all be read, because it often happens that when we think we understand what a sentence signifies, we give the wrong meaning to a word or phrase, and hence change the whole sense.

When this second reading has been completed, we will have a good understanding of the play, a more intimate acquaintance with the characters, and be ready for the more interesting studies which follow the play.

THE PERSONS

ALONSO, King of Naples.
SEBASTIAN, his Brother.
PROSPERO, the rightful Duke of Milan.
ANTONIO, his Brother, the usurping Duke of Milan.
FERDINAND, Son to the King of Naples.
GONZALO, an honest old Counsellor of Naples.
ADRIAN,
FRANCISCO, } Lords.
CALIBAN, a savage and deformed Slave.
TRINCULO, a Jester.

STEPHANO, a drunken Butler.
Master of a Ship, Boatswain, and Mariners.
MIRANDA, Daughter to Prospero.
ARIEL, an airy Spirit.
Other Spirits attending on Prospero.
IRIS,
CERES,
JUNO, } presented by Spirits.
Nymphs,
Reapers,

SCENE, *a Ship at Sea; afterwards an uninhabited Island.*

ACT I

SCENE I.—*On a Ship at sea. A Storm, with Thunder and Lightning.*

Enter Master *and* Boatswain *severally.*

MASTER *speaks.*

OATSWAIN!

Boats. Here, master: what cheer?

Mast. Good,[1] speak to the mariners: fall to't yarely,[2] or we run ourselves a-ground: bestir, bestir. [*Exit.*

Enter Mariners.

Boats. Heigh, my hearts! cheerly, cheerly, my hearts! yare, yare! Take in the topsail. Tend to the master's whistle. [*Exeunt* Mariners.]—Blow till thou burst thy wind,[3] if room enough![4]

Enter ALONSO, SEBASTIAN, ANTONIO, FERDINAND, GONZALO, *and Others.*

Alon. Good boatswain, have care. Where's the master? Play the men.[5]

Boats. I pray now, keep below.

Anto. Where is the master, boatswain?

Boats. Do you not hear him? You mar our labour: keep your cabins; you do assist the storm.

1. *Good* was often used in Shakespeare's time as we use the word *well*, to introduce a sentence.

2. *Fall to't yarely* means *get to work briskly.*

3. Perhaps the line should read, "Blow till thou burst *thee*, wind."

4. If there is sea-room enough. The boatswain is not alarmed if he can have room to handle his ship.

5. We still say "play the man" when we wish to encourage any one to be brave and manly.

Gonza. Nay, good, be patient.

Boats. When the sea is. Hence! What care these roarers for the name of king? To cabin: silence! trouble us not.

Gonza. Good, yet remember whom thou hast aboard.

Boats. None that I more love than myself. You are a counsellor: if you can command these elements to silence, and work the peace of the present,[6] we will not hand a rope more; use your authority: if you cannot, give thanks you have lived so long, and make yourself ready in your cabin for the mischance of the hour, if it so hap.[7]—Cheerly, good hearts!—Out of our way, I say.   [*Exit.*

Gonza. I have great comfort from this fellow: methinks he hath no drowning-mark upon him; his complexion[8] is perfect gallows.—Stand fast, good Fate, to his hanging! make the rope of his destiny our cable, for our own doth little advantage! If he be not born to be hang'd, our case is miserable.   [*Exeunt.*

Re-enter Boatswain.

Boats. Down with the top-mast! yare; lower, lower! Bring her to try wi' th' main-course.[9] [*A cry within.*] A plague upon this howling! they are louder than the weather or our office.[10]—

6. The word *time* may be understood after *present*. The boatswain infers that they cannot make peaceful weather of the present storm.

7. *Hap* means *happen*.

8. The word *complexion* here means *bent* or *inclination*. Gonzalo says the boatswain is born to be hung; he cannot be drowned.

9. The boatswain finds he has not sea-room enough so he calls upon the sailors to take down the topmast and to bring the ship as close into the wind as possible and hold her there with the main sail.

10. This sentence means *they are noisier than the tempest and the commands of our officers.*

Re-enter SEBASTIAN, ANTONIO, *and* GONZALO.

Yet again! what do you here? Shall we give
o'er, and drown? Have you a mind to sink?

Sebas.   A pox o' your throat, you bawling, blasphemous, incharitable dog!

Boats.   Work you, then.

Anto.   Hang, cur, hang! you insolent noise-
maker, we are less afraid to be drown'd than thou
art.

Gonza.   I'll warrant him for drowning,[11] though
the ship were no stronger than a nut-shell.

Boats.   Lay her a-hold, a-hold! set her two
courses![12] off to sea again; lay her off!

Re-enter Mariners, *wet.*

Mariners.   All lost! to prayers, to prayers! all
lost!   [*Exeunt.*

Boats.   What, must our mouths be cold?

Gonza.   The King and Prince at prayers! let
   us assist them,
For our case is as theirs.

Sebas.   I'm out of patience.

Anto.   We're merely[13] cheated out of our lives
by drunkards.
This wide-chopp'd rascal—would thou mightst lie
   drowning,
The washing of ten tides!

Gonza.   He'll be hang'd yet,
Though every drop of water swear against it,
And gape at widest to glut[14] him.

11. Gonzalo still thinks the boatswain was born to be hanged, and
warrants that he will not be drowned.

12. The boatswain is still trying to bring her to the wind, so she
may get out to sea. The *courses* are the largest lower sails.

13. *Merely*, here, means *entirely* or *absolutely.*

14. *Glut* means *swallow.*

(*A confused noise within.*) Mercy on us! We
split, we split!—Farewell, my wife and children!—
Farewell, brother!—We split, we split, we split!

[*Exit* Boatswain.

Anto. Let's all sink wi' th' King. [*Exit.*

Sebas. Let's take leave of him. [*Exit.*

Gonza. Now would I give a thousand furlongs
of sea for an acre of barren ground; ling, heath,
broom, furze,[15] anything. The wills[16] above be
done! but I would fain die a dry death. [*Exit.*

SCENE II.—*The Island: before the Cell of* PROS-
PERO.

Enter PROSPERO *and* MIRANDA.

Mira. If by your art, my dearest father, you
have
Put the wild waters in this roar, allay them.
The sky, it seems, would pour down stinking pitch,
But that the sea, mounting to th' welkin's cheek,[1]
Dashes the fire out. O, I have suffer'd
With those that I saw suffer! a brave[2] vessel,
Who had no doubt some noble creatures in her,
Dash'd all to pieces. O, the cry did knock
Against my very heart! Poor souls, they perish'd!
Had I been any god of power, I would
Have sunk the sea within the earth, or e'er[3]
It should the good ship so have swallow'd, and

15. These are all plants that grow in England, and were to Shakespeare the familiar signs of barren ground.

16. *The wills above be done* means *the will of the Powers above be
done.* Gonzalo interests us from the start by his rather humorous
view of everything.

1. *Welkin* means *sky.*

2. *Brave* means *fine.*

3. *Or e'er* means *before* or *sooner than.*

The fraughting[4] souls within her.

Pros.   Be collected;
No more amazement:[5] tell your piteous heart
There's no harm done.

Mira.   O, woe the day!

Pros.   No harm.
I have done nothing but in care of thee,—
Of thee, my dear one, thee, my daughter,—who
Art ignorant of what thou art, nought knowing
Of whence I am; nor that I am more better[6]
Than Prospero, master of a full-poor cell,
And thy no greater father.

Mira.   More to know
Did never meddle[7] with my thoughts.

Pros.   'Tis time
I should inform thee further. Lend thy hand,
And pluck my magic garment from me.—So:
                        [*Lays down his robe.*
Lie there, my art.[8]—Wipe thou thine eyes; have
      comfort.
The direful spectacle of the wreck, which touch'd
The very virtue of compassion in thee,
I have with such prevision in mine art
So safely order'd, that there is no soul[9]—

4. *Fraughting* means *freighting*. The human souls were the
freight of the ship.

5. *Amazement* means *anguish* and *deep distress* rather than astonishment.

6. In the time of Shakespeare it was not considered inelegant
English to use two forms of the comparative and superlative degrees.
More better, most best are good examples.

7. *Meddle* means *mix*. Miranda says she never thought of knowing more about herself or her father.

8. Prospero means that with his garment he lays his magic arts
aside and becomes the loving, human father.

9. Prospero does not complete his sentence, but expresses the
same thought in different form.

TELL YOUR PITEOUS HEART

No, not so much perdition as an hair
Betid to any creature in the vessel
Which thou heard'st cry, which thou saw'st sink.
    Sit down;
For thou must now know further.
    Mira.   You have often
Begun to tell me what I am; but stopp'd
And left me to a bootless inquisition,[10]
Concluding, *Stay, not yet.*
    Pros.   The hour's now come;
The very minute bids thee ope thine ear:
Obey, and be attentive.   Canst thou remember
A time before we came unto this cell?
I do not think thou canst; for then thou wast not
Out[11] three years old.
    Mira.   Certainly, sir, I can.
    Pros.   By what? by any other house or person?
Of any thing the image tell me that
Hath kept with thy remembrance.
    Mira.   'Tis far off,
And rather like a dream than an assurance
That my remembrance warrants.   Had I not
Four or five women once that tended me?
    Pros.   Thou hadst, and more, Miranda.   But
      how is it
That this lives in thy mind?   What see'st thou else
In the dark backward and abysm of time?
If thou remember'st aught ere thou camest here,
How thou camest here, thou mayst.[12]

10. *Bootless inquisition* means *fruitless questioning.*   The father
has before begun to tell Miranda who she is, but has interrupted
himself, and said, "Stay, not yet."

11. *Out* means *fully.*

12. Prospero says, in these two lines, "If you can remember anything that happened before we came here, you may remember *how* we
came here."

Mira.   But that I do not.

Pros.   Twelve year since, Miranda, twelve year
   since,
Thy father was the Duke of Milan, and
A prince of power.

Mira.   Sir, are you not my father?

Pros.   Thy mother was a piece of virtue, and
She said thou wast my daughter; and thy father
Was Duke of Milan; thou his only heir,
A princess—no worse issued.

Mira.   O the Heavens!
What foul play had we, that we came from thence?
Or blessèd was't we did?

Pros.   Both, both, my girl:
By foul play, as thou say'st, were we heaved thence;
But blessedly holp[13] hither.

Mira.   O, my heart bleeds
To think o' the teen[14] that I have turn'd you to,
Which is from my remembrance!   Please you,
   further.[15]

Pros.   My brother, and thy uncle, call'd An-
   tonio,—
I pray thee, mark me;—that a brother should
Be so perfidious!—he whom, next thyself,
Of all the world I loved, and to him put
The manage[16] of my State; as, at that time,
Through all the signiories[17] it was the first,
And Prospero the prime[18] Duke; being so reputed
In dignity, and for the liberal arts

13. *Holp* is an old form of *helped.*
14. *Teen* is an old word that means *trouble* or *anxiety.*
15. *Please you, further,* means *Please you, tell me further.*
16. *Manage* means *management.*
17. *Signiories* is a name for *principalities.*
18. *Prime* means *first* or *leading.*

Without a parallel: those being all my study,
The government I cast upon my brother,
And to my State grew stranger, being transported
And rapt in secret studies. Thy false uncle,—
Dost thou attend me?

Mira.   Sir, most heedfully.

Pros.—Being once perfected how to grant suits,
How to deny them; who[19] t' advance, and who
To trash[20] for over-topping[21]—new-created
The creatures that were mine, I say, or changed
    'em,
Or else new-form'd 'em; having both the key[22]
Of officer and office, set all hearts i' the State
To what tune pleased his ear; that[23] now he was
The ivy which had hid my princely trunk,
And suck'd the verdure out on't. Thou attend'st
    not.

Mira. O good sir, I do.

Pros.   I pray thee, mark me.
I thus neglecting worldly ends, all dedicated
To closeness,[24] and the bettering of my mind
With that which, but[25] by being so retired,
O'er-prized all popular rate,[26] in my false brother

19. *Who* is used for *whom*, as it was not considered ungrammatical in Shakespeare's day.

20. *Trash* means *check* or *set back*.

21. *Over-topping* means *rising too high*. Prospero means that his brother knew what persons to check when they tried to rise too high, to gain too much power.

22. The brother understood the *key* that kept officer and office in tune, and so set the minds of all Prospero's subjects thinking as the usurper wished. That is, Antonio took Prospero's friends away from him.

23. We would say *so that* instead of merely *that*.

24. *To closeness* means *to privacy*, to studies in his own home.

25. *But* in this sense means *except*.

26. This is a difficult clause to understand. What Prospero means is probably that his studies would have exceeded all popular estimate

Awaked an evil nature; and my trust,
Like a good parent, did beget of him
A falsehood, in its contrary as great
As my trust was; which had indeed no limit,
A confidence sans[27] bound. He being thus lorded,
Not only with what my revenue yielded,
But what my power might else exact,—like one
Who having unto truth, by falsing of it,[28]
Made such a sinner of his memory
To[29] credit his own lie,—he did believe
He was indeed the Duke; out o' the substitution,[30]
And executing the outward face of royalty,
With all prerogative: hence his ambition grow-
    ing,—
Dost thou hear?[31]
    Mira. Your tale, sir, would cure deafness.
    Pros. To have no screen between this part he
    play'd
And them he play'd it for, he needs will be
Absolute Milan.[32] Me,[33] poor man, my library

in value, but that they (if they had not) kept him so retired from
public life. Prospero sees the mistake he made, but cannot give up
the idea that his studies were valuable.

27. *Sans* is a French word that means *without*.

28. *By falsing it* means *by falsifying it* or *forging it*.

29. Shakespeare omits the word *as* before *to*. Antonio made so
great a sinner of his memory unto truth as to credit his own lie.

30. *Out of the substitution* may be understood to mean *because of
his being my substitute.*

31. Prospero's tale is not clearly told. He is evidently thinking
of other things, and his sentences are often imperfect. His mind
wanders to the things he intends doing, to the storm, the strangers
on the island and to his plans for the future. Miranda is not in-
attentive—she is fascinated by the story—but her father attributes
his own wandering thoughts to her.

32. Tired of ruling behind a screen, for that is what Prospero
really was, Antonio planned to remove his brother and become absolute Duke of Milan.

33. Shakespeare omits the word *for* before *me*.

Was dukedom large enough: of temporal royalties
He thinks me now incapable; confederates—
So dry he was for sway[34]—wi' th' King of Naples
To give him annual tribute, do him homage,
Subject his coronet to his crown, and bend
The dukedom, yet unbow'd,—alas, poor Milan![35]—
To most ignoble stooping.[36]

Mira.   O the Heavens!

Pros.   This King of Naples, being an enemy
To me inveterate, hearkens my brother's suit;
Which was, that he, in lieu[37] o' the premises,—
Of homage, and I know not how much tribute,—
Should presently[38] extirpate me and mine
Out of the dukedom, and confer fair Milan,
With all the honours, on my brother: whereon,
A treacherous army levied, one midnight
Fated to th' practice[39] did Antonio open
The gates of Milan; and, i' the dead of darkness,
The ministers for th' purpose hurried thence
Me and thy crying self.[40]

Mira.   Alack, for pity!
I, not remembering how I cried on't then,

34. *So dry he was for sway*, might now be written as *so thirsty he was for power.*

35. Prospero bewails the fate of his principality, Milan.

36. The meaning of the last seven lines is that Antonio thought Prospero incapable of ruling, offered to pay the King of Naples an annual tribute, to do him homage and to make Milan subject to Naples.

37. *In lieu* now means *instead of*, but Shakespeare uses it in the sense of *in return for.*

38. *Presently* means *immediately.*

39. *Practice* means *plot* or *stratagem.*

40. The six lines mean that one midnight, suited to such a plot, a treacherous army having been levied, Antonio opened the gates of Milan, and in the dead of darkness hurried away Prospero and the crying Miranda.

Will cry it o'er again: it is a hint[41]
That wrings mine eyes to't.

Pros. Hear a little further,
And then I'll bring thee to the present business
Which now's upon's;[42] without the which this story
Were most impertinent.[43]

Mira. Wherefore did they not
That hour destroy us?

Pros. Well demanded, wench:[44]
My tale provokes that question. Dear, they durst
not—
So dear the love my people bore me—set
A mark so bloody on the business; but
With colours fairer painted their foul ends.
In few,[45] they hurried us aboard a bark,
Bore us some leagues to sea; where they prepared
A rotten carcass of a boat, not rigg'd,
Nor tackle, sail, nor mast; the very rats
Instinctively had quit it: there they hoist[46] us,
To cry to th' sea that roar'd to us; to sigh
To th' winds, whose pity, sighing back again,
Did us but loving wrong.

Mira. Alack, what trouble
Was I then to you!

Pros. O, a cherubin
Thou wast that did preserve me! Thou didst smile,
Infusèd with a fortitude from Heaven,

41. In this place *hint* means *theme* or *subject.*

42. *Upon's* is *upon us.*

43. *Impertinent* in this connection means *out of place.*

44. *Wench* means *girl,* and at the time of Shakespeare was a term of affection, like *dear girl.*

45. *In few* may be read as *in a few words,* that is, *to make the story brief.*

46. *Hoist us* means *hoisted us,* that is *left us.*

When I have degg'd[47] the sea with drops full salt,
Under my burden groan'd; which raised in me
An undergoing stomach,[48] to bear up
Against what should ensue.
    Mira.   How came we ashore?
    Pros. By Providence divine.
Some food we had, and some fresh water, that
A noble Neapolitan, Gonzalo,
Out of his charity,—being then appointed
Master of this design,—did give us; with
Rich garments, linens, stuffs, and necessaries,
Which since have steaded[49] much; so, of his gen-
    tleness,
Knowing I loved my books, he furnish'd me,
From mine own library, with volumes that
I prize above my dukedom.
    Mira.   Would I might
But ever see that man!
    Pros.   Now I arise:[50]
Sit still, and hear the last of our sea-sorrow.
Here in this island we arrived; and here
Have I, thy schoolmaster, made thee more profit[51]
Than other princesses can, that have more time
For vainer hours, and tutors not so careful.
    Mira. Heavens thank you for't! And now, I
        pray you, sir,—

47. *Degg'd* means *sprinkled.*

48. Shakespeare, as was the custom in those days, often used the word *stomach* for *courage;* an *undergoing stomach* is a *lasting courage.*

49. *Steaded* means *aided.* We might say, *which have since stood us in good stead.*

50. Readers of Shakespeare dispute about the meaning of this sentence. We might imagine Prospero to say half to himself "Now *I arise;*" that is, "My turn has come."

51. *Made thee more profit,* that is, *have made you to profit more,* have taught you to better advantage.

For still 'tis beating in my mind,—your reason
For raising this sea-storm?
    Pros.   Know thus far forth:
By accident most strange, bountiful Fortune—
Now my dear lady—hath mine enemies
Brought to this shore; and by my prescience
I find my zenith[52] doth depend upon
A most auspicious star, whose influence
If now I court not, but omit, my fortunes
Will ever after droop.[53] Here cease more questions:
Thou art inclined to sleep; 'tis a good dulness,
And give it way: I know thou canst not choose.[54]
                            [*MIRANDA sleeps.*
Come away, servant, come! I'm ready now:
Approach, my Ariel; come!

               Enter ARIEL.
    Ari. All hail, great master! grave sir, hail! I
      come
To answer thy best pleasure; be't to fly,
To swim, to dive into the fire, to ride
On the curl'd clouds: to thy strong bidding task
Ariel and all his quality.[55]
    Pros.   Hast thou, spirit,
Perform'd to point[56] the tempest that I bade thee?
    Ari. To every article.
I boarded the King's ship; now on the beak,[57]

52. The *zenith* is the *highest point.*
53. Prospero means that if he acts now his fortune will rise to their highest point, but that if he waits, he will lose his opportunity.
54. Prospero, by his magic, throws his daughter into a deep sleep so that he may carry on his plans without her knowledge.
55. This line may be understood to read, *Ariel, and all spirits of his kind.*
56. *Performed to point* means *performed in every respect.*
57. The *beak* of a ship is the *prow,* the projecting forward part.

Now in the waist,[58] the deck, in every cabin,
I flamed amazement: sometime I'd divide,
And burn in many places; on the top-mast,
The yards, and bowsprit, would I flame distinctly,[59]
Then meet and join. Jove's lightnings, the pre-
    cursors
O' the dreadful thunder-claps, more momentary[60]
And sight-outrunning were not: the fire, and cracks
Of sulphurous roaring, the most mighty Neptune
Seem'd to besiege, and make his bold waves tremble,
Yea, his dread trident shake.

    Pros.   My brave spirit!
Who was so firm, so constant, that this coil[61]
Would not infect his reason?

    Ari.   Not a soul
But felt a fever of the mad,[62] and play'd
Some tricks of desperation. All but mariners
Plunged in the foaming brine, and quit the vessel,
Then all a-fire with me: The King's son, Ferdi-
    nand,
With hair up-staring,[63]—then like reeds, not hair,—
Was the first man that leap'd; cried, *Hell is empty,*
And all the devils are here.

    Pros.   Why, that's my spirit!
But was not this nigh shore?

    Ari.   Close by, my master.

    Pros. But are they, Ariel, safe?

58. The *waist* of a ship is the middle portion.
59. *Distinctly* means here *separately.* Ariel caused light globes of flame to appear for a second in different parts of the rigging, and to move about and to join.
60 *Momentary* means *instantaneous.*
61. *Coil* means *tumult* or *confusion.*
62. This clause means *There was not a soul that did not feel such a fever as madmen feel.*
63. In this place *upstaring* means *sticking up.*

Ari.   Not a hair perish'd;
On their unstaining[64] garments not a blemish,
But fresher than before: and, as thou badest me,
In troops I have dispersed them 'bout the isle.
The King's son have I landed by himself;
Whom I left cooling of the air with sighs
In an odd angle[65] of the isle, and sitting,
His arms in this sad knot.[66]

Pros.   Of the King's ship
The mariners, say, how hast thou disposed,
And all the rest o' the fleet?[67]

Ari.   Safely in harbour
Is the King's ship; in the deep nook, where once
Thou call'dst me up at midnight to fetch dew
From the still-vex'd Bermoothes,[68] there she's hid:
The mariners all under hatches stow'd;
Who, with a charm join'd to their suffer'd labour,
I've left asleep:[69] and, for the rest o' the fleet
Which I dispersed, they all have met again,

64. For *unstaining* we would say *unstained*.

65. *Odd angle* probably means *out-of-the-way place*.

66. Probably Ferdinand sat with his arms folded loosely, his head hanging on his breast.

67. This is a good example of the way Shakespeare sometimes changes the natural order in which the parts of a sentence should be placed. Naturally the sentence would read: "Say, how hast thou disposed of the mariners of the King's ship, and all the rest of the fleet?"

68. *Bermoothes* is the old form of the word *Bermudas*. It was supposed that witches haunted the Bermudas and filled the air with tempests, which kept the waters always stormy. *Still-vexed* means *always stormy*. The present errands of the spirit Ariel are not the first he has executed for Prospero. Dew from the Bermudas was probably wanted for some of his magical rites.

69. To enjoy *The Tempest*, we must lay aside our reason to the extent of believing in charms and in magic, in witchcraft and in Ariel's wonderful powers. Prospero's control of the magic art is part of what he gained from his studies while Antonio was stealing his principality.

And are upon the Mediterranean flote,[70]
Bound sadly home for Naples;
Supposing that they saw the King's ship wreck'd,
And his great person perish.

Pros.   Ariel, thy charge
Exactly is performed: but there's more work.
What is the time o' the day?

Ari.   Past the mid season,
At least two glasses.[71]

Pros.   The time 'twixt six and now
Must by us both be spent most preciously.

Ari. Is there more toil? Since thou dost give
     me pains,
Let me remember[72] thee what thou hast promised,
Which is not yet perform'd[73] me.

Pros.   How now! moody?
What is't thou canst demand?

Ari.   My liberty.

Pros. Before the time be out? no more![74]

Ari.   I pr'ythee,
Remember I have done thee worthy service;
Told thee no lies, made no mistakings, served
Without or grudge or grumblings: thou didst
     promise
To bate me a full year.[75]

Pros.   Dost thou forget
From what a torment I did free thee?

70. *Flote* is *flood*, therefore *wave* or *sea*.
71. This means that it was about two o'clock in the afternoon—past the mid-season by about the time it would take the sand to run twice through the hour-glass.
72. *Remember* here means *remind*.
73. *Perform'd me* means *performed for me*.
74. *Say* no more.
75. "To release me a full year before my time is up," is what Ariel says Prospero has promised.

Ari.   No.

Pros. Thou dost; and think'st it much to tread
       the ooze
Of the salt deep; to run upon the sharp
Wind of the North; to do me business in
The veins o' the earth when it is baked with frost.[76]

Ari. I do not, sir.

Pros. Thou liest, malignant thing![77] Hast thou
       forgot
The foul witch Sycorax, who with age and envy[78]
Was grown into a hoop? hast thou forgot her?

Ari. No, sir.

Pros.   Thou hast: where was she born?
       speak; tell me.

Ari. Sir, in Argier.[79]

Pros.   O, was she so? I must
Once in a month recount what thou hast been,
Which thou forgett'st. This damn'd witch Sycorax,
For mischiefs manifold, and sorceries terrible
To enter human hearing, from Argier,
Thou know'st, was banish'd. Is not this true?

Ari. Ay, sir.

Pros. This blue-eyed hag[80] was hither brought,
And here was left by th' sailors. Thou, my slave,
As thou report'st thyself, wast then her servant;
And, for[81] thou wast a spirit too delicate

76. This speech shows how marvelous are some of the things Ariel
has already done for Prospero.

77. Prospero is not speaking in earnest when he calls Ariel a
"malignant thing." He intends to release Ariel soon.

78. To Shakespeare and other writers of his time, the word *envy*
meant *malice*.

79. *Argier* is an old name for Algiers.

80. *Blue-eyed* means that the witch had dark blue circles around
her eyes, not that she had real blue eyes.

81. *For* means *because*.

To act her earthy and abhorr'd commands,
Refusing her grand hests,[82] she did confine thee,
By help of her more potent ministers,
And in her most unmitigable rage,
Into[83] a cloven pine; within which rift
Imprison'd thou didst painfully remain
A dozen years; within which space she died,
And left thee there; where thou didst vent thy
    groans
As fast as mill-wheels strike. Then was this
    island—
Save for the son that she did litter here,[84]
A freckled whelp, hag-born—not honour'd with
A human shape.
    Ari.   Yes, Caliban her son.
    Pros. Dull thing, I say so; he, that Caliban,
Whom now I keep in service. Thou best know'st
What torment I did find thee in: thy groans
Did make wolves howl, and penetrate the breasts
Of ever-angry bears. It was a torment
To lay upon the damn'd, which Sycorax
Could not again undo: it was mine art,
When I arrived and heard thee, that made gape
The pine, and let thee out.
    Ari.   I thank thee, master.
    Pros. If thou more murmur'st, I will rend an
    oak,
And peg thee in his knotty entrails, till
Thou'st howl'd away twelve Winters.
    Ari.   Pardon, master:
I will be correspondent[85] to command,

82. *Hests* means *behests* or *commands.*
83. The witch confined Ariel *in* a cloven pine tree.
84. This line means *save for the son that was born here.*
85. *Correspondent* means *obedient.*

And do my spriting gently.

Pros.   Do so; and after two days
I will discharge thee.

Ari.   That's my noble master!
What shall I do? say what; what shall I do?

Pros. Go make thyself like to a nymph o' the
sea:
Be subject to no sight but mine; invisible
To every eyeball else.   Go take this shape,
And hither come in't: hence, with diligence!—

                                        [*Exit* ARIEL.

Awake, dear heart, awake! thou hast slept well;
Awake!

Mira. [*Waking.*] The strangeness of your
story put
Heaviness in me.

Pros.   Shake it off.   Come on;
We'll visit Caliban my slave, who never
Yields us kind answer.

Mira.   'Tis a villain, sir,
I do not love to look on.

Pros.   But, as 'tis,
We cannot miss him:[86] he does make our fire,
Fetch in our wood, and serves in offices
That profit us.—What, ho! slave! Caliban!
Thou earth, thou! speak.

Cal. [*Within.*]   There's wood enough within.

Pros. Come forth, I say! there's other business
for thee:
Come forth, thou tortoise! when![87]—

Re-enter ARIEL, *like a Water-nymph.*

86. *Miss* means *spare.*
87. *When* was often used as an exclamation of impatience.

Fine apparition! My quaint[88] Ariel,
Hark in thine ear.

Ari.   My lord, it shall be done. [*Exit.*
Pros. Thou poisonous slave, come forth!

Enter CALIBAN.

Cal. As wicked[89] dew as e'er my mother brush'd
With raven's feather from unwholesome fen
Drop on you both! a south-west blow on ye,
And blister you all o'er![90]

Pros. For this, be sure, to-night thou shalt have
     cramps,
Side-stitches[91] that shall pen thy breath up;
     urchins[92]
Shall, for that vast[93] of night that they may work,
All exercise on thee; thou shalt be pinch'd
As thick as honeycomb, each pinch more stinging
Than bees that made 'em.

Cal.   I must eat my dinner
This island's mine, by Sycorax my mother,
Which thou takest from me. When thou camest
     here first,
Thou strokedst me, and madest much of me;
     wouldst give me
Water with berries in't[94] and teach me how
To name the bigger light, and how the less,
That burn by day and night: and then I loved thee,
And show'd thee all the qualities o' the isle,

88. Old meanings for *quaint* are *artful, ingenious.*
89. *Wicked dew* probably means *poisonous dew.*
90. Caliban, in cursing his master, alludes to the common belief of that time that a southwest wind was unwholesome.
91. *Side stitches* are *stitches* or *pains* in the side.
92. *Urchins* were troublesome *sprites* or *fairies.*
93. *Vast* alludes to the middle hours of night when in the stillness and vacancy evil spirits can do their work.
94. Just what Caliban means here is uncertain.

The fresh springs, brine-pits, barren place, and
    fertile.
Cursèd be that I did so! All the charms
Of Sycorax, toads, beetles, bats, light on you!
For I am all the subjects that you have,
Which first was mine own king: and here you sty[95]
    me
In this hard rock, whiles you do keep from me
The rest o' the island.

    Pros.   Abhorrèd slave,
Which any print of goodness wilt not take,
Being capable of all ill! I pitied thee,
Took pains to make thee speak, taught thee each
    hour
One thing or other: when thou didst not, savage,
Know thine own meaning,[96] but wouldst gabble like
A thing most brutish, I endow'd thy purposes
With words that made them known. But thy vile
    race,
Though thou didst learn, had that in't which good
    natures
Could not abide to be with; therefore wast thou
Deservedly confined into this rock,
Who hadst deserved more than a prison.

    Cal. You taught me language; and my profit
    on't
Is, I know how to curse. The red plague rid[97] you
For learning me your language!

    Pros.   Hag-seed, hence!
Fetch us in fuel; and be quick, thou'rt best,
To answer other business. Shrugg'st thou, malice?

    95. *Sty* here means *confine*, as in a sty.
    96. This clause means *did'st not, savage, know the meaning of
thine own words.*
    97. *Rid* means *destroy.*

If thou neglect'st, or dost unwillingly
What I command, I'll rack thee with old[98] cramps,
Fill all thy bones with achès, make thee roar,
That beasts shall tremble at thy din.

Cal.   No, pray thee.—
[*Aside.*]   I must obey: his art is of such power,
It would control my dam's god, Setebos,
And make a vassal of him.

Pros.   So, slave; hence!
[*Exit* CALIBAN.

Re-enter ARIEL, *invisible, playing and singing;*
FERDINAND *following.*

ARIEL'S SONG
Come unto these yellow sands,
    And then take hands:
Curtsied when you have, and kiss'd
    The wild waves whist,[99]
        Foot it featly here and there;
And, sweet sprites, the burden bear.

Hark, hark!	*Burden dispersedly.*
The watch-dogs bark:	Bow-wow.
Hark, hark! I hear	Bow-wow.
The s t r a i n of strutting chanticleer.	Cock-a-diddle-dow.

Ferd.   Where should this music be? i' the air,
    or th' earth?
It sounds no more: and, sure, it waits upon
Some god o' the island.   Sitting on a bank,
Weeping again the King my father's wreck,

98. *Old* here, as often in the writings of Shakespeare's time, is used merely to make stronger the meaning of the word that follows it.

99. *Kiss'd the wild waves whist* means *soothed the wild waves into peace.*

This music crept by me upon the waters,
Allaying both their fury and my passion[100]
With its sweet air: thence I have follow'd it,
Or it hath drawn me rather. But 'tis gone.
No, it begins again.

ARIEL *sings.*

Full fathom five thy father lies;
  Of his bones are coral made;
Those are pearls that were his eyes:
  Nothing of him that doth fade
But doth suffer a sea-change[101]
Into something rich and strange.
Sea-nymphs hourly ring his knell:
  Burden.   Ding-Dong.
Hark! now I hear them,—Ding-Dong, bell.

Ferd. The ditty does remember my drown'd
    father.
This is no mortal business, nor no sound
That the earth owes.[102] I hear it now above me.

Pros. The fringèd curtains of thine eyes ad-
    vance,[103]
And say what thou see'st yond.

Mira.   What is't? A spirit?
Lord, how it looks about! Believe me, sir,
It carries a brave[104] form. But 'tis a spirit.

Pros. No, wench; it eats and sleeps, and hath
    such senses

100. Ferdinand was suffering, and Shakespeare used the word *passion* to express the idea as we use it in speaking of the Passion of Christ.

101. This line means *without suffering a change from the effects of the sea.*

102. *Owes* here means *possesses.*

103. Prospero speaking to Miranda says, "Lift up your eyelids and tell me what you see yonder."

104. In this connection *brave* means *fine* or *noble.*

As we have, such. This gallant which thou see'st
Was in the wreck; and, but he's something stain'd
With grief, that's beauty's canker,[105] thou mightst
    call him
A goodly person: he hath lost his fellows,
And strays about to find 'em.
    Mira.   I might call him
A thing divine; for nothing natural
I ever saw so noble.[106]
    Pros. [*Aside.*]   It goes on,[107] I see,
As my soul prompts it.—Spirit, fine spirit! I'll
    free thee
Within two days for this.
    Ferd.   Most sure, the goddess
On whom these airs attend!—Vouchsafe my prayer
May know if you remain upon this island;
And that you will some good instruction give
How I may bear me here: my prime request,
Which I do last pronounce, is,—O you wonder!—
If you be maid or no?[108]
    Mira.   No wonder,[109] sir;
But certainly a maid.
    Ferd.   My language![110] Heavens!—
I am the best of them that speak this speech,

105. *Canker* means *rust* or *tarnish.* Prospero says, "Except for
the fact that he's somewhat stained with grief, which tarnishes
beauty, you might call him a goodly person."
106. Miranda, it must be remembered, has never seen any other
man than her father.
107. Prospero sees his plan going on well and gives Ariel credit
for it. Just what the plan is will soon become apparent.
108. Ferdinand speaks somewhat aside when he sees the beautiful Miranda, and then directly addresses her. He is embarrassed,
calls her a goddess, asks her how he shall behave, calls her a wonder,
but above all, wishes to know if she is mortal or not.
109. The word *Miranda* means *wonderful.*
110. "She speaks my language!"

Were I but where 'tis spoken.

Pros.   How! the best?
What wert thou, if the King of Naples heard thee?

Ferd.   A single thing,[111] as I am now, that won-
ders
To hear thee speak of Naples.   He does hear me;
And that he does I weep: myself am Naples;[112]
Who with mine eyes, ne'er since at ebb, beheld
The King my father wreck'd.

Mira.   Alack, for mercy!

Ferd.   Yes, faith, and all his lords; the Duke of
Milan
And his brave son[113] being twain.

Pros. [*Aside.*]   The Duke of Milan
And his more braver daughter could control thee,[114]
If now t'were fit to do't.   At the first sight
They have changed eyes.—Delicate Ariel,
I'll set thee free for this!—A word, good sir;
I fear you've done yourself some wrong:[116] a word.

Mira.   Why speaks my father so ungently?
This
Is the third man that e'er I saw; the first
That e'er I sigh'd for: pity move my father
To be inclined my way!

Ferd.   O, if a virgin,
And your affection not gone forth, I'll make you

111.   *A single thing* means *a weak and companionless thing.*
112.   *Myself am Naples* means *I am now the King of Naples.*
113.   Notice that this is the only mention of a son to Antonio,
the usurping Duke of Milan.
114.   *Control* means here *confute*, that is, *tell you differently.*
115.   Prospero notices the interest the two young people have
taken in each other, and as this furthers his plan he feels more
grateful to Ariel.
116.   What Prospero says is, "I fear that in claiming to be the
King of Naples you have done some wrong to your character."

The Queen of Naples.

    Pros.   Soft, sir! one word more.—
[*Aside.*] They're both in either's powers: but this
    swift business
I must uneasy make, lest too light winning
Make the prize light.[117]—One word more; I charge
    thee
That thou attend me: Thou dost here usurp
The name thou owest not; and hast put thyself
Upon this island as a spy, to win it
From me, the lord on't.

    Ferd.   No, as I'm a man.

    Mira. There's nothing ill can dwell in such a
    temple:
If the ill spirit have so fair a house,
Good things will strive to dwell with't.

    Pros. [*To* Ferd.]   Follow me—
Speak not you for him; he's a traitor.—Come;
I'll manacle thy neck and feet together:
Sea-water shalt thou drink; thy food shall be
The fresh-brook muscles, wither'd roots, and husks
Wherein the acorn cradled: follow.

    Ferd.   No;
I will resist such entertainment, till
Mine enemy has more power.

    [*He draws, and is charmed from moving.*
    Mira.   O dear father,
Make not too rash a trial of him, for
He's gentle, and not fearful.[118]

    Pros.   What, I say,
My fool my tutor!—Put thy sword up, traitor;

117. Prospero wishes to test the love he sees in Ferdinand, and make him earn his prize. So he charges the young man with deceit and threatens him.

118. *Fearful* here means *timid.*

Who makest a show, but darest not strike, thy
    conscience
Is so possess'd with guilt: come from thy ward;[119]
For I can here disarm thee with this stick,
And make thy weapon drop.
   Mira.   Beseech you, father!—
   Pros. Hence! hang not on my garments.
   Mira.   Sir, have pity;
I'll be his surety.
   Pros.   Silence! one word more
Shall make me chide thee, if not hate thee. What!
An advocate for an impostor? hush!
Thou think'st there are no more such shapes as he,
Having seen but him and Caliban: foolish wench!
To th' most of men this is a Caliban,
And they to him are angels.
   Mira.   My affections
Are, then, most humble; I have no ambition
To see a goodlier man.
   Pros. [*To* FERD.] Come on; obey:
Thy nerves[120] are in their infancy again,
And have no vigour in them.
   Ferd.   So they are:
My spirits, as in a dream, are all bound up.
My father's loss, the weakness which I feel,
The wreck of all my friends, and this man's
    threats
To whom I am subdued, are light to me,
Might I but through my prison once a day
Behold this maid: all corners else o' the Earth
Let liberty make use of; space enough
Have I in such a prison.

119. *Ward* is his position of defense to ward off a blow.
120. *Nerves* is here used for *muscles* and *sinews*.

Pros. [*Aside.*] It works.—[*To* Ferd.] Come on.—
Thou hast done well, fine Ariel!—Follow me.—
[*To* Ariel.]   Hark, what thou else shalt do me.
   Mira.   Be of comfort;
My father's of a better nature, sir,
Than he appears by speech: this is unwonted
Which now came from him.
   Pros.   [*To* Ariel.]   Thou shalt be as free
As mountain winds: but then exactly do
All points of my command.
   Ari.   To th' syllable.
   Pros.   Come, follow.—Speak not for him.
                                 [*Exeunt.*

ACT II

Scene I.—*Another part of the Island.*

Enter Alonso, Sebastian, Antonio, Gonzalo,
Adrian, Francisco, *and Others.*—

Gonzalo *speaks.*

ESEECH you, sir, be merry: you have
     cause—
     So have we all—of joy; for our escape
     Is much beyond our loss. Our hint of
     woe
     Is common; every day some sailor's
     wife,
The master of some merchant,[1] and the merchant,
Have just our theme of woe: but for the miracle—
I mean our preservation—few in millions
Can speak like us: then wisely, good sir, weigh
Our sorrow with our comfort.
   Alon.   Pr'ythee, peace.
   Sebas.   He receives comfort like cold porridge.

1. This word means a ship—the *merchantman.*

Anto. The visitor[2] will not give him o'er so.

Sebas. Look, he's winding up the watch of his wit; by-and-by it will strike.

Gonza. Sir,—

Sebas. One:—tell.[3]

Gonza.—When every grief is entertain'd that's offer'd,

Comes to the entertainer—

Sebas. A dollar.

Gonza. Dolour[4] comes to him, indeed; you have spoken truer than you purposed.

Sebas. You have taken it wiselier than I meant you should.

Gonza. Therefore, my lord,—

Anto. Fie, what a spendthrift is he of his tongue!

Alon. I pr'ythee, spare me.

Gonza. Well, I have done: but yet—

Sebas. He will be talking.

Anto. Which, of he or Adrian,[5] for a good wager, first begins to crow?

Sebas. The old cock.[6]

Anto. The cockerel.

Sebas. Done! The wager?

Anto. A laughter.

Sebas. A match![7]

2. A *visitor* in this sense is one who visits the sick to comfort them. Antonio and Sebastian are ridiculing Gonzalo for his efforts to cheer and console them.

3. *Tell* means *keep tally.* Sebastian means that the clock of Gonzalo's wit has struck one.

4. *Dolour* means *grief* or *sadness.*

5. Instead of *of he or Adrian,* we would say merely *he or Adrian.* Antonio offers to bet a good sum on which will speak first, Gonzalo or Adrian.

6. Gonzalo.

7. *A match* means *I take the bet.*

Adri. Though this island seem to be desert,—

Sebas. Ha, ha, ha!—So, you're paid.[8]

Adri.—uninhabitable, and almost inaccessible,—

Sebas. Yet—

Adri.—yet—

Anto. He could not miss't.

Adri.—it must needs be of subtle, tender, and delicate temperance.[9]

Anto. Temperance was a delicate wench.[10]

Sebas. Ay, and a subtle; as he most learnedly delivered.

Adri. The air breathes upon us here most sweetly.

Sebas. As if it had lungs, and rotten ones.

Anto. Or as 'twere perfumed by a fen.

Gonza. Here is everything advantageous to life.

Anto. True; save means to live.

Sebas. Of that there's none, or little.

Gonza. How lush[11] and lusty the grass looks! how green!

Anto. The ground, indeed, is tawny.

Sebas. With an eye[12] of green in't.

Anto. He misses not much.

Sebas. No; he doth but mistake the truth totally.

Gonza. But the rarity of it is,—which is indeed almost beyond credit,—

Sebas. As many vouch'd rarities are.

Gonza.—that our garments, being, as they were,

---

8. Sebastian has lost his bet, and he pays with a laugh.

9. Adrian means *temperature* when he says *temperance.*

10. People often named their girls *Temperance, Prudence, Faith,* etc. It is to this fact that Antonio jokingly alludes.

11. *Lush* means *juicy.*

12. *Eye* here means *tint* or *shade.*

drenched in the sea, are now as fresh as when we put them on first in Afric, at the marriage of the King's fair daughter Claribel to the King of Tunis.

Sebas. 'Twas a sweet marriage, and we prosper well in our return.

Adri. Tunis was never graced before with such a paragon to[13] their Queen.

Gonza. Not since widow Dido's time.[14]

Anto. Widow? a pox o' that! How came that widow in? Widow Dido!

Sebas. What if he had said widower Æneas too? Good Lord, how you take it!

Adri. Widow Dido, said you? you make me study of that: she was of Carthage, not of Tunis.

Gonza. This Tunis, sir, was Carthage.

Adri. Carthage!

Gonza. I assure you, Carthage.

Anto. His word is more than the miraculous harp.[15]

Sebas. He hath raised the wall and houses too.

Anto. What impossible matter will he make easy next?

Sebas. I think he will carry this island home in his pocket, and give it his son for an apple.

Anto. And, sowing the kernels of it in the sea, bring forth more islands.

Alon. Ah!

Anto. Why, in good time.

13. We would now say *for* instead of *to.*

14. Tunis is near the supposed site of Carthage. The story of Dido and Æneas is told in Virgil's *Æneid.*

15. One of the stories of the god Mercury is that he gave to Amphion, King of Thebes, a magic harp upon which the king played and so charmed the stones that they sprang into place to make the walls of his city.

Gonza.   Sir, we were talking that our garments seem now as fresh as when we were at Tunis at the marriage of your daughter, who is now Queen.

Anto.   And the rarest that e'er came there.

Sebas.   Bate, I beseech you, widow Dido.

Anto.   O, widow Dido! ay, widow Dido.

Gonza.   Is not, sir, my doublet as fresh as the first day I wore it, at your daughter's marriage?

Alon.   You cram these words into mine ears against

The stomach of my sense.[16]   Would I had never
Married my daughter there! for, coming thence,
My son is lost; and, in my rate,[17] she too,
Who is so far from Italy removed,
I ne'er again shall see her.   O thou mine heir
Of Naples and of Milan, what strange fish
Hath made his meal on thee?

Fran.   Sir, he may live:
I saw him beat the surges under him,
And ride upon their backs; he trod the water,
Whose enmity he flung aside, and breasted
The surge most swoln that met him: his bold head
'Bove the contentious waves he kept, and oar'd
Himself with his good arms in lusty stroke
To th' shore, that o'er his[18] wave-worn basis bow'd,
As[19] stooping to relieve him: I not doubt
He came alive to land.

Alon.   No, no; he's gone.

---

16.   The meaning of *stomach* in this line is *appetite* or *desire*. Alonso says they crowd their words into his ears when his feelings do not relish such nonsense.

17.   *Rate* means *estimation*.

18.   *His* is used for *its* and refers to *shore*.

19.   For *as*, read *as if*.

Sebas. Sir, you may thank yourself for this
    great loss,
That would not bless our Europe with your
    daughter,
But rather lose her to an African;
Where she at least is banish'd from your eye,
Who[20] hath cause to wet the grief on't.
  Alon.   Pr'ythee, peace.
  Sebas. You were kneel'd to, and impòrtuned
    otherwise,
By all of us; and the fair soul herself
Weigh'd, between loathness and obedience, at
Which end the beam should bow.[21] We've lost
    your son,
I fear, for ever: Milan and Naples have
More widows in them of this business' making
Than we bring men to comfort them: the fault's
Your own.
  Alon. So is the dear'st[22] o' the loss.
  Gonza.   My lord Sebastian,
The truth you speak doth lack some gentleness,
And time to speak it in: you rub the sore,
When you should bring the plaster.
  Sebas.   Very well.
  Anto. And most chirurgeonly.[23]
  Gonza. It is foul weather in us all, good sir,

20. *Who* is used for *which.* This is but another illustration of
the changes that have taken place in the use of words since Shakespeare's time.

21. Sebastian tells the King that he alone is responsible for the
loss. Even his daughter weighed her wish to be obedient against
her loathing of the match.

22. *Dearest* here means the same as *heaviest* or *worst.*

23. *Chirurgeon* is the old word for *surgeon.* Antonio says,
"And in the most surgeon-like manner."

When you are cloudy.[24]

　Sebas.　　　　　　　　Foul weather!

　Anto.　　　　　　　　　　Very foul.

　Gonza.　Had I plantation[25] of this isle, my
　　lord,—

　Anto.　He'd sow't with nettle-seed.

　Sebas.　　　　　　Or docks, or mallows.

　Gonza.—And were the King on't, what would
I do?

　Sebas.　'Scape being drunk for want of wine.

　Gonza.　I' the commonwealth I would by con-
　　traries

Execute all things; for no kind of traffic

Would I admit; no name of magistrate;

Letters should not be known; riches, poverty,

And use of service, none; contract, succession,[26]

Bourn,[27] bound of land, tilth,[28] vineyard, none;

No use of metal, corn, or wine, or oil;

No occupation; all men idle, all,

And women too, but innocent and pure;

No sovereignty:—

　Sebas.　　　　　　Yet he would be king on't.

　Anto.　The latter end of his commonwealth forgets the beginning.

　Gonza.—All things in common Nature should
　　produce

Without sweat or endeavour: treason, felony,

24. Gonzalo says, literally, "When you are sad, we all share
your sorrow."

25. "Had I the colonizing" is what Gonzalo means. Antonio
makes it appear that Gonzalo was speaking of *planting* the island.

26. *Succession* means *inheritance*, as a son *succeeds* to his
father's property.

27. *Bourn* means *brook*, hence *boundary*, as of land.

28. *Tilth* means *tillage* or *cultivation*, as of land.

Sword, pike, knife, gun, or need of any engine,[29]
Would I not have; but Nature should bring forth,
Of its own kind, all foison,[30] all abundance,
To feed my innocent people.

Sebas. No marrying 'mong his subjects?

Anto. None, man; all idle.

Gonza. I would with such perfection govern,
sir,
T' excel the golden age.[31]

Sebas. God save his Majesty!

Anto. Long live Gonzalo!

Gonza. And—do you mark me, sir?—

Alon. Pr'ythee, no more: thou dost talk nothing to me.

Gonza. I do well believe your Highness; and
did it to minister occasion to these gentlemen, who
are of such sensible[32] and nimble lungs, that they
always use to laugh at nothing.

Anto. 'Twas you we laugh'd at.

Gonza. Who in this kind of merry fooling am
nothing to you:[33] so you may continue, and laugh
at nothing still.

Anto. What a blow was there given!

Sebas. An it had not fallen flat-long.[34]

Gonza. You are gentlemen of brave mettle; you

29. He probably means any *engine of war*.
30. *Foison* means *plenty* of grain or fruits.
31. The *Golden Age* is that period of the world's history when
there was no sin, sorrow or suffering, and when all mankind was so
good that there was no need of government of any sort. The Greeks,
especially, but other peoples to some extent, have mythical tales of
such a time.
32. *Sensible* is here used for *sensitive*.
33. Gonzalo admits that in witty talk he is nothing in comparison to Antonio and Sebastian.
34. A blow with the *flat* of a sword is harmless; so is Gonzalo's
wit.

would lift the Moon out of her sphere, if she would[35] continue in it five weeks without changing.

Enter ARIEL, *invisible, playing solemn music.*

Sebas. We would so, and then go a-bat-fowling.[36]

Anto. Nay, good my lord, be not angry.

Gonza. No, I warrant you; I will not adventure[37] my discretion so weakly. Will you laugh me asleep? for I am very heavy.

Anto. Go sleep, and hear us not.

[*All sleep*[38] *but* ALON., SEBAS., *and* ANTO.

Alon. What, all so soon asleep! I wish mine eyes
Would, with themselves, shut up my thoughts: I find
They are inclined to do so.

Sebas.   Please you, sir,
Do not omit[39] the heavy offer of it:
It seldom visits sorrow; when it doth,
It is a comforter.

Anto.   We two, my lord,
Will guard your person while you take your rest,
And watch your safety.

35. We would say *should* instead of *would* in this case.

36. When they used to hunt birds in the night, they called it *bat-fowling.* Sometimes at night they took a light into the woods, and while one of the hunters held a net in front of the light, the others would beat the bushes round about. Some of the frightened birds would fly directly at the light and become entangled in the net.

37. *Adventure* here means *put in peril.*

38. Ariel is at work again, and in carrying out the plans of Prospero, he causes some to fall asleep that the others may plot.

39. *Omit* here means *neglect.* Sebastian suggests that it will be better for Alonso to go to sleep while he can. He has reasons for wishing the King asleep.

Alon. Thank you.—Wondrous heavy.[40]

[ALONSO *sleeps.* *Exit* ARIEL.

Sebas. What a strange drowsiness possesses them!

ANTONIO AND SEBASTIAN PLOTTING

Anto. It is the quality o' the climate.

Sebas. Why Doth it not, then, our eyelids sink? I find not Myself disposed to sleep.

40. Alonso grows more sleepy under Ariel's influence, and in these words alludes to what Sebastian has just said—"It is a wondrous heavy offer of sleep."

Anto.　　　　　　　Nor I; my spirits are nimble.
They[41] fell together all, as by consent;
They dropp'd, as by a thunder-stroke.　What
　　might,
Worthy Sebastian, O, what might![42]　No more:
And yet methinks I see it in thy face,
What thou shouldst be: th' occasion speaks thee;[43]
　　and
My strong imagination sees a crown
Dropping upon thy head.
　　Sebas.　　　　　　What, art thou waking?
　　Anto.　Do you not hear me speak?
　　Sebas.　　　　　　　I do; and surely
It is a sleepy language, and thou speak'st
Out of thy sleep.　What is it thou didst say?
This is a strange repose, to be asleep
With eyes wide open; standing, speaking, moving,
And yet so fast asleep.
　　Anto.　　　　　　Noble Sebastian,
Thou lett'st thy fortune sleep,—die rather; wink'st
Whiles thou art waking.[44]
　　Sebas.　　　　　Thou dost snore distinctly;
There's meaning in thy snores.
　　Anto.　I am more serious than my custom: you
Must be so too, if heed[45] me; which to do
Trebles thee o'er.[46]

41.　*They* refers to the other men.
42.　Probably we must understand Antonio to mean, "What might
you be!"　In this way Antonio begins to tempt Sebastian, whom he
finds ready to listen.
43.　*Speaks* means *proclaims.*
44.　Antonio says in effect, "You close your eyes when you are
awake.　You are blind to your opportunity."
45.　"If *you* heed me."
46.　Antonio means, "Which if you do, you shall be three times
as great as you are now."

Sebas.   Well, I am standing water.[47]

Anto. I'll teach you how to flow.

Sebas.   Do so: to ebb
Hereditary sloth instructs me.

Anto.   O,
If you but knew how you the purpose cherish
Whiles thus you mock it! how, in stripping it,
You more invest it![48] Ebbing men,[49] indeed,
Most often do so near the bottom run
By their own fear or sloth.

Sebas.   Pr'ythee, say on:
The setting of thine eye and cheek proclaim
A matter[50] from thee; and a birth indeed
Which throes thee much to yield.[51]

Anto.   Thus, sir:
Although this lord[52] of weak remembrance, this
Who shall be of as little memory[53]
When he is earth'd,[54] hath here almost persuaded—
For he's a spirit of persuasion, only
Professes to persuade—the King his son's alive,
'Tis as impossible that he's undrown'd
As he that sleeps here swims.

Sebas.   I have no hope

47. By *I am standing water*, Sebastian means that he is like the ocean standing between tides, ready to ebb or flow. That is, he is ready to accept suggestions from Antonio.

48. Antonio says in effect, "The more you ridicule the purpose I suggest, the more you welcome it."

49. *Ebbing men*, that is, *men whose fortunes are at a low ebb*.

50. *Matter* means *something of great importance*.

51. "It is difficult or painful for you to say what you think." While both have about the same idea in their minds, neither is quite willing to speak of it openly. It is too cruel and murderous a thought.

52. Francisco.

53. That is, "this lord who remembers little of the favors done him, and will be remembered no better."

54. *Earth'd* means *buried*.

That he's undrown'd.

Anto.   O, out of that no hope
What great hope have you! no hope that way is
Another way so high a hope, that even
Ambition cannot pierce a wink[55] beyond—
But doubt discovery there.[56] Will you grant with
    me
That Ferdinand is drown'd?

Sebas.   He's gone.

Anto.   Then, tell me,
Who's the next heir of Naples?

Sebas.   Claribel.

Anto. She that is queen of Tunis; she that
    dwells
Ten leagues beyond man's life;[57] she that from
    Naples
Can have no note,[58] unless the Sun were post,—[59]
The Man-i'-the-moon's too slow,—till new-born
    chins
Be rough and razorable. She 'twas for whom we
All were sea-swallow'd, though some cast again;[60]
And, by that destiny, to perform an act
Whereof what's past is prologue; what to come[61]
In yours and my discharge.

Sebas.   What stuff is this! How say you?

55. *A wink* here means *the least distance.*
56. It is difficult to say just what *But doubt discovery there* means. Antonio says, "But out of your certainty that Ferdinand is drowned, you have a great hope, a hope so high that ambition cannot see anything greater."
57. This means *ten leagues farther away than a man can travel in his life.*
58. *Can have no note* means *can receive no word.*
59. This clause means *unless the sun carried the mail.*
60. *Though some were cast up again.*
61. This sentence means, *you and I can manage what is to come.*

'Tis true, my brother's daughter's Queen of
    Tunis;
So is she heir of Naples; 'twixt which regions
There is some space.

   Anto.   A space whose every cubit
Seems to cry out, *How shalt thou, Claribel,*
Measure us back[62] *to Naples? Keep in Tunis,*
And let Sebastian wake! Say, this were death
That now hath seized them; why, they were no
    worse
Than now they are. There be[63] that can rule
    Naples
As well as he that sleeps; lords that can prate
As amply and unnecessarily
As this Gonzalo: I myself could make
A chough[64] of as deep chat.[65] O, that you bore
The mind that I do! what a sleep were this
For your advancement! Do you understand me?

   Sebas.   Methinks I do.

   Anto.   And how does your content
Tender your own good fortune?[66]

   Sebas.   I remember
You did supplant your brother Prospero.

   Anto.   True:
And look how well my garments sit upon me;
Much feater[67] than before: my brother's servants
Were then my fellows; now they are my men.

   Sebas.   But, for your conscience—

---

62. "*Measure us back,*" etc., means the same as *Return to us.*
63. The word *others* may be understood after *there be.*
64. A *chough* is a bird of the jackdaw kind.
65. This clause means, *I myself could breed a bird to talk as sensibly.*
66. This is difficult to understand. Perhaps it means, "And how does your present contentment advance or care for your interest?"
67. *Feater* means *more fittingly* or *more becomingly.*

Anto.   Ay, sir; and where lies that? if 'twere
a kibe,[68]
'Twould put me to my slipper: but I feel not
This deity in my bosom: twenty consciences,
That stand 'twixt me and Milan, candied[69] be they,
And melt, ere they molest! Here lies your brother,
No better than the earth he lies upon,
If he were that which now he's like; whom I,
With this obedient steel, three inches of it,
Can lay to bed for ever; whiles you, doing thus,
To the perpetual wink[70] for aye might put
This ancient morsel, this Sir Prudence, who
Should not upbraid our course. For all the rest,
They'll take suggestion[71] as a cat laps milk;
They'll tell the clock to any business that
We say befits the hour.[72]

Sebas.   Thy case, dear friend,
Shall be my precedent; as thou gott'st Milan,
I'll come by Naples. Draw thy sword: one stroke
Shall free thee from the tribute which thou pay'st;
And I the King shall love thee.

Anto.   Draw together;[73]
And when I rear my hand, do you the like,
To fall it on Gonzalo.

Sebas.   O, but one word.
                    [*They converse apart.*

68. A *kibe* is a sore on the heel.

69. *Candied* means here the same as crystallized.

70. This means, *while you, doing the same thing, might put Gonzalo to continuous sleep forever.*

71. *Suggestion* here means *temptation.*

72. *They'll tell the clock to any business,* etc., means *they will speak any words we tell them to.*

73. *Draw together* is *let us draw our swords together.*

Music. Re-enter ARIEL, *invisible.*

Ari. My master through his art foresees the
danger
That you, his friend, are in; and sends me forth—
For else his project dies—to keep thee living.

                        [*Sings in* GONZALO'S *ear.*
While you here do snoring lie,
  Open-eyed conspiracy
    His time doth take.
If of life you keep a care,
  Shake off slumber, and beware:
    Awake! Awake!

Anto. Then let us both be sudden.

Gonza. [*Waking.*]   Now, good angels
Preserve the King!—[*To* SEBAS. *and* ANTO.]
    Why, how now!—[*To* ALON.] Ho, awake!—
[*To* SEBAS. *and* ANTO.]   Why are you drawn?[74]
wherefore this ghastly looking?[75]

Alon. [*Waking.*]   What's the matter?

Sebas. Whiles we stood here securing your re-
pose,
Even now, we heard a hollow burst of bellowing
Like bulls, or rather lions: did't not wake you?
It struck mine ear most terribly.

Alon.   I heard nothing.

Anto. O, 'twas a din to fright a monster's ear,
To make an earthquake! sure, it was the roar
Of a whole herd of lions.

Alon.   Heard you this, Gonzalo?

Gonza. Upon mine honour, sir, I heard a hum-
ming,
And that a strange one too, which did awake me:

74. That is, *Why are your swords drawn?*
75. This means, *Why do you look so ghastly?*

I shaked you, sir, and cried: as mine eyes open'd,
I saw their weapons drawn: there was a noise,
That's verity.   'Tis best we stand upon our guard,
Or that we quit this place: let's draw our weapons.

   Alon.   Lead off this ground; and let's make further search
For my poor son.

   Gonza.   Heavens keep him from these beasts!
For he is, sure, i' the island.

   Alon.   Lead away.
                                 [*Exit with the others.*

   Ari.   Prospero my lord shall know what I have
done:—
So, King, go safely on to seek thy son.   [*Exit.*

SCENE II.—*Another part of the Island.*

Enter CALIBAN, *with a burden of wood.   A noise
of Thunder heard.*

   Cal.   All the infections that the Sun sucks up
From bogs, fens, flats, on Prosper fall, and make
him
By inch-meal[1] a disease! His spirits hear me,
And yet I needs must curse. But they'll nor pinch,
Fright me with urchin-shows,[2] pitch me i' the mire,
Nor lead me, like a fire-brand,[3] in the dark
Out of my way, unless he bid 'em: but
For every trifle are they set upon me;
Sometime[4] like apes, that mow[5] and chatter at me

1. *Inch-meal* means *piece-meal.*
2. *Urchin-shows* are *fairy-shows.*
3. *Fire-brand* refers to will o' the wisp, or dancing balls of light
seen sometimes at night in swampy places. People used to think
these lights were tended by naughty sprites who lured men into
trouble.
4. We would now say *sometimes.*
5. *Mow* means *make mouths* or *grin.*

And after bite me; then like hedgehogs, which
Lie tumbling in my barefoot way, and mount
Their pricks[6] at my foot-fall; sometime am I
All wound with adders, who with cloven tongues
Do hiss me into madness. Lo, now, lo!
Here comes a spirit of his; and to torment me
For bringing wood in slowly. I'll fall flat:
Perchance he will not mind me.[7]

Enter TRINCULO.

Trin. Here's neither bush nor shrub, to bear
off[8] any weather at all, and another storm brew-
ing; I hear it sing i' the wind: yond same black
cloud, yond huge one, looks like a foul bombard[9]
that would shed his liquor. If it should thunder
as it did before, I know not where to hide my head:
yond same cloud cannot choose but fall by pailfuls.
—What have we here? a man or a fish? Dead or
alive? A fish: he smells like a fish; a very ancient
and fish-like smell; a kind of not-of-the-newest
poor-john.[10] A strange fish! Were I in England
now, as once I was, and had but this fish painted,
not a holiday fool there but would give a piece of
silver: there would this monster make a man; any
strange beast there makes a man:[11] when they will

6. *Pricks*, here, means their *prickles* or *sharp quills*.
7. Caliban is a monster, part brute, part human, more fish-like
than man-like, probably. He works only when Prospero drives him
to it, and he hates his master bitterly in spite of all that the latter
has done for him. Now Caliban is under punishment for his wicked-
ness.
8. *To bear off* means *to keep off*.
9. A *bombard* is a black jar or jug to hold liquor.
10. *Poor-john* is an old name for dried and salted *hake*, a kind
of fish.
11. Trinculo means that any strange beast could be exhibited
and make a man's fortune.

not give a doit to relieve a lame beggar, they will lay out ten to see a dead Indian. Legg'd like a man! and his fins like arms! Warm, o' my troth! I do now let loose my opinion; hold it no longer: this is no fish, but an islander, that hath lately suffered by a thunder-bolt. [*Thunder.*] Alas, the storm is come again! my best way is to creep under his gaberdine;[12] there is no other shelter hereabout: misery acquaints a man with strange bed-fellows. I will here shroud till the dregs of the storm be past.

[*Creeps under* CALIBAN'S *garment.*

Enter STEPHANO, *singing; a bottle in his hand.*

Steph.   *I shall no more to sea, to sea,*
                  Here shall I die ashore;—
This is a very scurvy tune to sing at a man's funeral: well, here's my comfort.   [*Drinks.*

[Sings.] *The master, the swabber,*[13] *the boatswain,*
                  and I,
          The gunner, and his mate,
     Loved Mall, Meg, and Marian, and
          Margery,
          But none of us cared for Kate;
     For she had a tongue with a tang,[14]
     Would cry to a sailor, Go hang!
     She loved not the savour of tar nor of
          pitch:
          Then to sea, boys, and let her go hang!
This is a scurvy tune too: but here's my comfort.
                                        [*Drinks.*

----

12.   A *gaberdine* was a coarse outer garment or frock.
13.   A *swabber* is a man who scrubs the decks of a ship.
14.   *Tang* means *sharp taste;* here it means that Kate spoke sharply.

Cal. Do not torment me:—O!

Steph. What's the matter? Have we devils here? Do you put tricks upon's with savages and men of Inde,[15] ha? I have not 'scaped drowning, to be afeared now of your four legs; for it hath been said, As proper a man as ever went on four legs cannot make him give ground; and it shall be said so again, while Stephano breathes at's nostrils.

Cal. The spirit torments me:—O!

Steph. This is some monster of the isle with four legs, who hath got, as I take it, an ague. Where the Devil should he learn our language? I will give him some relief, if it be but for that. If I can recover him, and keep him tame, and get to Naples with him, he's a present for any emperor that ever trod on neat's-leather.[16]

Cal. Do not torment me, pr'ythee:
I'll bring my wood home faster.

Steph. He's in his fit now, and does not talk after the wisest. He shall taste of my bottle: if he have never drunk wine afore, it will go near to remove his fit. If I can recover him, and keep him tame, I will not take too much for him;[17] he shall pay for him that hath him, and that soundly.

Cal. Thou dost me yet but little hurt;
Thou wilt anon, I know it by thy trembling:
Now Prosper works upon thee.

Steph. Come on your ways; open your mouth; here is that which will give a language to you, cat:[18]

15. *Inde* may mean India as we understand it, or West India, that is, America. Stephano probably alludes to the sham wonders from America that were often exhibited by lying showmen.

16. *Neat's-leather* is *calfskin.*

17. Stephano means that he will take all he can get.

open your mouth; this will shake your shaking, I can tell you, and that soundly: [*Gives him drink.*] you cannot tell who's your friend; open your chops again. [*Gives him more drink.*

Trin. I should know that voice: it should be—but he is drown'd; and these are devils:—O, defend me!

Steph. Four legs, and two voices—a most delicate monster? His forward voice now is to speak well of his friend; his backward voice is to utter foul speeches and to detract. If all the wine in my bottle will recover him, I will help his ague: [*Gives him drink.*]—Come,—Amen![19] I will pour some in thy other mouth.

Trin. Stephano!

Steph. Doth thy other mouth call me?—Mercy, mercy! This is a devil and no monster: I will leave him; I have no long spoon.[20]

Trin. Stephano!—If thou be'st Stephano, touch me, and speak to me; for I am Trinculo,—be not afeared,—thy good friend Trinculo.

Steph. If thou be'st Trinculo, come forth: I'll pull thee by the lesser legs: if any be Trinculo's legs, these are they. [*Pulls* TRINCULO *out.*] Thou art very Trinculo indeed! How camest thou to be the siege[21] of this moon-calf?[22]

Trin. I took him to be kill'd with a thunder-

18. He alludes to an old saying, "Good liquor will make a cat talk."

19. This is probably the nearest to a prayer that Stephano can remember in his fright.

20. This alludes to an old proverb, "He that would eat with the devil must use a long spoon."

21. *Siege* here means *seat.*

22. A moon-calf was any shapeless monster; supposed to be made so through the influence of the moon.

stroke. But art thou not drown'd, Stephano? I hope, now, thou art not drown'd?[23] Is the storm overblown? I hid me under the dead moon-calf's gaberdine for fear of the storm. And art thou living, Stephano? O Stephano, two Neapolitans 'scaped!

Steph. Pr'ythee, do not turn me about; my stomach is not constant.[24]

Cal. [*Aside.*] These be fine things, an if[25] they be not sprites.
That's a brave god, and bears celestial liquor: I will kneel to him.

Steph. How didst thou 'scape? How camest thou hither? swear, by this bottle, how thou camest hither. I escaped upon a butt of sack,[26] which the sailors heaved o'erboard, by this bottle! which I made of the bark of a tree with mine own hands, since I was cast ashore.

Cal. I'll swear, upon that bottle, to be thy True subject; for the liquor is not earthly.

Steph. Here; swear, man, how thou escapedst.

Trin. Swam ashore, man, like a duck: I can swim like a duck, I'll be sworn.

Steph. Here kiss the book. [*Gives him drink.*] Though thou canst swim like a duck, thou art made like a goose.

Trin. O Stephano, hast any more of this?

23. The superstitious Trinculo is still a little afraid that Stephano may be a ghost.

24. *Constant* here means *settled,* from his recent experiences in the sea.

25. The word *an* may be omitted from before *if* without altering the meaning. Caliban fears the men may be evil spirits, but thinks Stephano must be a god.

26. *Sack* is an old-fashioned intox:cating drink. A *butt* is a big cask holding about two hogsheads.

Steph. The whole butt, man: my cellar is in a rock by the sea-side, where my wine is hid. — How now, moon-calf! how does thine ague?

Cal. Hast thou not dropp'd from heaven?

Steph. Out o' the Moon, I do assure thee: I was the Man-i'-the-moon when time was.

Cal. I've seen thee in her, and I do adore thee: My mistress show'd me thee, and thy dog, and thy bush.[27]

Steph. Come, swear to that; kiss the book: I will furnish it anon with new contents: swear.

　　　　　　　　　　　[*Gives* CALIBAN *drink.*

Trin. By this good light, this is a very shallow monster!—I afeared of him!—a very weak monster!—*The Man-i'-the-moon!*—a most poor credulous monster!—Well drawn,[28] monster, in good sooth.

Cal. I'll show thee every fertile inch o' the island;
And I will kiss thy foot: I pr'ythee, be my god.

Trin. By this light, a most perfidious and drunken monster! when his god's asleep, he'll rob his bottle.

Cal. I'll kiss thy foot; I'll swear myself thy subject.

Steph. Come on then; down, and swear.

Trin. I shall laugh myself to death at this puppy-headed monster. A most scurvy monster! I could find in my heart to beat him,—

Steph.　　Come, kiss. [*Gives* CALIBAN *drink.*

27. All these things the fanciful used to think they could see in the face of the moon.

28. This probably means that Caliban had taken a long hearty draught at the bottle.

Trin.—but that the poor monster's in drink: an abominable monster!

Cal. I'll show thee the best springs; I'll pluck
  thee berries;
I'll fish for thee, and get thee wood enough.
A plague upon the tyrant that I serve!
I'll bear him no more sticks, but follow thee,
Thou wondrous man.

Trin. A most ridiculous monster, to make a wonder of a poor drunkard!

Cal. I pr'ythee, let me bring thee where crabs
  grow;
And I with my long nails will dig thee pig-nuts;[29]
Show thee a jay's nest, and instruct thee how
To snare the nimble marmozet; I'll bring thee
To clustering filberts, and sometimes I'll get thee
Young staniels[30] from the rock. Wilt thou go with
  me?

Steph. I pr'ythee now, lead the way without any more talking. Trinculo, the King and all our company else being drown'd, we will inherit here. Here, bear my bottle: fellow Trinculo, we'll fill him by-and-by again.

Cal. [*Sings drunkenly.*] Farewell, master;
  farewell, farewell.

Trin. A howling monster; a drunken monster!

Cal. No more dams I'll make for fish;
  Nor fetch in firing at requiring;
 Nor scrape trencher, nor wash dish:
  'Ban, 'Ban, Ca—Caliban
  Has a new master; get a new man.

29. *Pig-nuts* were probably *ground-nuts,* the small bulbous growths on the roots of certain vines.

30. A *staniel* is a *kestril,* a beautiful hawk.

Freedom, hey-day, hey-day, freedom! freedom,
    hey-day, freedom!

    Steph.   O brave monster! lead the way.

                             [*Exeunt.*

ACT III

SCENE I.—*Before* PROSPERO'S *Cell.*

Enter FERDINAND, *bearing a log.*

HERE be some sports are painful,
    and their labour
Delight in them sets off:[1] some kinds
    of baseness[2]
Are nobly undergone; and most poor
    matters
Point to rich ends. This my mean
task would be
As heavy to me as 'tis odious, but
The mistress which I serve quickens what's dead,
And makes my labours pleasures:[3] O, she is
Ten times more gentle than her father's crabbed,
And he's composed of harshness. I must remove
Some thousands of these logs, and pile them up,
Upon a sore injunction: my sweet mistress
Weeps when she sees me work; and says such
    baseness
Had never like executor. I forget:
But these sweet thoughts do even refresh my
    labour;

    1.   Ferdinand says, "Some sports are painful, and the delight we take in them offsets the labor."

    2.   *Baseness* here means *lowliness*, rather than anything base or evil.

    3.   Prospero has set Ferdinand to carrying logs, a hard task and a lowly one, to test his love for Miranda, to find out how manly he really is.

Most busy when I do it least.[4]

Enter MIRANDA; *and* PROSPERO *behind.*

Mira.   Alas, now, pray you,
Work not so hard: I would the lightning had
Burnt up those logs that you're enjoin'd to pile!
Pray, set it down, and rest you: when this burns,
'Twill weep for having wearied you. My father
Is hard at study; pray now, rest yourself:
He's safe for these three hours.

Ferd.   O most dear mistress,
The Sun will set before I shall discharge
What I must strive to do.

Mira.   If you'll sit down,
I'll bear your logs the while: pray, give me that;
I'll carry't to the pile.

Ferd.   No, precious creature;
I'd rather crack my sinews, break my back,
Than you should such dishonour undergo,
While I sit lazy by.

Mira.   It would become me
As well as it does you: and I should do it
With much more ease; for my good will is to it,
And yours it is against.

Pros. [*Aside.*] Poor worm, thou art infected!
This visitation shows it.

Mira.   You look wearily.

Ferd. No, noble mistress; 'tis fresh morning
        with me
When you are by at night. I do beseech you,—
Chiefly that I might set it in my prayers,—

4. The meaning of this line probably is that when he works the
least he is really most wearied because he does not have Miranda's
sympathetic words to cheer him, or the sweet thought that he is
working for her.

What is your name?

Mira.   Miranda—O my father,
I've broke your hest to say so!

Ferd.   Admired Miranda!
Indeed the top of admiration; worth
What's dearest to the world! Full many a lady
I've eyed with best regard; and many a time
The harmony of their tongues hath into bondage
Brought my too diligent ear: for several virtues
Have I liked several women; never any
With so full soul, but some defect in her
Did quarrel with the noblest grace she owed,
And put it to the foil:[5] but you, O you,
So perfect and so peerless, are created
Of every creature's best!

Mira.   I do not know
One of my sex; no woman's face remember,
Save, from my glass, mine own; nor have I seen
More that I may call men, than you, good friend,
And my dear father: how features are abroad,
I'm skilless of; but, by my modesty,—
The jewel in my dower,—I would not wish
Any companion in the world but you;
Nor can imagination form a shape,
Besides yourself, to like of. But I prattle
Something too wildly, and my father's precepts
I therein do forget.

Ferd.   I am, in my condition,
A prince, Miranda; I do think, a king,—
I would not so![6]—and would no more endure

5. *Put it to the foil*, means *put it on the defensive*. Foil was a
general name for swords.

6. Ferdinand thinks his father has been drowned, but wishes it
were not so, even though he is thereby made King.

PRAY YOU, WORK NOT SO HARD

This wooden slavery than to suffer
The flesh-fly blow[7] my mouth. Hear my soul
   speak:
The very instant that I saw you, did
My heart fly to your service; there resides,
To make me slave to it; and for your sake
Am I this patient log-man.

    Mira.   Do you love me?

    Ferd. O Heaven, O Earth, bear witness to this
   sound,
And crown what I profess with kind event,
If I speak true! if hollowly,[8] invert
What best is boded me to mischief! I,
Beyond all limit of what else[9] i' the world,
Do love, prize, honour you.

    Mira.   I am a fool
To weep at what I'm glad of.

    Pros. [*Aside.*]   Fair encounter
Of two most rare affections! Heavens rain grace
On that which breeds between them!

    Ferd.   Wherefore weep you?

    Mira. At mine unworthiness, that dare not
   offer
What I desire to give; and much less take
What I shall die to want.[10] But this is trifling;
And all the more it seeks to hide itself,
The bigger bulk it shows. Hence, bashful cunning!
And prompt me, plain and holy innocence!
I am your wife, if you will marry me;

7. The flesh-fly is the blow-fly, which lays its eggs in meat and
helps its decay.

8. *Hollowly* here means *falsely.*

9. We would now say, "*Whatsoever* else."

10. Instead of *to want,* we would say *from wanting.*

If not, I'll die your maid: to be your fellow[11]
You may deny me; but I'll be your servant,
Whether you will or no.

Ferd. My mistress, dearest,
And I thus humble ever.

Mira. My husband, then?

Ferd. Ay, with a heart as willing
As bondage[12] e'er of freedom: here's my hand.

Mira. And mine, with my heart in't: and now
farewell
Till half an hour hence.

Ferd. A thousand thousand![13]

[*Exeunt* FERDINAND *and* MIRANDA.

Pros. So glad of this as they, I cannot be,
Who am surprised withal;[14] but my rejoicing
At nothing can be more. I'll to my book;
For yet, ere supper-time, must I perform
Much business appertaining. [*Exit.*

SCENE II.—*Another part of the Island.*

Enter CALIBAN, STEPHANO, *and* TRINCULO, *with
a bottle.*

Steph. Tell not me: when the butt is out, we
will drink water; not a drop before: therefore bear
up, and board 'em.[1]—Servant-monster, drink to me.

Trin. Servant-monster! the folly of this island!
They say there's but five upon this isle: we are

11. *Fellow* here means *equal.*
12. *Bondman* may be read for *bondage.* He accepts her as
willingly as a slave ever accepted freedom.
13. "A thousand thousand *farewells.*"
14. Prospero desires Ferdinand to love and marry Miranda and
has planned for it, but he is surprised at the suddenness and strength
of their love.
1. As in a naval battle one ship runs alongside another, and the
sailors leap aboard.

three of them; if th' other two be brain'd like us, the State totters.

Steph. Drink, servant-monster, when I bid thee: thy eyes are almost set[2] in thy head.

CALIBAN drinks.

Trin. Where should they be set else? he were a brave monster indeed, if they were set in his tail.

Steph. My man-monster hath drown'd his tongue in sack: for my part, the sea cannot drown me; I swam, ere I could recover the shore, five-and-thirty leagues, off and on, by this light.—Thou shalt be my lieutenant, monster, or my standard.[3]

Trin. Your lieutenant, if you list: he's no standard.[4]

Steph. We'll not run, Monsieur Monster.

Trin. Nor go neither: but you'll lie like dogs, and yet say nothing neither.

Steph. Moon-calf, speak once in thy life, if thou be'st a good moon-calf.

Cal. How does thy Honour? Let me lick thy shoe. I'll not serve him, he is not valiant.

Trin. Thou liest, most ignorant monster: I am in case to justle a constable.[5] Why, thou debosh'd[6] fish, thou, was there ever man a coward that hath drunk so much sack as I to-day? Wilt thou tell a monstrous lie, being but half a fish and half a monster?

Cal. Boo, how he mocks me! wilt thou let him, my lord?

2. *Set* means *fixed and staring.*
3. *Standard* may be read *standard-bearer.*
4. Trinculo means that Caliban is too drunk to stand.
5. Trinculo is always jesting, even at his own expense. He means he is so drunk he would pick a quarrel with a constable.
6. *Debosh'd* means *debauched.*

Trin. Lord, quoth he. That a monster should be such a natural! [7]

Cal. Lo, lo, again! bite him to death, I pr'ythee.

Steph. Trinculo, keep a good tongue in your head: if you prove a mutineer,—the next tree.[8] The poor monster's my subject, and he shall not suffer indignity.

Cal. I thank my noble lord. Wilt thou be pleased
To hearken once again the suit I made thee?

Steph. Marry, will I: kneel, and repeat it; I will stand, and so shall Trinculo.

Enter ARIEL, *invisible.*

Cal. As I told thee before, I am subject to a tyrant; a sorcerer, that by his cunning hath cheated me of the island.

Ari. Thou liest.[9]

Cal. Thou liest, thou jesting monkey, thou
I would my valiant master would destroy thee!
I do not lie.

Steph. Trinculo, if you trouble him any more in's tale, by this hand, I will supplant some of your teeth.

Trin. Why, I said nothing.

Steph. Mum, then, and no more.—
[*To* CAL.] Proceed.

Cal. I say, by sorcery he got this isle;
From me he got it. If thy Greatness will
Revenge it on him,—for, I know, thou darest,
But this thing[10] dare not,—

7. A *natural* is a fool or a simpleton.
8. Stephano means "You shall be hanged on the next tree."
9. As Ariel is invisible, each thinks another has spoken.
10. "*This thing*" is Caliban himself.

Steph. That's most certain.

Cal. Thou shalt be lord of it, and I will serve thee.

Steph. How now shall this be compass'd? Canst thou bring me to the party?

Cal. Yea, yea, my lord; I'll yield him thee asleep,
Where thou mayst knock a nail into his head.

Ari. Thou liest; thou canst not.

Cal. What a pied ninny's[11] this!—Thou scurvy patch![12]—
I do beseech thy Greatness, give him blows,
And take his bottle from him: when that's gone,
He shall drink nought but brine; for I'll not show him
Where the quick freshes[13] are.

Steph. Trinculo, run into no further danger: interrupt the monster one word further, and, by this hand, I'll turn my mercy out of doors, and make a stock-fish[14] of thee.

Trin. Why, what did I? I did nothing. I'll go further off.

Steph. Didst thou not say he lied?

Ari. Thou liest.

Steph. Do I so? take thou that. [*Strikes him.*] As you like this, give me the lie another time.

Trin. I did not give thee the lie. Out o' your wits and hearing too? A pox o' your bottle! this

11. The court fools or jesters of that day wore clothes of many colors—were *pied*, that is, *dappled*.

12. *Patch* is another word referring to the parti-colored clothing of the jester.

13. The *quick freshes* are the running springs of fresh water.

14. *Stock-fish* is a word used in the writings of that period to mean some kind of a fixture, which men struck with their fists or with cudgels in practicing boxing and fighting.

can sack and drinking do. A murrain on your monster, and the Devil take your fingers!

Cal. Ha, ha, ha!

Steph. Now, forward with your tale.—Pr'ythee
stand further off.[15]

Cal. Beat him enough: after a little time, I'll
beat him too.

Steph. Stand further.—Come, proceed.

Cal. Why, as I told thee, 'tis a custom with him
I' the afternoon to sleep; then thou mayst brain
    him,
Having first seized his books; or with a log
Batter his skull, or paunch him with a stake,
Or cut his weazand[16] with thy knife. Remember
First to possess his books; for without them
He's but a sot,[17] as I am, nor hath not
One spirit to command: they all do hate him
As rootedly as I. Burn but his books.
He has brave[18] utensils,—for so he calls them,—
Which, when he has a house, he'll deck't withal:
And that most deeply to consider is
The beauty of his daughter; he himself
Calls her a nonpareil: I ne'er saw woman,
But only Sycorax my dam and she;
But she as far surpasseth Sycorax
As great'st does least.

Steph.   Is it so brave a lass?

Cal. Ay, lord.

Steph. Monster, I will kill this man: his daugh-

15. Stephano speaks first to Caliban, then to Trinculo.
16. The *weazand* is the windpipe or throat.
17. *Sot* in this place means *fool*, not *drunkard*. Caliban thinks
Prospero's books are the source of his magic power over such spirits
as Ariel and those he commands.
18. *Brave* here means *beautiful* or *showy*.

ter and I will be king and queen,—save our Graces!
—and Trinculo and thyself shall be viceroys.—Dost
thou like the plot, Trinculo?

Trin. Excellent.

Steph. Give me thy hand: I am sorry I beat
thee; but, while thou livest, keep a good tongue in
thy head.

Cal. Within this half-hour will he be asleep:
Wilt thou destroy him then?

Steph. Ay, on mine honour.

Ari. This will I tell my master.[19]

Cal. Thou makest me merry; I am full of
    pleasure:
Let us be jocund: will you troll the catch[20]
You taught me but while-ere?[21]

Steph. At thy request, monster, I will do reason,[22] any reason.—Come on, Trinculo, let us sing.

                                          [*Sings.*

*Flout 'em and scout 'em, and scout 'em and flout
    'em;
Thought is free.*

Cal. That's not the tune.

    [ARIEL *plays the tune on a tabor and pipe.*

Steph. What is this same?[23]

Trin. This is the tune of our catch, play'd by
the picture of Nobody.[24]

19. This speech of Ariel's is made aside, that is, out of hearing
of the three conspirators.

20. *Troll the catch* means *sing the jolly song.*

21. *While-ere* means *awhile since.*

22. "I will do anything reasonable," says Stephano.

23. "What is this music I hear?"

24. A common sign in those times was called the picture of
Nobody. It consisted of a head upon two legs, with arms.

Steph. If thou be'st a man, show thyself in thy
likeness: if thou be'st a devil—take't as thou
list.[25]

Trin. O, forgive me my sins!

Steph. He that dies pays all debts: I defy
thee.—Mercy upon us!

Cal. Art thou afeard?

Steph. No, monster, not I.

Cal. Be not afeard; the isle is full of noises,
Sounds and sweet airs that give delight and hurt
not.
Sometime[26] a thousand twangling instruments
Will hum about mine ears; and sometimes
voices,
That, if I then had waked after long sleep,
Will make me sleep again: and then, in dreaming,
The clouds methought would open, and show
riches
Ready to drop upon me; that, when I waked,
I cried to dream again.

Steph. This will prove a brave kingdom to me,
where I shall have my music for nothing.

Cal. When Prospero is destroy'd.

Steph. That shall be by-and-by: I remember
the story.

Cal. The sound is going away; let's follow it,
And after do our work.

Steph. Lead, monster; we'll follow.—I would
I could see this taborer! he lays it on.—Wilt come?

Trin. I'll follow, Stephano.   [*Exeunt.*

25. Stephano probably means, "Take a blow from my fist," and
speaks to the invisible spirit or devil that he now thinks to be near
them, because of Ariel's curious interruptions.

26. *Sometime* is again used for *sometimes*.

SCENE III.—*Another part of the Island.*

Enter ALONSO, SEBASTIAN, ANTONIO, GONZALO,
ADRIAN, FRANCISCO, *and Others.*

Gonza. By'r lakin,[1] I can go no further, sir;
My old bones ache: here's a maze trod, indeed,
Through forth-rights[2] and meanders![3] by your
    patience,
I needs must rest me.

Alon.   Old lord, I cannot blame thee,
Who am myself attach'd with[4] weariness,
To th' dulling of my spirits: sit down, and rest.
Even here I will put off my hope, and keep it
No longer for my flatterer: he is drown'd
Whom thus we stray to find; and the sea mocks
Our frustrate[5] search on land. Well, let him go.

Anto. [*Aside* to SEBAS.] I am right glad that
    he's so out of hope.
Do not, for one repulse, forgo the purpose
That you resolved t' effect.

Sebas. [*Aside to* ANTO.] The next advantage
Will we take throughly.[6]

Anto. [*Aside to* SEBAS.] Let it be to-night.
For, now they are oppress'd with travel, they
Will not, nor cannot, use such vigilance
As when they're fresh.

SEBAS. [*Aside to* ANTO.] I say, to-night: no
    more.   ·   [*Solemn and strange music.*

1. *By our lady!* was a common exclamation. A diminutive form
of this was *by our ladykin* which was contracted into *by our lakin.*
2. *Forth-rights* are straight lines.
3. *Meanders* are crooked lines.
4. *Attach'd with* means *seized by.*
5. *Frustrate* means *defeated* or *baffled.*
6. *Throughly* means the same as *through.* Sebastian means that
the next time he will carry his purpose through.

Alon. What harmony is this? My good
friends, hark!

Gonza. Marvellous sweet music!

Enter PROSPERO *above, invisible. Enter, below,
several strange Shapes, bringing in a Banquet:
they dance about it with gentle actions of saluta-
tion; and, inviting the* KING, &c., *to eat, they
depart.*

Alon. Give us kind keepers, Heavens!—
What were these?

Sebas. A living drollery.⁷ Now I will believe
That there are unicorns; that in Arabia
There is one tree, the phœnix throne;⁸ one phœnix
At this hour reigning there.

Anto.   I'll believe both;
And what does else want credit, come to me,
And I'll be sworn 'tis true; travellers ne'er did lie,
Though fools at home condemn 'em.

Gonza.   If in Naples
I should report this now, would they believe me?
If I should say I saw such islanders,—
For, certes,⁹ these are people of the island,—
Who, though they are of monstrous shape, yet,
   note,
Their manners are more gentle-kind than of
Our human generation you shall find

7. A *drollery* was an amusing show of the *Punch and Judy* kind,
where the characters were puppets. In a *living* drollery, the characters would be alive instead of puppets.

8. The *phœnix* was a fabled bird of antiquity which lived a
hundred years and then died in flames, only to rise young and strong
again from its ashes. There was but one such bird in the world, and
somewhere in Arabia was a tree, different from any other in the
world, in which the phœnix built its nest.

9. *Certes* means *for a certainty.*

Many, nay, almost any.

Pros. [*Aside.*]   Honest lord,
Thou hast said well; for some of you there present
Are worse than devils.

Alon.   I cannot too much muse[10]
Such shapes, such gesture, and such sound, ex-
    pressing—
Although they want the use of tongue—a kind
Of excellent dumb discourse.

Pros. [*Aside.*]   Praise in departing.[11]

Fran. They vanish'd strangely.

Sebas.   No matter, since
They've left their viands behind; for we have
    stomachs.—
Will't please you taste of what is here?

Alon.   Not I.

Gonza. Faith, sir, you need not fear. When
    we were boys,
Who would believe that there were mountaineers
Dew-lapp'd like bulls, whose throats had hanging
    at 'em
Wallets of flesh? or that there were such men
Whose heads stood in their breasts?[12] which now
    we find,
Each putter-out of one for five[13] will bring us
Good warrant of.

10. *Muse* here means *wonder at.*

11. Probably Prospero alludes to an old saying which meant, "Do
not praise your banquet too soon; wait till it is over."

12. Among the *strange shapes* that danced about the banquet
were deformed men from whose throats the flesh hung down in huge
pockets, like goitres, and others whose heads grew from their breasts
without neck and shoulders.

13. Sometimes in Shakespeare's days they practiced a curious
kind of insurance. If a man were going on a long journey, he *put out*
in the hands of agents a sum of money, under the agreement that if

Alon.   I will stand to, and feed,
Although my last: no matter, since I feel
The best is past.—Brother, my lord the Duke,
Stand to, and do as we.

Thunder and lightning. Enter ARIEL, *like a
harpy; claps his wings upon the table; and by
a quaint device, the banquet vanishes.*

Ari. You are three men of sin, whom Destiny—
That hath to instrument[14] this lower world
And what is in't—the never-surfeited sea
Hath caused to belch up; yea, and on this island
Where man doth not inhabit; you 'mongst men
Being most unfit to live. I've made you mad;
And even with such like valour men hang and
      drown
Their proper selves.
      [*Seeing* ALON., SEBAS., &c., *draw their swords.*
                  You fools! I and my fellows
Are ministers of Fate: the elements,
Of whom your swords are temper'd, may as well
Wound the loud winds, or with bemock'd-at stabs
Kill the still-closing[15] waters, as diminish

he returned he was to have a certain number of times the money he
put out. If the journey was perilous, the agreement might call for
five times the sum; if a safer journey, perhaps twice the amount. If
the traveler did not return, the agents kept the sum put out. Gonzalo uses the phrase "*Each putter-out of one for five*," to mean each
man who goes on a perilous journey. He means that every traveler
returning vouches for, or gives good warrant for, the wonders he has
seen.

14. Instead of *That hath to instrument*, we might read *That has
control of.* The whole sentence means: "You are three sinful men
whom Destiny, that rules this lower world and what is in it, has
caused the never-surfeited sea to throw on shore; yes, and on this
island which man does not inhabit; you who are among men the
most unfit to live."

15. Water closes immediately over any cut made in it.

One dowle[16] that's in my plume: my fellow-
  ministers
Are like invulnerable. If you could hurt,
Your swords are now too massy for your strengths,
And will not be uplifted. But remember,—
For that's my business to you,—that you three
From Milan did supplant good Prospero;
Exposed unto the sea, which hath requit[17] it,
Him and his innocent child: for which foul deed
The powers, delaying, not forgetting, have
Incensed the seas and shores, yea, all the creatures,
Against your peace. Thee of thy son, Alonso,
They have bereft; and do pronounce, by me,
Lingering perdition—worse than any death
Can be at once—shall step by step attend
You and your ways; whose[18] wraths to guard you
  from,—
Which here, in this most desolate isle, else falls
Upon your heads,—is nothing, but heart-sorrow
And a clear life ensuing.

*He vanishes in thunder; then, to soft music, enter
    the Shapes again, and dance with mocks and
    mowes, and carry out the table.*

  Pros. [*Aside.*] Bravely the figure of this
    harpy hast thou
Perform'd, my Ariel; a grace it had, devouring:
Of my instruction hast thou nothing 'bated

  16. *Dowle* means *down,* and the comparison means, *as cut off a
single thread of down from my plumes.*
  17. *Requit* means here *revenged.*
  18. *Whose* refers to the word *powers* six lines before. The meaning of the remainder of Ariel's speech is as follows: "Nothing but
repentance and a clear life hereafter can guard you from the wrath
that otherwise will fall upon your heads in this desolate isle."

In what thou hadst to say: so, with good life,
And observation strange, my meaner ministers
Their several kinds have done.[19] My high charms
    work,
And these mine enemies are all knit up
In their distractions: they now are in my power;
And in these fits I leave them, while I visit
Young   Ferdinand, — who   they   s u p p o s e   is
    drown'd,—
And his and my loved darling. [*Exit from above.*
    Gonza. I' the name of something holy, sir, why
        stand you
In this strange stare?
    Alon.   O, it is monstrous, monstrous!
Methought the billows spoke, and told me of it;[20]
The winds did sing it to me; and the thunder,
That deep and dreadful organ pipe, pronounced
The name of Prosper: it did bass my trespass.[21]
Therefore my son i' the ooze is bedded;[22] and
I'll seek him deeper than e'er plummet sounded,
And with him there lie mudded.[23]   [*Exit.*
    Sebas.   But one fiend at a time,
I'll fight their legions o'er.
    Anto.   I'll be thy second.
                [*Exeunt* SEBASTIAN *and* ANTONIO.
    Gonza. All three of them are desperate: their
        great guilt,

19. The meaning of the preceding clause is: "Thus with the
skill of life and keen observance of the ways of men, my humbler
servants have done their work, each according to his nature or kind."
20. *It* refers to his sin against Prospero.
21. That is: "It sang my misdeed in a terrible bass."
22. This clause means: "My son sleeps in the ooze on the bottom of the ocean."
23. *Mudded* means *buried in mud.* Alonso threatens to drown
himself.

Like poison given to work a long time after,[24]
Now 'gins to bite the spirits.—I do beseech you,
That are of suppler joints, follow them swiftly,
And hinder them from what this ecstasy[25]
May now provoke them to.

 Adri.   Follow, I pray you. [*Exeunt.*

ACT IV

SCENE I.—*Before* PROSPERO'S *Cell.*

Enter PROSPERO, FERDINAND, AND MIRANDA.
PROSPERO *speaks.*

I F I have too austerely punish'd you,
  Your compensation makes amends; for I
  Have given you here a thread of mine own life,
  Or that for which I live; who once again
  I tender to thy hand: all thy vexations
Were but my trials of thy love, and thou
Hast strangely stood the test: here, afore Heaven,
I ratify this my rich gift. O Ferdinand,
Do not smile at me that I boast her off,
For thou shalt find she will outstrip all praise
And make it halt behind her.

 Ferd.   I do believe it
Against an oracle.

 Pros. Then, as my gift, and thine own acquisition
Worthily purchased, take my daughter, thou.
Sit, then, and talk with her; she is thine own.—
What, Ariel! my industrious servant, Ariel!

---

 24. There are said to be poisons which will not work until a long time after a person takes them.
 25. For *ecstasy,* read *fit of madness.*

Enter ARIEL.

Ari. What would my potent master? Here I am.

Pros. Thou and thy meaner fellows your last
   service
Did worthily perform; and I must use you
In such another trick. Go bring the rabble,
O'er whom I give thee power, here, to this place:
Incite them to quick motion; for I must
Bestow upon the eyes of this young couple
Some vanity[1] of mine art: it is my promise,
And they expect it from me.

Ari.   Presently?

Pros. Ay, with a twink.[2]

Ari. Before you can say *Come* and *Go,*
   And breathe twice, and cry *So, so.*
   Each one, tripping on his toe,
   Will be here with mop[3] and mow.[4]
   Do you love me, master?—no?   [*Exit.*

Pros. Now come, my Ariel! bring a corollary,[5]
Rather than want a spirit: appear, and pertly![6]
No tongue; all eyes; be silent.

                   [*Soft music.*

Enter IRIS.[7]

Iris. Ceres,[8] most bounteous lady, thy rich leas
Of wheat, rye, barley, vetches, oats, and peas;

1. *Vanity* probably means *fine display.*
2. *With a twink* means *in the twinkling of an eye.*
3. *Mop* means *chattering.*
4. *Mow* means *making faces.* *Mop and mow* were words applied
to such chattering and grinning as a monkey makes.
5. A *corollary* here means *more than enough.*
6. *Pertly* means *alertly.*
7. Iris was the fleet messenger of the Greek gods. She had
beautiful golden wings, and as she flew across the heavens, she left
the many-colored rainbow as her trail.
8. Ceres was the Greek goddess of the earth, who especially
watched over the growth of grain and fruits. She it is who brings

Thy turfy mountains, where live nibbling sheep,
And flat meads thatch'd with stover,[9] them to keep;
Thy banks with peonéd[10] and twilled[11] brims,
Which spongy[12] April at thy hest betrims,
To make cold nymphs chaste crowns;[13] and thy
     brown groves,
Whose shadow the dismissed bachelor loves,
Being lass-lorn;[14] thy pole-clipt vineyard;[15]
And thy sea-marge, steril, and rocky-hard,
Where thou thyself dost air;—the Queen o' the
     Sky,[16]
Whose watery arch[17] and messenger am I,
Bids thee leave these, and with her sovereign Grace,
Here on this grass-plot, in this very place,
To come and sport. Her peacocks[18] fly amain:
Approach, rich Ceres, her to entertain.

Enter Ceres.

Cer. Hail, many-color'd messenger, that ne'er
Dost disobey the wife of Jupiter;[19]

rich harvests, or when her attention is called away, permits drought
to kill the vegetation.

    9. *Stover* is fodder. A mead thatched with stover is a meadow
covered with rich grass and hay.

    10. The common marsh-marigold was called *peony* in some lo-
calities.

    11. Reeds were called *twills* in some localities.

    12. The frequent rains of April make the ground like a water-
soaked sponge.

    13. This passage means: "Thy banks with edges bordered with
marsh-marigolds and reeds which rainy April trims to make cold
crowns for chaste nymphs."

    14. *Lass-lorn* means *forsaken by his lass.*

    15. The poles in a vineyard are *clipt* or *embraced* by the vines.

    16. Juno was Queen of the sky and Iris was her special mes-
senger.

    17. Rainbow.

    18. Peacocks were sacred to Juno and are represented as ac-
companying her.

    19. Jupiter was the chief god of the ancient Greeks, and Juno
was his wife.

CERES ENTERS, AT IRIS'S CALL

Who, with thy saffron wings, upon my flowers
Diffusest honey-drops, refreshing showers;
And with each end of thy blue bow dost crown
My bosky[20] acres and my unshrubb'd down,[21]
Rich scarf to my proud Earth;—why hath thy
    Queen
Summon'd me hither, to this short-grass'd green?

   Iris. A contract of true love to celebrate;
And some donation freely to estate
On the bless'd lovers.

   Cer.   Tell me, heavenly Bow,
If Venus[22] or her son, as thou dost know,
Do now attend the Queen? Since they did plot
The means that dusky Dis[23] my daughter got,[24]
Her and her blind boy's[25] scandal'd company
I have forsworn.

   Iris.   Of her society
Be not afraid: I met her deity
Cutting the clouds towards Paphos,[26] and her son
Dove-drawn with her.

   Cer.   Here, Queen of highest state,
Great Juno comes; I know her by her gait.[27]

Enter JUNO.[28]

   Juno. How does my bounteous sister? Go
  with me

    20. *Bosky* means *wooded.*
    21. *Unshrubbed downs* are tracts of land on which no bushes
grow.
    22. Venus was the Greek goddess of love and beauty.
    23. *Dis* is another name for Pluto, who according to the Greek
mythology ruled in the dismal lower world.
    24. By the aid of Venus, Pluto stole Proserpina, the daughter of
Ceres and Jupiter, and carried her away to be his queen in Hades.
    25. Her *blind boy* is Cupid, the mischievous little god of love.
    26. Paphos was a city in Cyprus, where Venus loved to live.
    27. Juno's walk was very stately and dignified.

To bless this twain, that they may prosperous be,
And honour'd in their issue.

SONG.

Juno. *Honour, riches, marriage-blessing,*
Long continuance, and increasing,
Hourly joys be still upon you!
Juno sings her blessings on you.

Cer. *Earth's increase, and foison plenty,*[29]
Barns and garners never empty;
Vines with clustering bunches growing;
Plants with goodly burden bowing;
Spring come to you at the farthest
In the very end of harvest![30]
Scarcity and want shall shun you;
Ceres' blessing so is on you.

Ferd. This is a most majestic vision, and
Harmonious charmingly. May I be bold
To think these spirits?[31]
Pros. Spirits, which by mine art
I have from their confines call'd to enact
My present fancies.

---

28. Juno was a large, noble, motherly-looking woman, who is
represented in art as attended by the nymphs and the hours, as well
as by Iris. The goose and the cuckoo were as much Juno's birds as
the peacock. She was the protectress of young married people and
infants, and so was worshipped especially by women.

29. *Foison* and *plenty* mean about the same thing. The phrase
might be read, *overflowing plenty*, a great plenty.

30. This means, may a new spring come as soon as you have
gathered the harvest of the old one. May there be no winter in your
lives.

31. Ferdinand is still amazed, and inquires if they are really
spirits that he sees.

Ferd.   Let me live here ever;
So rare a wonder'd[32] father and a wife
Make this place Paradise.   [Juno *and* Ceres
                        whisper, and send
             Iris *on employment.*

     Pros.   Sweet, now, silence!
Juno and Ceres whisper seriously;
There's something else to do: hush, and be mute,
Or else our spell is marr'd.

     Iris.   You nymphs, call'd Naiads, of the wind-
       ing brooks,
With your sedge crowns and ever-harmless looks,
Leave your crisp[33] channels, and on this green land
Answer our summons; Juno does command:
Come, temperate nymphs, and help to celebrate
A contract of true love; be not too late.—

                  Enter certain Nymphs.

You sun-burn'd sicklemen,[34] of August weary,
Come hither from the furrow, and be merry:
Make holiday; your rye-straw hats put on,
And these fresh nymphs encounter every one
In country footing.

Enter certain Reapers, *properly habited: they join
     with the* Nymphs *in a graceful dance; towards
     the end whereof* Prospero *starts suddenly, and
     speaks; after which, to a strange, hollow, and
     confused noise, they heavily vanish.*

    32. *So rare a wonder'd father* means, *so rarely wonderful a
father.*
    33. *Crisp* means *curled,* alluding to the wavelets that the breezes
make on the surface of the water.
    34. The *sicklemen* are reapers called from the harvest fields to
make merry.

Pros. [*Aside.*] I had forgot that foul con-
    spiracy
Of the beast Caliban and his confederates
Against my life: the minute of their plot
Is almost come.—[*To the* Spirits.] Well done;
    avoid;[35] no more!
  Ferd. This is most strange: your father's in
    some passion
That works him strongly.
  Mira.   Never till this day
Saw I him touch'd with anger so distemper'd.
  Pros. You do, my son, look in a moved sort,
As if you were dismay'd: be cheerful, sir.
Our revels now are ended. These our actors,
As I foretold you, were all spirits, and
Are melted into air, into thin air:
And, like the baseless fabric of this vision,
The cloud-capp'd towers, the gorgeous palaces,
The solemn temples, the great globe itself,
Yea, all which it inherit, shall dissolve,
And, like this insubstantial pageant faded,
Leave not a rack[36] behind. We are such stuff
As dreams are made on,[37] and our little life
Is rounded[38] with a sleep. Sir, I am vex'd;
Bear with my weakness; my old brain is troubled:
Be not disturb'd with my infirmity:
If you be pleased, retire into my cell,
And there repose: a turn or two I'll walk,
To still my beating mind.
  Ferd. ⎫
          ⎬ We wish you peace.
  Mira. ⎭

35. *Avoid* means *begone.*
36. The thin fleecy clouds, highest in the sky, were called *rack.*
37. *On* is here used for *of.*
38. We would say *rounded off* or *finished.*

Pros. [*To* ARIEL.]   Come with a thought!—
I thank ye.[39] [*Exeunt* FERD. *and* MIRA.]—Ariel,
   come!

Re-enter ARIEL.

Ari.   Thy thoughts I cleave to: what's thy
   pleasure?
Pros.   Spirit,
We must prepare to meet with[40] Caliban.
Ari.   Ay, my commander: when I presented
   Ceres,
I thought t' have told thee of it; but I fear'd
Lest I might anger thee.
Pros.   Well, say again, where didst thou leave
   these varlets?
Ari.   I told you, sir, they were red-hot with
   drinking;
So full of valour, that they smote the air
For breathing[41] in their faces; beat the ground
For kissing of their feet; yet always bending
Towards their project.   Then I beat my tabor;
At which, like unback'd[42] colts, they prick'd their
   ears,
Advanced[43] their eyelids, lifted up their noses
As they smelt music: so I charm'd their ears,
That, calf-like, they my lowing follow'd through
Tooth'd briers, sharp furzes, pricking goss, and
   thorns,
Which enter'd their frail shins: at last I left them

39. *I thank ye* is spoken to Ferdinand and Miranda, and is Prospero's reply to their good wishes.

40. *Meet with* means *oppose* or *counteract.*

41. *For breathing* means *because it breathed.* In the next line,
for kissing means *because it kissed.*

42. *Unback'd* means *unridden.*

43. *Advanced* means *raised.*

I' the filthy-mantled[44] pool beyond your cell,
There dancing up to th' chins, that[45] the foul lake
O'erstunk their feet.

 Pros.   This was well done, my bird.
Thy shape invisible retain thou still:
The trumpery in my house, go bring it hither,
For stale[46] to catch these thieves.

 Ari.   I go, I go. [*Exit.*

 Pros. A devil, a born-devil,[47] on whose nature
Nurture can never stick;[48] on whom my pains,
Humanely taken, all are lost, quite lost;
And as with age his body uglier grows,
So his mind cankers.[49] I will plague them all,
Even to roaring.—

   Re-enter ARIEL *loaden with glistering*
     apparel, &c.

    Come, hang them on this line.[50]

PROSPERO *and* ARIEL *remain invisible.* *Enter* CAL-
IBAN, STEPHANO, *and* TRINCULO, *all wet.*

 Cal. Pray you, tread softly, that the blind mole
  may not
Hear a foot fall: we now are near his cell.

 Steph. Monster, your fairy, which you say is

---

44. The pool was mantled, or covered over, with filth.

45. For *that* read *so that* or *insomuch that.*

46. *Stale* means *bait.* It was a term used by hunters for a bait that would lure birds.

47. Caliban.

48. *Nurture* can never stick on his *nature*: that is, he can never be improved by culture or education.

49. *Cankers* means *rusts*, or here, *eats into itself.*

50. It is not known whether *line* refers to a clothesline or to a line tree. Only Shakespeare himself could tell us to a certainty.

a harmless fairy, has done little better than play'd
the Jack with us.[51]

Trin. Monster, I do smell all horse-stale; at
which my nose is in great indignation.

Steph. So is mine.—Do you hear, monster? If
I should take a displeasure against you, look you,—

Trin. Thou wert but a lost monster.

Cal. Nay, good my lord, give me thy favour
still.
Be patient, for the prize I'll bring thee to
Shall hoodwink this mischance:[52] therefore speak
softly;
All's hush'd as midnight yet.

Trin. Ay, but to lose our bottles in the pool,—

Steph. There is not only disgrace and dishonour
in that, monster, but an infinite loss.

Trin. That's more to me than my wetting: yet
this is your harmless fairy, monster.

Steph. I will fetch off my bottle, though I be
o'er ears for my labour.

Cal. Pr'ythee, my King, be quiet. See'st thou
here?
This is the mouth o' the cell: no noise, and enter.
Do that good mischief which may make this island
Thine own for ever, and I, thy Caliban,
For aye thy foot-licker.

Steph. Give me thy hand. I do begin to have
bloody thoughts.

Trin. O King Stephano! O peer![53] O worthy
Stephano! look what a wardrobe here is for thee!

51. *Play'd the Jack with us.* "Led us astray as a Jack-o'-
lantern might."

52. *To hoodwink this mischance* means *to make it forgotten* or
overlooked.

53. In Hudson's Shakespeare this is explained as an allusion to

Cal. Let it alone, thou fool; it is but trash.

Trin. O, ho, monster! we know what belongs to a frippery.[54]—O King Stephano!

Steph. Put off that gown, Trinculo; by this hand, I'll have that gown.

Trin. Thy Grace shall have it.

Cal. The dropsy drown this fool!—what do you mean,
To dote thus on such luggage? Let's along,
And do the murder first: if he awake,
From toe to crown he'll fill our skins with pinches;
Make us strange stuff.

Steph. Be you quiet, monster.—Mistress line, is not this my jerkin? Now is the jerkin under the line:[55] now, jerkin, you are like to lose your hair, and prove a bald jerkin.

Trin. Do, do; we steal by line and level,[56] an't like your Grace.

Steph. I thank thee for that jest; here's a garment for't: wit shall not go unrewarded while I am king of this country. *Steal by line and level* is an

the old ballad entitled "Take thy old Cloak about thee." The following stanza is quoted:

> "*King Stephen* was a worthy *peer*,
> His breeches cost him but a crown;
> He held them sixpence all too dear,
> Therefore he called the tailor lown."

54. A *frippery* was a shop where old clothes were sold. Trinculo has found the clothing Ariel hung upon the line.

55. *Under the line.* We can imagine that Stephano has pulled the leather jerkin or coat from the line. When he says *under the line*, he thinks of that as an expression sailors use when they are near the equinoctial line or equator, where the heat is intense, so strong as to take the hair or fur off the coat and make it a *bald jerkin*.

56. *By line and level*, that is, as architects build, by plumb line and level. Trinculo picks up the word *line* and makes a new pun on it.

excellent pass of pate;[57] there's another garment
for't.

Trin. Monster, come, put some lime[58] upon
your fingers, and away with the rest.

STEPHANO AND TRINCULO QUARREL

Cal. I will have none on't: we shall lose our
        time,
And all be turn'd to barnacles,[59] or to apes
With foreheads villainous low.

57. A *pass* is a *thrust; pate* is *head. Pass of pate* is a *thrust* or
sally of *wit.*
58. *Lime* is a sticky substance used to catch birds.
59. *Barnacles* here means *barnacle-geese*, a kind of geese sup-

Steph. Monster, lay-to your fingers: help to bear this away, where my hogshead of wine is, or I'll turn you out of my kingdom: go to, carry this.

Trin. And this.

Steph. Ay, and this.

A noise of hunters heard. Enter divers Spirits *in shape of hounds, and hunt them about;* PROS-PERO *and* ARIEL *setting them on.*

Pros. Hey, Mountain, hey!

Ari. Silver! there it goes, Silver!

Pros. Fury, Fury! there, Tyrant, there! hark! hark!— [CAL., STEPH. *and* TRIN. *are driven out.*

Go charge my goblins that they grind their joints
With dry convulsions; shorten up their sinews
With aged cramps; and more pinch-spotted make them
Than pard or cat-o'-mountain.[60]

Ari. Hark, they roar!

Pros. Let them be hunted soundly. At this hour
Lie at my mercy all mine enemies:
Shortly shall all my labours end, and thou
Shalt have the air at freedom: for a little
Follow, and do me service. [*Exeunt.*

posed by the superstitious to be produced when certain barnacles or shell-fish fell into the sea water.

60. *Pard* is a contraction for *leopard; cat-o'-mountain* may be another name for wild-cat, though wild-cats are not spotted. Probably the term is loosely used to mean any spotted animal of the cat tribes.

ACT V

SCENE I.—*Before the Cell of* PROSPERO.

Enter PROSPERO *in his magic robes, and* ARIEL.
PROSPERO *speaks:*

N OW does my project gather to a head:
My charms crack not; my spirits obey;
and Time
Goes upright with his carriage.[1] How's
the day?
 Ari. On the sixth hour; at which
time, my lord,
You said our work should cease.
 Pros.   I did say so,
When first I raised the tempest. Say, my spirit,
How fares the King and's followers?
 Ari.   Confined together
In the same fashion as you gave in charge;
Just as you left them; all are prisoners, sir,
In the line-grove which weather-fends your cell;[2]
They cannot budge till your release.[3] The King,
His brother, and yours, abide all three distracted;
And the remainder mourning over them,
Brimful of sorrow and dismay; but chiefly
He that you term'd *The good old lord, Gonzalo:*
His tears run down his beard, like winter-drops
From eaves of reeds. Your charm so strongly
works 'em,

1. *Goes upright with his carriage* means, *goes erectly under his burden,* that is, there is time enough to accomplish what Prospero wishes to do.

2. That is, "In the grove of line-trees which protects your cell from the weather."

3. *Till your release* means *till you release them.*

That, if you now beheld them, your affections
Would become tender.

Pros.   Dost thou think so, spirit?

Ari.   Mine would, sir, were I human.

Pros.   And mine shall.
Hast thou, which art but air, a touch, a feeling
Of their afflictions, and shall not myself,
One of their kind, that relish all as sharply
Passion as they,[4] be kindlier moved than thou art?
Though with their high wrongs I am struck to th'
    quick,
Yet with my nobler reason 'gainst my fury
Do I take part: the rarer action is
In virtue than in vengeance: they being penitent,
The sole drift of my purpose doth extend
Not a frown further. Go release them, Ariel:
My charms I'll break, their senses I'll restore,
And they shall be themselves.

Ari.   I'll fetch them, sir. [*Exit.*

Pros. Ye elves of hills, brooks, standing lakes,
    and groves;
And ye that on the sands with printless foot
Do chase the ebbing Neptune,[5] and do fly him
When he comes back; you demi-puppets that
By moonshine do the green-sour ringlets[6] make,
Whereof the ewe not bites; and you whose pastime

4. In this place *all* has the sense of *quite; relish* means *feel; passion* has the sense of *suffering.* The meaning of the clause is, that feel suffering quite as sharply as they.

5. *Neptune,* the name of the god of the seas, is used for *sea* or *ocean.*

6. "Fairy rings" are green circles in the grass. They were supposed to be caused by fairies dancing in a circle, but are now known to be caused by mushrooms which grow in circles and which enrich the ground as they decay. Because it contained some peculiar quality which Shakespeare calls sourness, the sheep would not eat the grass of the rings.

Is to make midnight mushrooms;[7] that rejoice
To hear the solemn curfew;[8] by whose aid—
Weak masters[9] though ye be—I have be-dimm'd
The noon-tide Sun, call'd forth the mutinous winds,
And twixt the green sea and the azure vault
Set roaring war: to the dread-rattling thunder
Have I given fire, and rifted Jove's[10] stout oak
With his own bolt: the strong-based promontory
Have I made shake, and by the spurs[11] pluck'd up
The pine and cedar: graves at my command
Have waked their sleepers, oped, and let 'em forth
By my so potent art. But this rough magic
I here abjure; and, when I have required
Some heavenly music,—which even now I do,—
To work mine end upon their senses that
This airy charm is for, I'll break my staff,
Bury it certain fathoms in the earth,
And deeper than did ever plummet sound
I'll drown my book.   [*Solemn music.*

Re-enter ARIEL: *after him,* ALONSO, *with a frantic
    gesture, attended by* GONZALO; SEBASTIAN *and*
    ANTONIO *in like manner, attended by* ADRIAN
    and FRANCISCO: *they all enter the circle which*
    PROSPERO *has made, and there stand charmed;
    which* PROSPERO *observing, speaks.*

7. Because mushrooms and toadstools spring up so quickly in
the night, they were supposed to be the work of fairies.

8. The curfew rings at night, and the fairies rejoice to hear it,
for it is the signal for them to begin their frolics.

9. The fairies are weak masters, that is, they can accomplish
little if left to themselves, but under the direction of a human mind
like Prospero's they could work such wonders as he describes.

10. The oak was sacred to Jove (Jupiter), and lightning and
thunder-bolts were his chief weapons.

11. The spurs are the long *roots* of the pines and cedars.

A solemn air, as the best comforter
To an unsettled fancy, cure the brains,
Now useless, boil'd[12] within the skull! — There
    stand,
For you are spell-stopp'd.—
Holy Gonzalo, honourable man,
Mine eyes, even sociable to[13] the show of thine,
Fall fellowly drops.[14]—The charm dissolves apace;
And as the morning steals upon the night,
Melting the darkness, so their rising senses[15]
Begin to chase the ignorant fumes that mantle[16]
Their clearer reason.—O thou good Gonzalo,
My true preserver, and a loyal sir
To him thou follow'st! I will pay thy graces
Home[17] both in word and deed.—Most cruelly
Didst thou, Alonso, use me and my daughter:
Thy brother was a furtherer in the act:—
Thou'rt pinch'd for't now, Sebastian.—Flesh and
    blood,
You, brother mine, that entertain'd ambition
Expell'd remorse[18] and nature;[19] who, with Sebas-
    tian,—
Whose inward pinches therefore are most strong,—
Would here have kill'd your King; I do forgive
    thee,
Unnatural though thou art.—Their understanding

12. *Boil'd* is used for *boiling* or *seething.*
13. *Sociable to* means *sympathizing with.*
14. *Fall fellowly drops* means *shed tears in sympathy.*
15. *Rising senses* means *clearing mental faculties.*
16. *Ignorant fumes that mantle* alludes to the confusion that the charm has caused in their ideas. The whole passage means simply that they are recovering their senses.
17. This sentence means, *I will reward thee to the utmost.*
18. *Remorse* here means *pity.*
19. *Nature* here means *brotherly love.*

Begins to swell; and the approaching tide
Will shortly fill the reasonable shore,[20]
That now lies foul and muddy. Not one of them
That yet looks on me, or would know me.—Ariel,
Fetch me the hat and rapier in my cell:—

         [Exit ARIEL.

I will discase me,[21] and myself present
As I was sometime Milan:[22]—quickly, spirit;
Thou shalt ere long be free.

  ARIEL *re-enters, singing, and helps to attire*
      PROSPERO.

Ari. Where the bee sucks, there suck I:
  In a cowslip's bell I lie,—
  There I couch: when owls do cry,
  On the bat's back I do fly
  After Summer, merrily.[23]
Merrily, merrily shall I live now
Under the blossom that hangs on the bough.
Pros. Why, that's my dainty Ariel! I shall
 miss thee;
But yet thou shalt have freedom:—so, so, so.
To the King's ship, invisible as thou art:
There shalt thou find the mariners asleep
Under the hatches; the master and the boatswain
Being awaked, enforce them to this place,

20. *The reasonable shore* means *the shore of reason.* As the
tide rises to the shore of the sea, so their clearing thoughts fill their
minds.

21. *Discase me* means *remove my disguise.*

22. *As I was sometime Milan* means *as I was once, the Duke of
Milan.*

23. The meaning of the three lines preceding has been much
disputed. No one knows exactly what the poet meant. Perhaps Ariel
sings with this meaning: "When the owls cry and foretell the approach of winter, I fly on the back of a bat in a merry search for
summer."

Ins Weddell White

WHERE THE BEE SUCKS, THERE SUCK I

And presently, I pr'ythee.

    Ari.   I drink the air before me,[24] and return
Or e'er your pulse twice beat.   [*Exit* ARIEL.

    Gonza. All torment, trouble, wonder, and
    amazement
Inhabit here: some heavenly power guide us
Out of this fearful country!

    Pros.   Behold, sir King,
The wronged Duke of Milan, Prospero:
For more assurance that a living prince
Does now speak to thee, I embrace thy body;
And to thee and thy company I bid
A hearty welcome.

    Alon.   Whêr[25] thou be'st he or no,
Or some enchanted trifle[26] to abuse me,
As late I have been, I not know: thy pulse
Beats, as of flesh and blood; and, since I saw thee,
Th' affliction of my mind amends, with which,
I fear, a madness held me: this must crave—
An if this be at all[27]—a most strange story.
Thy dukedom I resign and do entreat
Thou pardon me my wrongs.[28] But how should
    Prospero
Be living and be here?

    Pros.   First, noble friend,[29]
Let me embrace thine age, whose honour cannot
Be measured or confined.

---

    24. Ariel uses this fanciful way of saying that he will go as fast
as human thought.

    25. *Wher* is a contraction of *whether.*

    26. *Trifle* here means *phantom* or *spirit.*

    27. This clause means, *if this be at all true.*

    28. *My wrongs* means *the wrongs I have done.*

    29. He speaks to Gonzalo.

Gonza.   Whether this be
Or be not, I'll not swear.
　　Pros.   You do yet taste
Some subtilties[30] o' the isle, that will not let you
Believe things certain. — Welcome, my friends
　　all:—
[*Aside to* SEBAS. *and* ANTO.]　But you, my brace
　　of lords, were I so minded,
I here could pluck his Highness' frown upon you,
And justify you traitors:[31] at this time
I'll tell no tales.
　　Sebas. [*Aside to* ANTO.]　The Devil speaks in
　　him.
　　Pros.   Now,
For you, most wicked sir, whom to call brother
Would even infect my mouth, I do forgive
Thy rankest fault; all of them; and require
My dukedom of thee, which perforce, I know,
Thou must restore.
　　Alon.   If thou be'st Prospero,
Give us particulars of thy preservation;
How thou hast met us here, who three hours since
Were wreck'd upon this shore; where I have lost—
How sharp the point of this remembrance is!—
My dear son Ferdinand.
　　Pros.   I'm woe[32] for't, sir.
　　Alon. Irreparable is the loss; and patience
Says it is past her cure.
　　Pros.   I rather think
You have not sought her help; of whose soft grace,
For the like loss I have her sovereign aid,

30. *Taste some subtilties* means *feel some deceptions.*
31. *Justify you traitors* means *prove that you are traitors.*
32. *Woe* here means *sorry.*

And rest myself content.

Alon.   You the like loss!

Pros.   As great to me, as late;[33] and, portable
To make the dear loss, have I means much weaker
Than you may call to comfort you; for I
Have lost my daughter.

Alon.   A daughter!
O Heavens, that they were living both in Naples,
The King and Queen there! that they were, I wish
Myself were mudded in that oozy bed
Where my son lies.   When did you lose your
    daughter?

Pros.   In this last tempest. I perceive, these
    lords
At this encounter do so much admire,[34]
That they devour their reason, and scarce think
Their eyes do offices of truth, these words
Are natural breath:[35] but, howsoe'er you have
Been justled from your senses, know for certain
That I am Prospero, and that very Duke
Which was thrust forth of Milan; who most
    strangely
Upon this shore, where you were wreck'd, was
    landed
To be the lord on't. No more yet[36] of this;
For 'tis a chronicle of day by day,[37]
Not a relation for a breakfast, nor

33. *As late* means *as recent.*

34. In this place *admire* means *wonder.*

35. *Are natural breath* means *are the breath of a human being.* The lords are still amazed; they cannot reason, they can
scarcely believe their eyes or that the words they hear come from
a living human being.

36. In this connection *yet* means *now,* or *for the present.*

37. That is, it is a story to be told day after day.

Befitting this first meeting. Welcome, sir;
This cell's my Court: here have I few attendants,
And subjects none abroad: pray you, look in.
My dukedom since you've given me again,
I will requite you with as good a thing;
At least bring forth a wonder to content ye
As much as me my dukedom.

The entrance of the Cell opens, and discovers FER-
DINAND *and* MIRANDA *playing at chess.*

Mira. Sweet lord, you play me false.[38]

Ferd. No, my dear'st love,
I would not for the world.

Mira. Yes, for a score of kingdoms you should
wrangle,[39]
And I would call it fair play.

Alon. If this prove
A vision of the island, one dear son
Shall I twice lose.[40]

Sebas. A most high miracle!

Ferd. Though the seas threaten, they are mer-
ciful!
I've cursed them without cause. [*Kneels to* ALON.

Alon. Now all the blessings
Of the glad father compass thee about!
Arise, and say how thou camest here.

Mira. O, wonder!
How many goodly creatures are there here!

38. Miranda playfully accuses Ferdinand of cheating in the game.

39. The exact meaning of *wrangle* has not been determined, and critics still disagree. However, what Miranda says is, "you might cheat me for a score of kingdoms and yet I would call it fair play."

40. Alonzo means that if this sight of Ferdinand is one of the witcheries of the island, he will feel that he has lost his son a second time.

How beauteous mankind is! O brave new world,
That has such people in't!
　　Pros.　　　　　　　　　'Tis new to thee.
　　Alon.　What is this maid with whom thou wast
　　　at play?
Your eld'st acquaintance cannot be three hours:
Is she the goddess that hath sever'd us,
And brought us thus together?
　　Ferd.　　　　　　　　　　Sir, she's mortal;
But by immortal Providence she's mine:
I chose her when I could not ask my father
For his advice, nor thought I had one.　She
Is daughter to this famous Duke of Milan,
Of whom so often I have heard renown,
But never saw before; of whom I have
Received a second life; and second father
This lady makes him to me.[41]
　　Alon.　　　　　　　　　I am hers:
But, O, how oddly will it sound that I
Must ask my child forgiveness!
　　Pros.　　　　　　　　　There, sir, stop:
Let us not burden our remembrance with
A heaviness that's gone.
　　Gonza.　　　　　　　I've inly wept,
Or should have spoke ere this.—Look down, you
　　gods,
And on this couple drop a blessed crown!
For it is you that have chalk'd forth the way
Which brought us hither.
　　Alon.　　　　　　　I say, Amen, Gonzalo!
　　Gonza.　Was Milan thrust from Milan, that his
　　issue

41.　And this lady by becoming my wife makes him a second
father to me.

LOOK DOWN, YOU GODS, ON THIS COUPLE

Should become Kings of Naples! O, rejoice
Beyond a common joy! and set it down
With gold on lasting pillars: In one voyage
Did Claribel her husband find at Tunis;
And Ferdinand, her brother, found a wife
Where he himself was lost; Prospero, his dukedom,
In a poor isle; and all of us, ourselves,
When no man was his own.[42]

  Alon. [*To* FERD. *and* MIRA.]   Give me your
    hands:
Let grief and sorrow still embrace his heart
That doth not wish you joy!

  Gonza.   Be't so! Amen!—

Re-enter ARIEL, *with the* Master *and* Boatswain
    amazedly following.

O, look, sir, look, sir! here is more of us:
I prophesied, if a gallows were on land,
This fellow could not drown.[43]—Now, blasphemy,
That swear'st grace o'erboard, not an oath on
   shore?[44]
Hast thou no mouth by land? What is the news?

  Boats.   The best news is, that we have safely
    found
Our King and company; the next, our ship—
Which, but three glasses since, we gave out split—
Is tight, and yare, and bravely rigg'd, as when
We first put out to sea.

  Ari. [*Aside to* PROS.]   Sir, all this service
Have I done since I went.

42. That is, "all of us have found our senses, when no man was
in possession of his own."

43. See Act I—Scene I.

44. This sentence means, "Now you blasphemous man who swore
so on board the ship that we could be saved, have you not an oath
to swear on shore?"

Pros. [*Aside to* ARIEL.] My tricksy[45] spirit!

Alon. These are not natural events; t h e y strengthen
From strange to stranger.—Say, how came you hither?

Boats. If I did think, sir, I were well awake,
I'd strive to tell you. We were dead of sleep,
And — how we know not — all clapp'd under hatches;
Where, but even now, with strange and several noises
Of roaring, shrieking, howling, jingling chains,
And more diversity of sounds, all horrible,
We were awaked; straightway, at liberty:
When we, in all her trim, freshly beheld
Our royal, good, and gallant ship; our master
Capering to eye her:[46] on a trice, so please you,
Even in a dream, were we divided from them,
And were brought moping[47] hither.

Ari. [*Aside to* PROS.] Was't well done?

Pros. [*Aside to* ARI.] Bravely, my diligence.
Thou shalt be free.

Alon. This is as strange a maze as e'er men trod;
And there is in this business more than Nature
Was ever conduct of:[48] some oracle
Must rectify our knowledge.[49]

Pros. Sir, my liege,
Do not infest your mind with beating on[50]

45. *Tricksy* means *clever.*
46. *Capering to eye her* means *dancing with joy at seeing her.*
47. *Moping* here means *bewildered.*
48. *Conduct of* is used for *conductor* or *leader of.*
49. That is, "some wise man must make it clear to us."
50. This sentence means "Do not trouble your mind by hammering away at the strangeness of these happenings."

The strangeness of this business; at pick'd leisure,[51]
Which shall be shortly, single I'll resolve[52] you—
Which to you shall seem probable—of every
These happen'd accidents:[53] till when, be cheerful,
And think of each thing well.—[*Aside to* ARIEL.]
    Come hither, spirit:
Set Caliban and his companions free;
Untie the spell. [*Exit* ARI.]—How fares my gra-
    cious sir?
There are yet missing of your company
Some few odd lads that you remember not.

Re-enter ARIEL, *driving in* CALIBAN, STEPHANO,
    and TRINCULO, *in their stolen apparel.*

    Steph. Every man shift for all the rest,[54] and
let no man take care for himself; for all is but fortune.—Coragio,[55] bully-monster, coragio!

    Trin. If these be true spies which I wear in my
head,[56] here's a goodly sight.

    Cal. O Setebos, these be brave spirits indeed!
How fine my master is! I am afraid
He will chastise me.

    Sebas. Ha, ha!
What things are these, my Lord Antonio?
Will money buy 'em?

    Anto.   Very like; one of them
Is a plain fish, and, no doubt, marketable.

    51. *At pick'd leisure* is *at a chosen time when we have the op-
portunity.*
    52. *Single I'll resolve* means *I will explain singly.*
    53. *Of every these happen'd accidents* means *how every one of
these things happened.*
    54. Stephano is still a little drunk and his tongue uncertain in
its speech. He means, *Let us every man shift for himself.*
    55. *Coragio* is used for *courage!*
    56. Trinculo means, "If my eyes do not deceive me."

Pros. Mark but the badges of these men, my
   lords,
Then say if they be true. This mis-shaped knave,—
His mother was a witch; and one so strong
That could control the Moon, make flows and ebbs,
And deal in her command without[57] her power.
These three have robb'd me; and this demi-devil—
For he's but half a one—had plotted with them
To take my life: two of these fellows you
Must know and own; this thing of darkness I
Acknowledge mine.

Cal.   I shall be pinch'd to death.

Alon. Is not this Stephano, my drunken butler?

Sebas. He is drunk now: where had he wine?

Alon. And Trinculo is reeling ripe: where
   should they
Find this grand liquor that hath gilded[58] 'em?—
How camest thou in this pickle?

Trin. I have been in such a pickle since I saw
you last, that I fear me, will never out of my bones:
I shall not fear fly-blowing.[59]

Sebas. Why, how now, Stephano!

Steph. O, touch me not! I am not Stephano,
but a cramp.

Pros. You'd be king o' the isle, sirrah?

Steph. I should have been a sore[60] one, then.

---

57. *Without* here means *outside of* or *beyond.*

58. *Gilded* is a word that was commonly applied to a man who
was drunk.

59. Meat that is infested with maggots which have hatched from
eggs laid by flies is said to be fly-blown. These will not lay their eggs
in pickled meat. Trinculo says he has been so pickled, that is drunk,
that the flies will not blow him.

60. Stephano is sore from his torments, but as the word *sore*
also means *harsh* and *severe*, he makes a good pun in his speech.

Alon. [*Pointing to* CAL.] This is as strange
a thing as e'er I look'd on.

Pros. He is as disproportion'd in his manners
As in his shape.—Go, sirrah, to my cell;
Take with you your companions; as you look
To have my pardon, trim it handsomely.

Cal. Ay, that I will; and I'll be wise hereafter,
And seek for grace. What a thrice double ass
Was I, to take this drunkard for a god,
And worship this dull fool!

Pros. Go to; away!

Alon. Hence, and bestow your luggage where
you found it.

Sebas. Or stole it, rather.

[*Exeunt* CAL., STEPH., *and* TRIN.

Pros. Sir, I invite your Highness and your
train
To my poor cell, where you shall take your rest
For this one night; which, part of it, I'll waste
With such discourse as, I not doubt, shall make it
Go quick away,—the story of my life,
And the particular accidents gone by,
Since I came to this isle: and in the morn
I'll bring you to your ship, and so to Naples,
Where I have hope to see the nuptial
Of these our dear-beloved solemnized;
And thence retire me[61] to my Milan, where
Every third thought shall be my grave.[62]

Alon. I long
To hear the story of your life, which must

61. *Retire me* means *withdraw myself.*

62. Prospero has accomplished his purpose; he has recovered his
dukedom, has found a suitable husband for his daughter, and now
feels that life has little in store for him. So every third thought will
be in preparation for his death.

Take the ear strangely.

Pros. I'll deliver all;
And promise you calm seas, auspicious gales,
And sail so expeditious, that shall catch
Your royal fleet far off.—[*Aside to* ARI.] My
    Ariel, chick,
That is thy charge: then to the elements
Be free, and fare thou well!—Please you, draw
    near. [*Exeunt.*

EPILOGUE[63]

SPOKEN BY PROSPERO

Now my charms are all o'erthrown,
And what strength I have's mine own,—[64]
Which is most faint: now, 'tis true,
I must be here confined by you,[65]
Or sent to Naples. Let me not,
Since I have my dukedom got,
And pardon'd the deceiver, dwell
In this bare island by your spell;
But release me from my bands,
With the help of your good hands.[66]
Gentle breath of yours my sails
Must fill, or else my project fails,
Which was to please: now I want

63. The Epilogue is a part spoken by one of the actors after the
play is over, and is addressed to the audience. Here *Prospero* steps
forward and speaks.

64. He has dismissed Ariel and laid aside all his magic arts.

65. The audience may hold him on the island or send him to
Naples, for he is still under a spell.

66. He asks the audience to applaud, to clap their hands, for
noise always breaks charms, and will release him from the enchant-
ment so that he may return to his dukedom.

Spirits to enforce, art to enchant;
And my ending is despair,
Unless I be relieved by prayer;
Which pierces so, that it assaults
Mercy itself, and frees all faults.
As you from crimes would pardon'd be,
Let your indulgence set me free.

STUDIES FOR "THE TEMPEST"

 HE AUTHOR. Many times we have had occasion to say that an acquaintance with an author has much to do with our liking for his works, and as we read the great plays of our greatest poet, we wish we might know him more intimately. However, when we look for information concerning him, we quickly find that comparatively little is known of the man beyond what we can draw from his writings, and few authors have shown themselves less vividly. After doing our best, we can find only a great, shadowy Author who must have had a broad knowledge, a rare invention, a profound insight into human nature, a penetrating sympathy and a marvelous power of expression. As seen through his works, he appears more than human, but when we look into our histories, we wonder that so great a man could have lived and died, and left so light an impression on his times. In fact, some wise men have felt that the William Shakespeare we know could never have written the great plays that bear his name. That is a question, however, we need not discuss; it is better to leave the credit

where it has rested for centuries, and believe that the plays are better evidence of Shakespeare's greatness than his own life is evidence of his ability to write them.

William Shakespeare was born in Stratford-on-Avon, April 23, 1564. His father, John Shakespeare, was a respectable citizen, a wool-dealer and a glover, who at one time possessed considerable means, and was an alderman and a bailiff in the little town, but who later on lost most of his property and ceased to be prominent in the affairs of the village. William's mother was Mary Arden, a gentle, tender woman of Norman descent, who exerted a powerful influence over the lives of her children.

Until William was about fourteen years old he attended the free school in Stratford, and though there are many legends concerning his boyhood pranks and his gift for learning, we know practically nothing for a certainty. In one of the desks at the school, they still show the initials he is supposed to have cut during some idle moment. Of his youth we know still less, except that at about eighteen he married Ann Hathaway, a farmer's daughter who lived in the village of Shottery, a mile or two from Stratford. Ann was eight years older than William, but they seem to have lived happily and to have loved the children that were born to them.

The next thing we can be really certain of is, that about the time William was twenty-three he went to London and soon became connected with a company of actors. Here the genius of the poet began to make itself felt. He wrote some plays, he

recast others, and by the time he had been five years
in the city, he was prominent among the bright men
of his time, and was recognized as a rising man.
Unlike most actors and writers of that period,
Shakespeare was not a dissipated man, but attended carefully to his duties, saved his money, and
ten years after he left Stratford was able to return
to his native town and buy a fine estate, to which
he added from time to time. His money had not
all come from his writings and his acting, however, for he owned a large part of the stock in the
two leading theaters in London.

About 1604 he ceased to be an actor, although
he continued to write for the stage, and in fact
produced his greatest plays after that date. Seven
years later he returned finally to Stratford, and
there lived a quiet and delightful home life until
1616, when on the anniversary of his birth he died
suddenly of a fever. He was buried in the little
parish church at Stratford, where his remains rest
beside those of his wife. On the flat stone that
covers his body is inscribed this epitaph:

> "Good frend for Iesus sake forbeare,
> To digg the dvst encloased heare:
> Blesse be ye man yt spares thes stones,
> And Cvrst be he yt moves my bones."

Such are the principal facts that we know concerning the great man, and a simple biography it
certainly is. We must not, however, think that he
was not popular among his fellows, or that he was
merely a successful business man. He counted
among his friends the wisest and best men of his
time, and some of them have written their impressions of him. Ben Jonson, a rough but sincere and

honest man, says: "I loved the man, and do honor
his memory, on this side idolatry, as much as any.
He was indeed honest, and of an open, free nature; had an excellent phantasy, brave notions and
gentle expressions."

THE PLAY. *The Tempest* was one of the
last of the poet's dramas, though not the last,
as some writers have contended. It was not printed
until 1623, after the poet's death, but it was written, according to Hudson, between 1603 and 1613,
and probably between 1610 and 1613.

The story seems to have been original with
Shakespeare; at least no satisfactory evidence has
been given to show that he borrowed it. This is
rather unusual, for Shakespeare showed a fine contempt for originality, and borrowed the plots of
his plays from a great variety of sources. His
own version of each story, however, was so mas-
terly that no one regrets that he availed himself
of all the assistance he could get.

The scene of the play is laid on an island; what
island we do not know. Probably it is as mythical
as the events that happened on it.

The Tempest is one of Shakespeare's most perfect plays. In form it is perfect, and follows, more
closely than was customary with him, the strict
laws of the old Greek dramas, the laws which critics
still uphold as those governing the highest art. The
three unities are here observed: The events all occur in a single day; they happen in a single place;
from beginning to end there is one continuous line
of thought. Only the last characteristic is still
generally observed by dramatic writers.

Beside perfection in form, *The Tempest* shows the greatest nicety in the way the natural and supernatural move along together without a single interference. It is difficult to think of the magic art of Prospero as more marvelous than the coarse plotting of Sebastian, or to consider the delicate Ariel and the mis-shapen Caliban less human than the manly Ferdinand, or the honest old Gonzalo. Only a great writer could accomplish this, and none but a genius could make of his work a piece so fine that we delight in every line of it. It would be unfair too not to mention the beautiful expressions that abound in it, the high sentiments that prevail, and the great renunciation that Prospero makes when he has in his hands every means for swift and terrible revenge.

CHARACTERS. In reading the drama we become acquainted with the characters, and begin to be indifferent toward some, to have admiration for others and contempt for others. In real life we must not be governed by our first impressions of people. We must study their appearance, their speech, their actions, and make up our minds as to their characters before we decide to make them our friends. It is very unwise to trust every agreeable person we meet, and especially unwise to be suspicious of every person who at first impresses us unfavorably. The older we grow, the keener becomes our power to read character, and the less liable we are to be deceived if we try always to use our best judgment. One of the great benefits literature can offer us is the opportunity to study character, and Shakespeare had such a re-

markable insight into human nature, and so great
a power of drawing character that in his plays we
can see before us almost every type of human being, and from a study of them we can gain a knowledge of humanity that will help us every day of
our lives.

Accordingly, let us take up, one after another,
the principal characters in *The Tempest* and study
them in such a way that we shall be able to read
other plays with greater ease and quickened intelligence.

1. *Prospero.* The hero of the drama is a man
well advanced in years, grave, dignified and serene.
As Duke of Milan he was a prince of power, "without a parallel in dignity and knowledge." He was
popular with his subjects, for so dear was the love
his people bore him, that the conspirators did not
dare to destroy him. Yet he was not inclined to
rule his dukedom, for he grew a stranger to his
estate, so transported and wrapt was he in secret
studies. He confesses that his library was dukedom enough for him, and that he had volumes that
he prized above his dukedom. This was his weakness, and upon this his false brother preyed, until
one night in the dead of darkness the Duke and the
crying Miranda were set adrift in the rotten carcass of a boat, which the very rats instinctively
had quit.

On the island, with the books Gonzalo had preserved for him, he continued his studies and played
the schoolmaster to his gentle child until she was
better educated and more highly cultured than
other princesses that spend more time in vain en-
joyments and have less careful tutors. Prospero's

love for his daughter is the strong, central trait in his character. He has raised her judiciously, guarded her zealously, and now when he finds, brought to his very door, all the actors in the tragedy of his life, his one great care is to provide for Miranda's happiness. All his plans lead to that end, and when he has achieved it, the labors of his life are over.

The supernatural powers that Prospero has acquired seem natural to the studious, dignified old gentleman, and amazing as they are, we can discredit none of them. He tells us he caused the storm, and Miranda begs him to save the passengers on the doomed ship with perfect confidence in his ability to do it. He causes sleep to fall on Miranda, and he summons the gentle Ariel, who enters as naturally as a human being, and admits the marvelous acts that he has seen Prospero perform. Caliban testifies to the power of Prospero so convincingly that we know the magician has control of the destinies of every human being on the island, and can wreak a terrible vengeance if he is determined to do it. When Ferdinand draws his sword, the magician by a word makes him powerless as he stands. We see the magic banquet appear and disappear, and Iris, Ceres, Juno, the nymphs and the reapers come and converse, as a proof positive of his more than mortal power. How has he used this power and how will he continue to use it? When first he came upon the island it was full of evil, and the powers of darkness ruled. He has imprisoned and punished the evil spirits; freed the gentle and the good, banished all discord, and filled the island "full of noises, sounds and sweet airs that give delight and hurt not." That in the future he will use his vast power only for good, we feel assured. Only Caliban hates and abuses him, but the testimony of one so wicked rather proves the gentleness, wisdom and justice of the magician.

Prospero's passionate love for his daughter makes him cunning and wise. Before he will trust his daughter to Ferdinand, he tests both the character and the love of the latter most severely. He even feigns anger and appears to be cruel and unjust. That he is feigning, neither suspect, but Miranda says: "Never till this day saw I him touch'd with anger so distemper'd," and "My father's a better nature, sir, than he appears by speech." When he is assured of Ferdinand's worthiness, of the sincerity of his love for Miranda and of her devotion to her young lover, he is delighted, and becomes so interested in the entertainment he is giving them, that he forgets the plot against his life, although the hour of his danger has arrived. It is true the father stoops to listening, but his purpose is so worthy, no one is inclined to cavil at his watchfulness, and, in any event, his exceeding care but justifies the feeling that his love for Miranda is the mainspring of his every act.

On this small island Prospero is little less than a god, and controls affairs with almost supernatural justice and wisdom. Caliban, the ungrateful, terribly wicked monster, is punished unsparingly but with justice, for in the end with repentance he is forgiven, and the tortures cease. Ariel and the other obedient spirits, though reproved at times, are rewarded by freedom and placed beyond the reach of the evil powers of earth and air.

The sufferings Prospero has endured, the intensity of his studies, and the fierceness of his struggles with the supernatural powers of evil, have given a tinge of sadness to his thought, and have led him to feel that the result of all his labors may amount to little. The world is to him but an insubstantial pageant that shall dissolve and fade, leaving not the trace of the thinnest cloud behind. And as for ourselves,

> "We are such stuff
> As dreams are made on, and our little life
> Is rounded with a sleep."

Yet no sooner does he give way to this feeling than he sees how unkind it is to trouble the young with such musings, and says pathetically to Ferdinand,

> "Sir, I am vex'd;
> Bear with my weakness; my old brain is troubled:
> Be not disturbed with my infirmity."

It is, however, at the end of the play, when all his plans have been carried out successfully, and enemies and friends are alike at his mercy, that the character of Prospero shines out most gloriously. Rejoicing at the fruition of his hopes, he asks from his enemies only a sincere repentance, and then nobly resigning the great arts which have rendered the plotters powerless, he forgives them one and all: his brother Antonio; the scheming Sebastian; Caliban, the evil spirit; and the two weak but wicked ones, Stephano and Trinculo. Then with generosity unparalleled he restores Ferdinand to his father, the King, who has joined with Antonio, and promises to all "calm seas, auspicious gales and sail so expeditious that shall catch your

royal fleet far off." Remembering to set Ariel free,
he lays aside his magic gown, breaks his staff, buries
it fathoms deep in the earth, and drowns his magic
book deeper than did ever plummet sound. Thus
he leaves us, only a man once more, but a loving
father, a wise and gentle ruler.

2. *Miranda.* We have seen that the master
feeling in Prospero's soul is his love for his daughter. Is she worthy of so great an affection? Let
us draw our answers from the drama.

(a) She is beautiful.

Ferdinand says:

> "Most sure, the goddess
> On whom these airs attend!"

And:

> "O you wonder!
> If you be maid or no?"

Caliban says:

> "And that most deeply to consider is
> The beauty of his daughter; he himself
> Calls her a nonpareil: I ne'er saw woman
> But only Sycorax my dam and she;
> But she as far surpasseth Sycorax
> As great'st does least."

Alonzo says:

> "Is she the goddess that hath sever'd us,
> And brought us thus together?"

(b) She is educated, cultured and refined.

Prospero says:

> "And here
> Have I, thy schoolmaster, made thee more profit
> Than other princesses can, that have more time
> For vainer hours, and tutors not so careful."

(c)   She is tender-hearted, sympathetic and compassionate.

She says:

> "O, I have suffer'd
> With those that I saw suffer!"

And:

> "O, the cry did knock
> Against my very heart!"

Prospero speaks of these traits:

> "Wipe thou thine eyes; have comfort.
> The direful spectacle of the wreck, which touch'd
> The very virtue of compassion in thee,——"

Speaking of the trials which Prospero puts upon Ferdinand, she says:

> "Make not too rash a trial of him, for
> He's gentle and not fearful."

When she learns of her helplessness at the time they were set adrift, she says:

> "O, my heart bleeds
> To think o' the teen that I have turn'd you to."

When Miranda hears how her father was treated by her false uncle, she exclaims:

> "Alack, for pity!
> I, not remembering how I cried on't then,
> Will cry it o'er again: it is a hint
> That wrings mine eyes to't."

(d)   She is brave.

Prospero says of her childhood:

> "O, a cherubin
> Thou wast that did preserve me! Thou didst smile,
> Infused with a fortitude from Heaven."

(e)   She is innocent and unacquainted with mankind and hates the sight of evil.

When she first sees Ferdinand, she asks:

> "What is't? A spirit?
> Lord, how it looks about! Believe me, sir,
> It carries a brave form. But 'tis a spirit."

Again:

> "I do not know
> One of my sex; no woman's face remember,
> Save, from my glass, mine own; nor have I seen
> More that I may call men, than you, good friend."

And finally:

> "How beauteous mankind is! O brave new world,
> That has such people in't."

She says of Caliban:

> "'Tis a villain, sir,
> I do not love to look on."

(f)   She is grateful.

When she is told of Gonzalo's services to her and her father, she exclaims:

> "Would I might
> But ever see that man!"

(g)   She is a loving, faithful woman:

While Ferdinand is at work she pleads:

> "Alas, now, pray you,
> Work not so hard,———
> Pray, set it down, and rest you: when this burns,
> 'Twill weep for having wearied you."

Again:

> "If you'll sit down,
> I'll bear your logs the while."

Later Ferdinand asks, "Wherefore weep you?"
Miranda answers:

> "At mine unworthiness,————
> ————Hence, bashful cunning!
> And prompt me, plain and holy innocence!
> I am your wife, if you will marry me;
> If not, I'll die your maid: to be your fellow
> You may deny me; but I'll be your servant,
> Whether you will or no."

(h) Lover and father both bestow unqualified
praise upon her. Ferdinand says:

> "Admired Miranda!
> Indeed the top of admiration; worth
> What's dearest to the world!————
> ————but you, O you,
> So perfect and so peerless, are created
> Of every creature's best!"

Her father says:

> "O Ferdinand,
> Do not smile at me that I boast her off,
> For thou shalt find she will outstrip all praise,
> And make it halt behind her."

3. *Ferdinand.* The quotations we have made
from the text seem to have answered our question
as to Miranda's worthiness. Upon what sort of a
man has she set her affections? Will she find in
her husband the man she thinks she is to marry?
Answer these questions for yourselves by reading
the text and setting down the proofs as we did while
studying Miranda.

4. *Ariel.* Prospero's agent Ariel is an interesting study, for the poet has drawn him with lines
so clear and exact that he seems a veritable person.
Will you not seek to know him, and in doing so
follow these suggestions?

(a)   Ariel appears in the following scenes:

Act I	Scene II	(three times)
Act II	Scene I	(twice)
Act III	Scene II	(once)
	Scene III	(once)
Act IV	Scene I	(three times)
Act V	Scene I	(five times)

How many scenes are there in the play? In how many does Ariel appear? In what scenes does he make no appearance? What characters appear more times? What characters appear more prominently in the play?

(b)   Ariel does many different things. Make a list of the things Ariel does in this play, and a second list of the things that it appears Ariel has done elsewhere.

(c)   Ariel appears in different forms. What are these forms? Is Ariel ever visible to any of the characters besides Prospero? Does Ariel ever appear visibly to Prospero? If the play were to be acted on the stage, would it be necessary at any time to have a person come upon the stage to represent him?

(d)   Ariel has human characteristics. What acts like those of a human being does Ariel commit? What does Ariel say that shows him to have human traits?

(e)   Ariel is a spirit. What supernatural things does Ariel do? What does Ariel say that makes him seem more than human?

(f)   Ariel has a many-sided character. Find in the play where the following questions are answered: Is he faithful? Does he do his duties well? Does Ariel love music? Does he feel gratitude? Does he always favor the right? Is Ariel merry? Does he love fun? Does he play practical jokes? Does he love warmth and light, or cold and darkness? Is he sympathetic? Does he lessen the grief of any one? Does he lead any one to remorse for evil deeds? Does he assist love in the hearts of Ferdinand and Miranda? Do you think Prospero always treats him fairly? Does he seem so light and inconstant that he needs some discipline? What will he do when he is released from Prospero's control? Finally, does Ariel seem lovable to you, would you like him as a friend and companion as well as a powerful servant?

5. *Caliban.* It is difficult to tell just what the slave of Prospero looked like, and it is not at all unlikely that the poet intended we should not see him very clearly. He is a hideous spectacle, scarcely human, yet resembling a man in some respects. He is called in various places villain, slave and tortoise; a moon-calf, that is, a shapeless lump; a fish, with legs like a man and fins like arms; a puppy-headed monster; a man monster; half a fish and half a monster; a plain fish; a mis-shaped knave; "as strange a thing as e'er I looked upon;" and it is said of him that his manners are as disproportioned as his shape.

Is the character of Caliban apparently in keeping with his appearance? What does Prospero say of him? Do you place confidence in the opinion of such a man as Prospero, and do you feel that he is not unnecessarily severe? Does Caliban do anything to justify the bad character Prospero gives him early in the play? Why do you suppose Shakespeare introduces into the play such a character?

Does such a character heighten the effect of the others?

6. *Other Characters.* Classify the other characters as good or bad. Where did you place Alonso? Is there any doubt at all as to where Gonzalo should be placed? Are there any redeeming traits in Stephano? Do you think Trinculo's jesting is really funny? Would you like the play better if Stephano and Trinculo were left out of it? What can you find in the boatswain's words to justify the opinion Gonzalo holds of him? Which is the greater scoundrel, Sebastian or Antonio?

THE STORY OR PLOT. A certain duke has been by treachery driven from his principality with his infant daughter, and has found refuge on an uninhabited island. After many years those who plotted against him are thrown into his power, he recovers his dukedom and marries his daughter to the son of his king. Such, in brief, is the plot of *The Tempest,* but how wonderfully it is expanded, and how many characters have been created, how many incidents created to give interest and truthfulness to the narrative. Let us follow the play through, and by studying the relation of the incidents, one to another, learn to appreciate more fully the art of the great magician who wrote the play.

ACT I—SCENE I. *Purpose:* To introduce the enemies of Prospero. Do we know at the time of such a person as Prospero? Do we know why the persons are on the ship, where they intended to go or where they are now? When do we find out these things? What idea do you get of Gon-

zalo in the first scene? Why is his conversation
with the boatswain put into the play?

ACT I—SCENE II. *Purpose:* To bring before
us all the leading characters in the play, and to tell
us enough about them to secure our interest; also
to give us the history necessary to an understanding of the plot. When do we first learn that there
are miracles and magic in the play? How do we
learn what has happened to Prospero before the
time of the storm? How do we learn Ariel's history? How are we made acquainted with Caliban?
How do we learn that Prospero raised the storm?
How were the mariners confused, and by whom
were all saved? What did Prospero whisper in the
ear of Ariel when the latter came in after Prospero has called Caliban? What incident followed
as a result of this command? How did Ariel lead
Ferdinand? Are there other places in the play
where Ariel leads people in the same way? What
do you call the three most important incidents in
this scene? What incidents could be left out of
this scene without interfering with the development
of the plot?

ACT II—SCENE I. *Purpose:* To account for
the presence of the plotters, and to show the character of the men. Is it necessary to the development of the main plot that Sebastian and Antonio
should scheme to kill the king? Do any of the incidents of this scene have any direct bearing on the
main plot? Could any of the incidents of this
scene be omitted without injury to the play?

ACT II—SCENE II. *P u r p o s e:* To create
amusement, lighten the play and by contrast make
the fine parts more beautiful. Is any character in

the scene absolutely essential to the completion of
the story? Would you understand the story as well
if the entire scene were omitted?

ACT III—SCENE I. *Purpose:* To disclose
Prospero's purpose more fully, and to secure our
interest in Ferdinand and Miranda.

ACT III—SCENE II. What is the purpose of
this scene? What bearing do the incidents of this
scene have upon the main plot?

ACT III—SCENE III. What effect is the magic
banquet to have on the persons who saw it? What
was Prospero's purpose in showing it? Did it con-
tribute in any way to the success of his general
plan?

ACT IV—SCENE I. What incidents in this scene
are necessary, and what are introduced to give light
and beauty to the play? What is the effect of in-
troducing Caliban and his companions right after
Ariel and the spirits have been entertaining Ferdinand and Miranda? What are Mountain, Silver,
Fury and Tyrant, mentioned in this scene?

ACT V—SCENE I. What is the purpose of this
scene? Is the plot brought to a satisfactory conclusion? Are there any characters left unaccounted
for? Does every character in the play appear in
this scene? Are they all on the stage when the
curtain falls?

Make a list of the incidents which to you seem
unnecessary, which could be left out without injury
to the real story. Make another list of incidents
that could not be omitted without spoiling the story.
Find two little plots that make complete stories in
themselves, but that help only in a moderate degree to make the main story clearer.

POETRY AND PROSE. Do any of the characters speak always in prose? Do any speak always in poetry? Do some speak partly in prose and partly in poetry? Can you see any connection between each character and his method of speech? How many songs are sung in the play? Who sings them? Do you like any of the songs? What effect do the songs have upon the play? Can you find rhyming lines anywhere excepting in the songs? Does any character speak in rhyme?

CONCLUSION. If we study a play too long or continue to read it after our interest ceases for a time, we are liable to be prejudiced against it, and to feel that it is not worth the labor we have put upon it. If, however, a person will stop studying when he begins to lose interest and work seems a drudgery, he will come back a little later with renewed interest. Again, when we study a play minutely as we have been doing, and view it from many sides, we may lose sight for a time of the unity and beauty of the whole composition. This is peculiarly unfortunate, for the poet intends us to view his work as a whole, and to produce his effect with the whole. It is *The Tempest* that we will remember as a work of art, and, if our studies are fruitful, that will draw us back to it at intervals for many years to come. Before we leave it, we must take it and read it through in a leisurely manner, pausing merely to enjoy its beauty, to smile at its playfulness and to feel our hearts expand under the benign influence of the grand old man Prospero. Now Miranda, Ferdinand and Ariel have passed the line of mere acquaintances, and have become to us fast friends, who, though they may be forever silent, have yet given us a fragment of their lives to cheer us on our way.

OTHER PLAYS OF SHAKESPEARE.   Shakespeare wrote a great many plays, and all are not equally good; a few seem so inferior that many who study them think they were not written by the same hand that penned *The Tempest*. Some of the plays are more difficult than others, and some cannot be comprehended until the reader has had some experience in life. There are several, on the other hand, that may be read with great interest and profit by almost any one, while those who have read *The Tempest* as we have recommended, should find some measure of enjoyment in all. *A Midsummer Night's Dream* is a charming fairy story; *The Merchant of Venice* is a good story, contains fine characters and shows some of Shakespeare's most beautiful thoughts, although some people are inclined to believe he has dealt too severely with the Jew. *Much Ado About Nothing* is a jolly comedy to match with *The Comedy of Errors*. *Julius Cæsar, Richard III* and *Coriolanus* are interesting historical plays, and *Hamlet, Macbeth* and *Romeo and Juliet* are among the best of his tragedies. If a person would read just the plays mentioned in the thoughtful way we have indicated here, he would gain a benefit whose great value never can be estimated, and thereafter all reading would seem easier and more delightful.

PRONUNCIATION OF PROPER NAMES

NOTE.—The pronunciation of difficult words is indicated by respelling them phonetically. *N* is used to indicate the French nasal sound; *K* sound of *ch* in German; *ü* the sound of the German *ü* and French *u*; *ö* the sound of *ö* in foreign languages.

ABOUKIR, *ah boo keer'*
ACHILLES, *a kil' leez*
ACIS, *ay' sis*
AIX, *ayx*
AJAX TELAMON, *ay' jacks tel' a mon*
ALAMO, *al' a mo*
ALAMEDA, *ah la may' dah*
ALAVA, *ah' la vah*
ALGIERS, *al jeerz'*
ALGONQUIN, *al gon' kwin*
ALLOUEZ, *al loo ay'*
ALONSO, *a lon' zo*
ALPUXARRAS, *ahl" poo hahr' ras*
ALVARADO, *ahl vah rah' do*
ANTIGUA, *an tee' gwa*
APHRODITE, *af ro di' tee*
ARDENNES, *ahr den'*
ARGONAUTA, *ahr go naw' tah*
ARIEL, *ay' ry el*
AYACANORA, *i a kahn o' rah*
BOABDIL, *bo ahb deel'*
CADIZ, *kay' diz*

CANOVA, *kah no' vah*
CASABIANCA, *kas" a bee an' kah*
CHARLEVOIX, *shahr" lev wah'*
CHARYBDIS, *ka rib' dis*
COLIGNI, *ko" leen" yee'*, or *ko leen' yee*
COMMUNIPAW, *kom mun' y paw*
CORIOLANUS, *kor y o lay' nus*
COROMANTEES, *ko ro mahn' teez*
CUNDINAMARCA, *koon" dee nam ahr' kah*
DAMFREVILLE, *doN freh veel'*
D'AUMALE, *do mahl'*
DEMARTUS, *de mar' a tus*
DENT BLANCHE, *doN bloN' sh*
DIAZ, *dee' ahs*, or *dee' ath*
DIOGENES, *di oj' ee neez*
DISCOBOLUS, *dis kob' o lus*
ELIA, *ee' ly a*
EPHIALTES, *ef y al' teez*
EURYALUS, *u ri' a lus*
FERROL, *fer role'*
FINISTERRE, *fin" is tayr'*
FLIEDNER, *fleet' ner*
FRONTENAC, *fron' te nak*
GALATEA, *gal a tee' a*
GHENT, *gent*
GONZALES, *gon zah' leez*
GONZALO, *gon zah' lo*
GRANADA, *gran ah' dah*
GRÈVE, *grayv'*
HERNANDO CORTES, *her nahn' do kor tays'*
HERVÉ RIEL, *her vay" ree el'*
IVRY, *eev ree'*
JOLIET, *zho lee yay'*
KIKABEAUX, *kee ka bo'*

Koran, *ko' ran,* or *ko rahn'*
La Chine, *lah sheen'*
Leigh, Amyas, *lee, a mi' as*
Leonidas, *lee on' y das*
Lethe, *lee' thee*
Lochiel, *lo keel'*
Louvre, *loo' vr'*
Maelstrom, *mayl' strum*
Malouins, *mah loo aN'*
Marco Bozzaris, *mahr' ko bo tsa' rees,* popularly
   bo zar' is
Mayenne, *mi en'*
Megistias, *me gis' ty as*
Miamis, *mi ah' miz*
Michillimackinac, *mee'' shil y mack' in ak*
Miguel, *mee gayl'*
Milan, *mil' an,* or *mil an'*
Mycenae, *mi see' nee*
Nacogdoches, *nak o do' chez*
Navarre, *nah vahr'*
Nombre de Dios, *nom' bray day de os'*
Nyack, *ni' ak*
Œta, *ee' ta*
Olmedo, *ol may' do*
Orchomenus, *or kom' ee nus*
Ordaz, *or dath'*
Pedrillo, *pay dreel' yo*
Peloponnesus, *pel'' o pon nee' sus*
Pere Marquette, *payr mar ket'*
Phoenicians, *fee nish' anz*
Picardy, *pik' ar dy*
Pizarro, *pee zahr' ro*
Plataea, *pla tee' a*
Plutarch, *plu' tark*

PROSPERO, *pros' pe ro*
PUEBLO NUEVA, *pweb' lah nuay' va*
ROCHEFORT, *rosh for'*
ST. GÉNÉVIÈVE, *saN zhen'' vy ayv'*
SALTO DE ALVARADO, *sahl'' to day ahl vah rah' do*
SAN ANTONIO DE BEXAR, *day bay hahr'*
SANDOVAL, *sahn do vahl'*
SAN JACINTO, *san ja sin' to*
SANTA FÉ, *san'' ta fay'*
SAULT SAINTE MARIE, *soo saint may' ry*
SCYLLA, *sil' la*
SEGUIN, *se geen'*
STUYVESANT, *sti' ves sant*
TALADEGA, *tah lah day' ga*
TEGEA, *tee' gee a*
TEMERAIRE, *tem e rayr'*
THERMOPYLAE, *thur mop' y lee*
TLASCALANS, *tlahs kah' lahns*
TOURVILLE, *toor veel'*
TRAFALGAR, *traf al gahr'* or *tra fal' gar*
TYROLESE, *tir ol ees'*
VIGO, *vee' go*
VILLENEUVE, *veel neuv'*
WILHELMUS KIEFT, *vil hel' mus keeft'*
XENIL, *hay' neel*
XERXES, *zurks' eez*